Moderato Cantabile

MASTERPIECES OF FRENCH LITERATURE SERIES

The aim of this series is to provide outstanding works of French literature of all periods to students at all levels by means of carefully selected, judiciously annotated, unabridged paperbound editions.

ROBERT L. POLITZER

Series Editor

Stanford University

DURAS

Moderato Cantabile

E 70

Edited by
THOMAS BISHOP
New York University

PRENTICE-HALL, INC. *Englewood Cliffs, New Jersey*

Prentice-Hall International, Inc., *London*
Prentice-Hall of Australia, Pty. Ltd., *Sydney*
Prentice-Hall of Canada, Ltd., *Toronto*
Prentice-Hall of India Private Ltd., *New Delhi*
Prentice-Hall of Japan, Inc., *Tokyo*

Library of Congress Catalog Card No.: 68-15848

843.91
D952m

Current printing (last digit)
10 9 8 7 6 5 4 3 2 1

Printed in the United States of America

TABLE DES MATIÈRES

Moderato Cantabile

Introduction

A LA RECHERCHE DE MARGUERITE DURAS

MARGUERITE DURAS EST PARMI LES AUTEURS CONTEMPORAINS les plus difficiles à classer[1] sous une étiquette.[2] Celle qu'on lui applique le plus souvent, c'est le «nouveau roman», mais Marguerite Duras semble par bien des égards aussi éloignée de romanciers tels que Michel Butor, Alain Robbe-Grillet, et Nathalie Sarraute qu'elle ne leur ressemble par d'autres. La qualité sobre de son écriture, la simplicité, voire[3] l'austérité de ses récits permettent de parler de classicisme tout en évoquant cette tradition du roman français «classique» qui nous parvient depuis Madame de Lafayette en passant par Gide et Camus. Néanmoins, l'œuvre de Marguerite Duras n'est classique que par certains aspects et il faut en chercher une définition plus complexe.

Les critiques littéraires citent beaucoup de noms lorsqu'ils veulent lui attribuer une ascendance: Proust, Melville, Antonioni, la romancière anglaise, Ivy Compton-Burnett. Il existe en effet des liens plus ou moins palpables entre Marguerite Duras et ces artistes si différents les uns des autres. On a même écrit que *Moderato Cantabile*, c'était *Madame Bovary* récrite[4] par Béla Bartók, idée inimaginable si jamais il en fut, et pourtant Anne Desbaresdes n'est-elle pas une sorte d'Emma Bovary (dans le sens générique), et l'écriture de Marguerite Duras n'est-elle pas moderne dans le sens où l'écriture musicale de Bartók est moderne (sans vouloir trop insister sur de véritables rapprochements qui ne se défendraient[5] pas)? Certes, ces références aident à situer l'écrivain, mais il faut chercher plus loin pour trouver sa qualité particulière. En allant donc à la recherche de Marguerite Duras, il y a plusieurs points de départ possibles, mais c'est par le «nouveau roman» qu'il convient de commencer.

---

[1] **classer:** mettre dans un certain ordre.
[2] **étiquette:** «label».
[3] **voire:** et même.
[4] **récrit:** écrit de nouveau.
[5] **se défendre:** ici, «to be substantiated».

QU'EST-CE QUE LE NOUVEAU ROMAN?

CE QU'ON APPELLE LE «NOUVEAU ROMAN» n'est pas une révolution subite dans l'art du roman. Bien que l'expression s'applique surtout à une esthétique du roman beaucoup utilisée et beaucoup discutée depuis le début des années cinquante, certains livres publiés tout de suite après—et même avant—la deuxième guerre mondiale figurent dans cette catégorie, et les antécédents directs de ces romanciers français contemporains comprennent des auteurs du xxᵉ siècle et de nationalités différentes: Joyce, Proust, Faulkner, Kafka, Sartre, Céline, Camus, pour ne nommer que ceux-là.

D'ailleurs, l'appellation «nouveau roman» est peu satisfaisante puisqu'elle n'explique rien: toute époque a son «nouveau» roman. Aussi certains critiques ont-ils préféré parler d'*anti-roman*, d'*école du regard*,[6] d'*alittérature*, d'*école de l'objet*, de *littérature du constat*.[7] Mais il ne s'agit point d'école littéraire proprement dite;[8] les auteurs en question partagent une certaine tendance tout en se distinguant sur bien des points importants. L'expression «nouveau roman» a donc cet avantage qu'à une époque particulière—la nôtre— elle désigne tous les romanciers d'une lignée[9] sans les séparer dans leurs spécificité individuelle.

Dans ses lignes les plus générales, le «nouveau roman» est une réaction contre le roman «traditionnel»—celui où, à l'instar des[10] grands maîtres du xixᵉ siècle, le romancier s'installe confortablement au centre de son œuvre et y joue Dieu, c'est-à-dire, qu'il sait tout, contrôle tout. Ce roman traditionnel le lecteur n'avait qu'à le lire passivement: tout lui était indiqué—les pensées de tel personnage, le passé du héros, sa psychologie dans un cadre souvent historique ou sociologique.

Jean-Paul Sartre s'était opposé à ce genre de roman en accusant le romancier traditionnel de mauvaise foi—ce romancier, disait-il, se voulait à la fois hors de son personnage et au dedans, tâche qui dans la réalité est impossible.[11] Si le roman doit reproduire la vie, il faut qu'il s'adapte à elle, et dans la vie il nous est impossible de voir autrement que de l'extérieur. Un narrateur, par exemple, peut bien nous conter ce qu'il pense lui-même; il ne peut pas *savoir* ce que pense un autre. Tout au plus peut-il faire des suppositions, mais même en supposant, ce narrateur doit se baser sur ce qu'il entend et ce qu'il voit, de sorte qu'il peut très bien se tromper car ce qu'on nous dit est souvent mensonger et nous interprétons tous de manière différente ce que nous voyons. Ainsi, le «nouveau roman» renonce aux suppositions, aux interprétations; il se contente de voir, de constater, de dire, et le romancier se refuse à donner des significations définitives, se refuse, en somme, à faire autre chose que ce que nous pouvons tous faire dans

---

6 **regard:** action de regarder.
7 **constat:** action de constater.
8 **proprement dit:** exactement.
9 **lignée:** descendance.
10 **à l'instar de:** comme; en suivant l'exemple de.
11 Dans sa préface à *Portrait d'un inconnu* de Nathalie Sarraute.

la vie. Or, si par exemple nous faisons la connaissance d'un homme dans une situation spécifique, nous ne le connaissons qu'à partir de ce moment-là et dans la situation précise. Son passé, nous l'ignorons; l'homme peut nous le raconter mais comment savoir s'il nous raconte la vérité? En plus, dans la vie les événements ne se passent pas suivant la logique rigoureuse du roman traditionnel, de A à B de B à C. Le plus souvent pour nous, les événements sont moins bien organisés et se déroulent de X à Y d'Y à Z. C'est cette anarchie et ce manque de *savoir* qui sont à la base du «nouveau roman» et c'est aussi ce qui constitue à la fois sa difficulté et sa séduction, car l'auteur exige que son lecteur reconstitue l'œuvre, qu'il se place au centre de l'univers créé et qu'il démêle[12] les choses (comme nous sommes obligés de le faire tout le temps dans la réalité) pour imposer notre propre logique, notre propre explication—qui n'est d'ailleurs pas forcément[13] celle de l'auteur.

Il en résulte que les romanciers en question s'attachent volontiers aux *choses* qui, elles au moins, se laissent appréhender[14] par le regard, et que leurs personnages deviennent eux aussi choses puisqu'ils ne *signifient* pas. N'étant pas chargé de significations, le monde des objets a en quelque sorte une existence pure. C'est Robbe-Grillet qui a le mieux décrit cette condition: «. . . le monde n'est ni signifiant, ni absurde. Il est tout simplement.»[15] Ainsi, les écrivains d'antan[16] recherchaient l'ordre; d'autres plus récents se basaient sur une conception d'un monde absurde. Pour le «nouveau roman», il n'est pas question de chercher des principes abstraits; on se limite aux choses, ces choses qui ne sont que surfaces sans profondeur cachée.

S'il est vrai que le «nouveau roman» en général s'oppose au roman traditionnel en dévalorisant[17] ce que celui-ci avait de plus caractéristique—l'intrigue, la psychologie, les personnages et le milieu social—il n'en est pas moins vrai que les écrivains de la nouvelle tendance emploient des procédés différents et parfois opposés. Par exemple, Michel Butor et Alain Robbe-Grillet utilisent volontiers comme thème de leurs romans l'impossibilité d'écrire (quoique par des moyens peu semblables); Marguerite Duras et Nathalie Sarraute préfèrent une recherche des zones mystérieuses chez l'être humain entre le conscient et le sub-conscient (des *tropismes*, suivant l'expression de Nathalie Sarraute), recherches qui n'ont rien de commun pourtant avec la psychologie habituelle; et Samuel Beckett pousse le roman jusqu'à ses ultimes limites en réduisant le personnage à une simple conscience qui ne peut cesser de parler même si elle n'appartient plus qu'à un bout[18] de chair pourrissante.

En ce qui concerne la structure du roman et son langage, là encore, autant de tentatives différentes que d'écrivains. Mais partout on rencontre une structure compliquée qui correspond à cette nouvelle manière de voir et au refus de «raconter».

---

12 **démêler:** «to unravel»; «to figure out».
13 **forcément:** nécessairement.
14 **appréhender:** attrapper.
15 Dans *Une Voie pour le roman futur.*
16 **antan:** autrefois.
17 **dévaloriser:** faire perdre de la valeur à.
18 **bout:** morceau.

MARGUERITE DURAS

MARGUERITE DURAS NE SE RÉCLAME PAS particulièrement du[19] «nouveau roman». Surtout, ce n'est pas une théoricienne du roman; contrairement à Robbe-Grillet, Butor et Sarraute, elle n'a pas l'intention de faire une œuvre expérimentale et n'explique pas dans ses essais ce qu'elle veut faire dans ses romans. Elle rejoint ces autres auteurs en ce que, elle aussi, crée des romans sans véritable intrigue, avec des personnages dont la vie antérieure et la profondeur nous restent cachées; par contre son œuvre vit d'une humanité plus intense que celles de la plupart des autres et son écriture se remarque par sa simplicité et son économie de moyens.

Née en Indochine en 1914, de parents français, Marguerite Duras vit à Paris depuis l'âge de dix-huit ans. Elle fit ses débuts en littérature avec des romans d'une veine néo-réaliste dont deux se firent très remarquer,[20] *Le Barrage*[21] *contre le Pacifique* en 1950 et *Le Marin de Gibraltar* en 1952. Ensuite ses livres se dépouillent[22] de plus en plus, se concentrent sur une seule situation assez banale et mettent en relief des personnages (dont le nombre est limité d'habitude à deux ou trois) qui vivent une expérience amoureuse peu réussie dans laquelle ils essaient sans succès de se réaliser. Les personnages des romans tels que *Les Petits Chevaux de Tarquinia* (1953), *Le Square* (1955), *Moderato Cantabile* (1958), *Dix Heures et demie du soir en été* (1960), *L'Après-midi de Monsieur Andesmas* (1962), *Le Ravissement de Lol V. Stein* (1964), *Le Vice-Consul* (1965) cherchent à se définir, à se comprendre sans jamais y parvenir. Aux prises avec[23] de graves remous[24] intérieurs qu'ils ressentent sans les comprendre, les personnages de Marguerite Duras tâtonnent dans le clair-obscur de leur solitude vers cet autre qu'ils réussiront à peine à frôler. Et pourtant, ce ne sont pas forcément des romans de l'échec, car on ne peut pas toujours résumer par l'échec un mouvement d'un être vers un autre, mouvement qui n'aboutit pas à l'unisson[25] de deux solitudes mais qui laisse néanmoins une empreinte ineffaçable.

Le succès considérable auprès du public aussi bien qu'auprès des critiques que lui ont valu ses romans, Marguerite Duras l'a retrouvé aussi au cinéma et au théâtre. Sur la scène, elle a donné *Les Viaducs de la Seine-et-Oise*, *La Musica*, *Les Eaux et les forêts*, *Des Journées entières dans les arbres* (tirée d'une nouvelle du même nom et qui eut un succès retentissant au Théâtre de France de Jean-Louis Barrault et Madeleine Renault) ainsi qu'une adaptation théâtrale du *Square*. C'est pourtant le cinéma qui assura la renommée internationale de Marguerite Duras: elle écrivit le magnifique scénario de

---

[19] **se réclamer de:** se dire disciple de.
[20] **se faire remarquer:** attirer de l'attention.
[21] **barrage:** ici, «dam».
[22] **se dépouiller:** ici, se dénuer, éliminer tout ce qu'il y a de superflu.
[23] **aux prises avec:** en proie à.
[24] **remous:** mouvements en sens divers.
[25] **unisson:** accord.

Hiroshima mon amour pour le film réalisé par Alain Resnais qui allait changer le langage même du cinéma contemporain. Comme dans les autres œuvres de cet écrivain, *Hiroshima mon amour*, c'est encore deux solitudes qui se retrouvent en tâtonnant, qui vivent un bref amour impossible et qui finissent inéluctablement par se séparer. Les romans de Marguerite Duras ont aussi attiré plusieurs des plus grands cinéastes[26] modernes; Peter Brook, Tony Richardson, René Clément et Jules Dassin ont chacun porté un de ses romans à l'écran et Marguerite Duras elle-même s'est faite réalisateur[27] pour faire un film de sa pièce, *La Musica*.

MODERATO CANTABILE

PARMI LES RÉUSSITES NOMBREUSES de Marguerite Duras, *Moderato Cantabile* me semble son œuvre la plus parfaite, la plus belle, celle qui attire le plus par un charme étrange et troublant. Rien de plus simple que cette «histoire» qui se résume facilement en une phrase: témoins d'un crime passionnel,[28] un homme et une femme de milieux très différents sont attirés l'un vers l'autre, se retrouvent cinq fois dans un café et puis se séparent à jamais. Mais que de richesses derrière cette façade simple et austère! Marguerite Duras fait vivre pour nous un drame bouleversant chez Anne Desbaresdes, cette femme qui, auprès d'un mari qui lui est indifférent et auquel elle aussi est indifférente, rêve du grand amour, pur et total. Or, quand le hasard la rend témoin de ce crime—un homme tue une femme et puis se jette sur son cadavre pour le couvrir de baisers—elle comprend instinctivement que l'amour absolu ne peut se réaliser que dans la mort. Avec Chauvin, elle va essayer de revivre cet amour fou qui a mené jusqu'au crime, qu'elle tentera de s'approprier pour devenir celle qui fut tuée. Jamais ne pourra-t-elle connaître les véritables raisons du meurtre, mais elle invente et laisse inventer Chauvin et elle finit par croire que c'est par amour que l'homme a tué la femme, que c'est par amour qu'elle l'avait supplié de la tuer.

Anne et Chauvin arriveront au même point que l'autre couple, mais symboliquement seulement. Une main froide qui se pose sur une autre, deux bouches froides qui se touchent suffisent pour que leurs désirs ardents soient consommés. «Je voudrais que vous soyez morte», dit Chauvin et Anne répond simplement «C'est fait.» L'amour et le crime des deux inconnus a été revécu, mais par les émotions uniquement et deux abîmes de vide et de solitude se sont rejoints temporairement dans un triste pastiche. Anne serait incapable de vivre un vrai amour avec Chauvin non seulement à cause de sa soif[29] de l'absolu mais aussi pour des raisons d'ordre social: parce que malgré elle, il y a un fossé[30] trop large entre cet ouvrier qu'est Chauvin et cette femme élégante

---

26 **cinéaste:** directeur de film.
27 **réalisateur:** ici, cinéaste.
28 **passionnel:** d'amour.
29 **soif:** ici, désir ardent.
30 **fossé:** ici, différence.

du directeur de l'usine, parce que, aussi, l'enfant serait toujours là entre eux, un obstacle que Chauvin ne veut ou ne peut surmonter. L'échec de cette liaison-qui-n'est-pas-une-liaison est donc inévitable, et Anne, qui rêvait de se réaliser dans l'amour, en est finalement anéantie.

L'expérience est encore plus tragique pour Anne que l'anéantissement[31] par l'amour. Les réunions avec Chauvin dans le café finiront par la séparer à jamais de son milieu bourgeois et elle sera obligée de se construire son monde à elle derrière cette façade d'ivresse par le vin. Cette aliénation d'Anne du monde qu'elle avait connu est suggérée admirablement dans la scène brillante du dîner qu'est le chapitre VII. Auprès de ses amis et de son mari, Anne est pitoyablement seule, seule avec la pensée que Chauvin erre dehors dans la rue, à la fois à cent mètres d'elle et à mille années-lumière, seule avec cette torpeur et ce désir que tant de vin fait brûler dans ses veines et qui l'isole au sein de conversations mondaines et de plats succulents. Et quand elle n'en peut plus de Pommard,[32] de canard à l'orange et de misère, Anne monte dans la chambre de son enfant pour vomir cette ivresse, cette nausée et ce malheur auprès du seul être qui lui importe. La rupture est totale et le monde qu'elle avait connu s'efface pour elle à jamais.

L'aspect le plus remarquable de *Moderato Cantabile* est sans doute la perfection des moyens utilisés. Tout se résume par le style et par la structure de l'œuvre. Cette structure—musicale, comme le laisse deviner le titre—est merveilleusement adaptée à la conception même de ce roman. Le thème de l'amour total allant jusqu'au crime passionnel est établi dès le premier chapitre; il sera repris avec des variations savantes dans les chapitres suivants et finira au huitième et dernier chapitre par être répété entièrement, mais avec des harmoniques bien différents du début. Au fur et à mesure qu'Anne[33] et Chauvin reconstruisent le crime, ils le revivent mais sous une forme altérée qui convient à leur situation et à leurs tempéraments.

Déjà aussi dans le premier chapitre se laisse entrevoir la fêlure[34] dans l'âme d'Anne qui ira en s'élargissant. Marguerite Duras décrit avec beaucoup d'humour la leçon de piano qui met aux prises le professeur de piano et le petit garçon entêté et dont l'enjeu[35] est la sonatine de Diabelli. Contre cet arrière-plan de la leçon, nous commençons à apercevoir la dualité de la mère. Elle voudrait que son fils apprenne le piano, mais en même temps, elle ne peut s'empêcher d'être joyeuse face à l'obstination du garçon qui s'oppose à la tyrannie du professeur. Cette liberté à laquelle elle aspire sans encore le savoir, elle la désire pour son fils et elle est heureuse de constater son indépendance d'esprit. Quand le garçon cède finalement à la manière impérieuse du professeur et se met à jouer la sonatine comme on le lui demande, «moderato cantabile», Anne va jusqu'à dire: «Quand il obéit de cette façon, ça me dégoûte un peu.» C'est à ce moment-

---

[31] **anéantissement:** réduction à rien, au néant.
[32] **Pommard:** un vin rouge de Bourgogne.
[33] **au fur et à mesure que:** en proportion que.
[34] **fêlure:** fente.
[35] **enjeu:** «stakes».

là d'ailleurs qu'elle entend un cri dans la rue et que commence pour elle l'étrange expérience au cours de laquelle ses deux tendances contradictoires, vers le conformisme et l'affirmation de son individualité, s'aiguiseront et l'amèneront jusqu'au bord de la folie.

Tout, dans *Moderato Cantabile*, dépend du dialogue. C'est lui qui crée une ambiance chargée et dramatique malgré le fait qu'il ne se passe quasiment rien; c'est encore lui, par les phrases dites et les phrases coupées, les propos qui ne se suivent pas, et surtout par ce qui n'est *pas* prononcé, qui révèle l'angoisse et le trouble de cet homme et de cette femme. Le style de Marguerite Duras est un «... art qui parvient à nous tenir en haleine[36] avec des silences et des vides».[37] Par ces dialogues souvent peu cohérents, les deux personnages se révèlent, se trahissent et nous permettent de les comprendre même si l'auteur ne se permet jamais de les illuminer de l'intérieur, c'est-à-dire, subjectivement. Le véritable drame se joue dans la région nébuleuse aux abords de la conscience, une région que nous comprenons mal en nous-mêmes mais qu'avec sensibilité et intuition nous pouvons saisir chez autrui. Ainsi, Chauvin et le lecteur comprennent Anne bien avant qu'elle ne sache, elle, ce qui la ronge.

Il est extraordinaire qu'à aucun moment Marguerite Duras ne cède à la sentimentalité là où il aurait été facile de le faire. Elle laisse se mouvoir ses personnages dans leur humanité sans les interpréter. Le dialogue peut nous faire croire parfois à des divagations[38] parce qu'il ne suit pas la logique à laquelle nous sommes accoutumés, mais la phrase est claire, le vocabulaire d'une simplicité totale et la narration directe. Marguerite Duras ne nous cache rien de ce qu'elle sait sur ses personnages; les ombres que nous apercevons sont en eux et font partie de la complexité de leurs personnalités. Et c'est dans leur complexité que Marguerite Duras saisit ses personnages, au moment d'une crise psychologique intense qui fait contraste avec l'ennui et l'isolement dans lesquels ils vivent. Pour aboutir à cela, Marguerite Duras ne nous permet jamais de devenir conscients de son style. Ces phrases courtes, saccadées, souvent incohérentes, sont là tout simplement, discrètes, pour laisser ressortir de manière plus frappante tout ce qui est tû, leur amour, leur désir, leur solitude.

Il faudrait finalement parler du cadre dans lequel a lieu *Moderato Cantabile*. C'est surtout le café, que nous connaîtrons sans que Marguerite Duras ne l'ait jamais vraiment décrit, avec ses tables mal éclairées, son comptoir où à la sortie des usines règne une vie intense, et son vin, surtout ce vin qui envahit Anne jusqu'à la posséder. Quand nous ne nous trouvons pas dans ce café, nous sommes sur les quais, chez le professeur de musique, ou au dîner mondain chez Anne—tous des lieux que l'auteur fait vibrer d'une vie intense. Cette rencontre en huit chapitres qu'est le roman se joue sur un fond de leitmotive qui donne sa grande subtilité au roman: l'enfant qui semble toujours être là entre Anne et Chauvin; les vedettes[39] du port et le bruit de la mer qui invitent

---

36 **tenir en haleine:** garder notre attention passionnée.
37 Gaëton Picon dans le *Mercure de France* (juin 1958).
38 **divagation:** digression.
39 **vedette:** «motorboat».

peut-être à fuir très loin; la sirène qui marque la fin du travail et qui, avec le crépuscule, signalera qu'Anne devra bientôt rentrer; et bien sûr ce vin omniprésent, vin du désir, de l'abrutissement et de l'évasion qui arrache Anne à son monde. En dix jours, tandis que les journées s'allongent et que le printemps devient été, une femme fut bouleversée, coupée de son passé et plongée dans un vide dont elle ne soupçonne même pas les profondeurs. C'est là, en toute simplicité, le récit émouvant que nous offre Marguerite Duras.

T.B.

Préface

On a très souvent parlé—dans les articles consacrés[1] à *Moderato Cantabile*—d'une histoire d'amour. J'ai essayé, oralement, à plusieurs reprises, d'expliquer qu'il s'agissait là d'une erreur due, à mon avis, à une lecture peut-être un peu superficielle. Je suis parvenue quelquefois à détourner certains lecteurs de l'habitude qui consiste à nommer sentiment ou amour toute relation entre un homme et une femme.

De quoi s'agit-il si ce n'est pas d'un amour? me demande-t-on.

Je réponds: il s'agit de l'amour mais pas d'un amour.

Chauvin, le héros du livre se présente, à mon avis, comme un accident secondaire, de nature interchangeable, dans la vie de l'héroïne, Anne Desbaresdes. Il se présente comme le conteur[2] d'une histoire, une seule: celle de la femme assassinée dans le café au premier chapitre du roman. Ce que connaît Anne Desbaresdes de Chauvin c'est seulement ceci—qu'il a vu, dans le même temps qu'elle, un crime obscur et qu'il paraît, lui, le comprendre et pouvoir l'expliquer.

Le récit de ce crime fait par Chauvin à Anne Desbaresdes est celui-là même que, sans le savoir, elle attendait d'entendre un jour. Elle demande à Chauvin de le lui faire. Mais, en fait, c'est elle qui mène ce récit. Tout en le réclamant elle le conduit et elle le mène vers le but qu'elle a choisi.

La femme qui a été assassinée dans le café, raconte Chauvin, a imploré son amant de la tuer. Anne Desbaresdes qui l'écoute est confirmée dans l'intuition qu'elle avait d'une possibilité de fulguration de l'amour ou, si on veut, d'un stade[3] de l'amour où plus rien ne peut la nourrir que la mort.

Aux yeux d'Anne Desbaresdes, ce récit fait à «sa mesure» par Chauvin, définit Chauvin. Elle n'a pas besoin d'autre chose pour avoir avec lui une histoire dangereuse, mortelle.

Ce que veut Anne Desbaresdes de Chauvin c'est ce qu'elle n'a jamais vécu mais c'est ce qu'elle aurait pu vivre avec et à travers d'autres hommes: son anéantissement

---

1 **consacré:** ici, concernant.
2 **conteur:** narrateur.
3 **stade:** étape.

dans l'amour même. Tout se passe entre eux comme si—ayant brûlé toutes les étapes[4] habituelles d'une histoire d'amour grâce à ce crime modèle—ils se trouvaient d'emblée[5] à la dernière de toutes: la mort. Eu égard à[6] celle-ci, la connaissance et même le désir paraissent superflus. *De l'amour est vécu*, de l'amour passe entre eux. C'est le même amour que celui qui a présidé au couple du café—débarrassé de sa contingence et seulement porté par sa vocation à la mort.

MARGUERITE DURAS

---

4 **brûler les étapes:** ici, «to skip over».
5 **d'emblée:** directement, dès le début.
6 **eu égard à:** en considération de.

Moderato Cantabile

I

— Veux-tu lire ce qu'il y a d'écrit au-dessus de ta partition?[1] demanda la dame.

— Moderato cantabile, dit l'enfant.

La dame ponctua cette réponse d'un coup de crayon sur le clavier.[2] L'enfant resta immobile, la tête tournée vers sa partition.

— Et qu'est-ce que ça veut dire, moderato cantabile?   5

— Je sais pas.[3]

Une femme, assise à trois mètres de là, soupira.

— Tu es sûr de ne pas savoir ce que ça veut dire, moderato cantabile? reprit la dame.

L'enfant ne répondit pas. La dame poussa un cri d'impuissance étouffé, tout en   10
frappant de nouveau le clavier de son crayon. Pas un cil de l'enfant ne bougea. La dame se retourna.

— Madame Desbaresdes, quelle tête[4] vous avez là, dit-elle.

Anne Desbaresdes soupira une nouvelle fois.

— A qui le dites-vous,[5] dit-elle.   15

L'enfant, immobile, les yeux baissés, fut seul à se souvenir que le soir venait d'éclater. Il en frémit.

— Je te l'ai dit la dernière fois, je te l'ai dit l'avant-dernière fois, je te l'ai dit cent fois, tu es sûr de ne pas le savoir?

L'enfant ne jugea pas bon de répondre. La dame reconsidéra une nouvelle fois   20
l'objet qui était devant elle. Sa fureur augmenta.

— Ça recommence, dit tout bas Anne Desbaresdes.

— Ce qu'il y a,[6] continua la dame, ce qu'il y a, c'est que tu ne veux pas le dire.

---

1 **partition:** «musical score».
2 **clavier:** «keyboard».
3 **je sais pas:** c'est-à-dire, je ne sais pas.
4 **tête:** ici, une personne têtue.
5 **à qui le dites-vous:** «you're telling me!».
6 **ce qu'il y a:** la difficulté, le problème.

Anne Desbaresdes aussi reconsidéra cet enfant de ses pieds jusqu'à sa tête mais d'une autre façon que la dame.

— Tu vas le dire tout de suite, hurla la dame.

L'enfant ne témoigna aucune surprise. Il ne répondit toujours pas. Alors la
5   dame frappa une troisième fois sur le clavier, mais si fort que le crayon se cassa. Tout à côté des mains de l'enfant. Celles-ci étaient à peine écloses,[7] rondes, laiteuses[8] encore. Fermées sur elles-mêmes, elles ne bougèrent pas.

— C'est un enfant difficile, osa dire Anne Desbaresdes, non sans une certaine timidité.

10   L'enfant tourna la tête vers cette voix, vers elle, vite, le temps de s'assurer de son existence, puis il reprit sa pose d'objet, face à la partition. Ses mains restèrent fermées.

— Je ne veux pas savoir s'il est difficile ou non, Madame Desbaresdes, dit la dame. Difficile ou pas, il faut qu'il obéisse, ou bien.[9]

15   Dans le temps qui suivit ce propos, le bruit de la mer entra par la fenêtre ouverte.

Et avec lui, celui, atténué, de la ville au cœur de l'après-midi de ce printemps.

— Une dernière fois. Tu es sûr de ne pas le savoir?

Une vedette passa dans le cadre de la fenêtre ouverte. L'enfant, tourné vers sa
20   partition remua à peine—seule sa mère le sut—alors que la vedette lui passait dans le sang. Le ronronnement[10] feutré[11] du moteur s'entendit dans toute la ville. Rares étaient les bateaux de plaisance.[12] Le rose de la journée finissante colora le ciel tout entier. D'autres enfants, ailleurs, sur les quais, arrêtés, regardaient.

— Sûr, vraiment, une dernière fois, tu es sûr?

25   Encore, la vedette passait.

La dame s'étonna de tant d'obstination. Sa colère fléchit et elle se désespéra de si peu compter aux yeux de cet enfant que d'un geste, pourtant, elle eût pu réduire à la parole, que l'aridité de son sort, soudain, lui apparut.

— Quel métier, quel métier, quel métier, gémit-elle.

30   Anne Desbaresdes ne releva pas le propos, mais sa tête se pencha un peu de la manière, peut-être, d'en convenir.

La vedette eut enfin fini de traverser le cadre de la fenêtre ouverte. Le bruit de la mer s'éleva, sans bornes, dans le silence de l'enfant.

— Moderato?

---

7 **éclos:** ouvert.
8 **laiteux:** couleur de lait.
9 **ou bien:** «or else».
10 **ronronnement:** «purring».
11 **feutré:** comme si c'était recouvert de feutre.
12 **plaisance:** plaisir.

L'enfant ouvrit sa main, la déplaça et se gratta légèrement le mollet.[13] Son geste fut désinvolte[14] et peut-être la dame convint-elle de son innocence.

— Je sais pas, dit-il, après s'être gratté.

Les couleurs du couchant[15] devinrent tout à coup si glorieuses que la blondeur de cet enfant s'en trouva modifiée. 5

— C'est facile, dit la dame un peu plus calmement.

Elle se moucha longuement.

— Quel enfant j'ai là, dit Anne Desbaresdes joyeusement, tout de même, mais quel enfant j'ai fait là, et comment se fait-il qu'il me soit venu avec cet entêtement-là . . . 10

La dame ne crut pas bon de relever tant d'orgueil.

— Ça veut dire, dit-elle à l'enfant—écrasée—pour la centième fois, ça veut dire modéré et chantant.

— Modéré et chantant, dit l'enfant totalement en allé où?[16]

La dame se retourna. 15

— Ah, je vous jure.

— Terrible, affirma Anne Desbaresdes, en riant, têtu comme une chèvre, terrible.

— Recommence, dit la dame.

L'enfant ne recommença pas. 20

— Recommence, j'ai dit.

L'enfant ne bougea pas davantage. Le bruit de la mer dans le silence de son obstination se fit entendre de nouveau. Dans un dernier sursaut, le rose du ciel augmenta.

— Je ne veux pas apprendre le piano, dit l'enfant. 25

Dans la rue, en bas de l'immeuble, un cri de femme retentit. Une plainte longue, continue, s'éleva et si haut que le bruit de la mer en fut brisé. Puis elle s'arrêta, net.

— Qu'est-ce que c'est? cria l'enfant.

— Quelque chose est arrivé, dit la dame. 30

Le bruit de la mer ressuscita de nouveau. Le rose du ciel, cependant commença à pâlir.

— Non, dit Anne Desbaresdes, ce n'est rien.

Elle se leva de sa chaise et alla vers le piano.

— Quelle nervosité, dit la dame en les regardant tous deux d'un air réprobateur. 35

---

13 **mollet:** partie inférieure de la jambe; «calf».
14 **désinvolte:** dégagé; «offhand».
15 **couchant:** ici, le soleil au moment où il se couche.
16 **en allé où:** distrait.

Anne Desbaresdes prit son enfant par les épaules, le serra à lui faire mal, cria presque.

— Il faut apprendre le piano, il le faut.

L'enfant tremblait lui aussi, pour la même raison, d'avoir eu peur.

5   — J'aime pas[17] le piano, dit-il dans un murmure.

D'autres cris relayèrent alors le premier, éparpillés, divers. Ils consacrèrent une actualité déjà dépassée, rassurante désormais. La leçon continuait donc.

— Il le faut, continua Anne Desbaresdes, il le faut.

La dame hocha la tête, la désapprouvant de tant de douceur. Le crépuscule
10 commença à balayer la mer. Et le ciel, lentement, se décolora. L'ouest seul resta rouge encore. Il s'effaçait.

— Pourquoi? demanda l'enfant.

— La musique, mon amour . . .

L'enfant prit son temps, celui de tenter de comprendre, ne comprit pas, mais
15 l'admit.

— Bon. Mais qui a crié?

— J'attends, dit la dame.

Il se mit à jouer. De la musique s'éleva par-dessus la rumeur d'une foule qui commençait à se former au-dessous de la fenêtre, sur le quai.

20 — Quand même, quand même, dit Anne Desbaresdes joyeusement, voyez.

— S'il voulait, dit la dame.

L'enfant termina sa sonatine. Aussitôt la rumeur d'en bas s'engouffra[18] dans la pièce, impérieuse.[19]

— Qu'est-ce que c'est? redemanda l'enfant.

25 — Recommence, répondit la dame. N'oublie pas: moderato cantabile. Pense à une chanson qu'on te chanterait pour t'endormir.

— Jamais je ne lui chante de chansons, dit Anne Desbaresdes. Ce soir il va m'en demander une, et il le fera si bien que je ne pourrai pas refuser de chanter.

La dame ne voulut pas entendre. L'enfant recommença à jouer la sonatine de
30 Diabelli.

— Si bémol à la clef,[20] dit la dame très haut, tu l'oublies trop souvent.

Des voix précipitées, de femmes et d'hommes, de plus en plus nombreuses, montaient du quai. Elles semblaient toutes dire la même chose qu'on ne pouvait distinguer. La sonatine alla son train,[21] impunément, mais cette fois, en son milieu,
35 la dame n'y tint plus.[22]

---

17 **j'aime pas:** c'est-à-dire, je n'aime pas.
18 **s'engouffre:** entrer avec violence (pour des choses intangibles).
19 **impérieux:** ici, *fig.* irrésistible.
20 **si bémol à la clef:** «there is a B-flat in the key signature».
21 **aller son train:** «to go along».
22 **ne pas y tenir:** ne plus pouvoir se contrôler.

— Arrête.

L'enfant s'arrêta. La dame se tourna vers Anne Desbaresdes.

— C'est sûr, il s'est passé quelque chose de grave.

Ils allèrent tous les trois à la fenêtre. Sur la gauche du quai, à une vingtaine de mètres de l'immeuble, face à la porte d'un café, un groupe s'était déjà formé. Des gens arrivaient en courant de toutes les rues avoisinantes[23] et s'aggloméraient à lui. C'était vers l'intérieur du café que tout le monde regardait.

— Hélas, dit la dame, ce quartier . . .—elle se tourna vers l'enfant, le prit par le bras—recommence une dernière fois, là où tu t'es arrêté.

— Qu'est-ce qu'il y a?

— Ta sonatine.

L'enfant joua. Il reprit la sonatine au même rythme que précédemment et, la fin de la leçon approchant, il la nuança comme on le désirait, moderato cantabile.

— Quand il obéit de cette façon, ça me dégoûte un peu, dit Anne Desbaresdes. Je ne sais pas ce que je veux, voyez-vous. Quel martyre.

L'enfant continua néanmoins à bien faire.

— Quelle éducation lui donnez-vous là, Madame Desbaresdes, remarqua la dame presque joyeusement.

Alors l'enfant s'arrêta.

— Pourquoi t'arrêtes-tu?

— Je croyais.

Il reprit sa sonatine comme on le lui demandait. Le bruit sourd de la foule s'amplifiait toujours, il devenait maintenant si puissant, même à cette hauteur-là de l'immeuble, que la musique en était débordée.

— Ce si bémol à la clef, n'oublie pas, dit la dame, sans ça ce serait parfait, tu vois.

La sonatine se déroula, grandit, atteignit son dernier accord[24] une fois de plus. Et l'heure prit fin. La dame proclama la leçon terminée pour ce jour-là.

— Vous aurez beaucoup de mal, Madame Desbaresdes, avec cet enfant, dit-elle, c'est moi qui vous le dis.[25]

— C'est déjà fait,[26] il me dévore.[27]

Anne Desbaresdes baissa la tête, ses yeux se fermèrent dans le douloureux sourire d'un enfantement sans fin. En bas, quelques cris, des appels maintenant raisonnables, indiquèrent la consommation d'un événement inconnu.

— Demain, nous le saurons bien, dit la dame.

L'enfant courut à la fenêtre.

---

23 **avoisinant:** proche, voisin.
24 **accord:** ici, «chord».
25 **c'est moi qui vous le dis:** «I know what I'm talking about».
26 **c'est déjà fait:** «it has already happened».
27 **dévorer:** ici, *fig.* «to overwhelm».

— Des autos qui arrivent, dit-il.

La foule obstruait le café de part et d'autre de l'entrée, elle se grossissait encore, mais plus faiblement, des apports[28] des rues voisines, elle était beaucoup plus importante qu'on n'eût pu le prévoir. La ville s'était multipliée. Les gens s'écartèrent, un courant se creusa au milieu d'eux pour laisser le passage à un fourgon noir.[29] Trois hommes en descendirent et pénétrèrent dans le café.

— La police, dit quelqu'un.

Anne Desbaresdes se renseigna.

— Quelqu'un qui a été tué. Une femme.

Elle laissa son enfant devant le porche de Mademoiselle Giraud, rejoignit le gros de la foule devant le café, s'y faufila[30] et atteignit le dernier rang des gens qui, le long des vitres ouvertes, immobilisés par le spectacle, voyaient. Au fond du café, dans la pénombre de l'arrière-salle,[31] une femme était étendue par terre, inerte. Un homme, couché sur elle, aggripé à[32] ses épaules, l'appelait calmement.

— Mon amour. Mon amour.

Il se tourna vers la foule, la regarda, et on vit ses yeux. Toute expression en avait disparu, exceptée celle, foudroyée, indélébile, inversée du monde, de son désir. La police entra. La patronne, dignement dressée près de son comptoir, l'attendait.

— Trois fois que j'essaye de vous appeler.

— Pauvre femme, dit quelqu'un.

— Pourquoi? demanda Anne Desbaresdes.

— On ne sait pas.

L'homme, dans son délire, se vautrait[33] sur le corps étendu de la femme. Un inspecteur le prit par le bras et le releva. Il se laissa faire. Apparemment, toute dignité l'avait quitté à jamais. Il scruta l'inspecteur d'un regard toujours absent du reste du monde. L'inspecteur le lâcha, sortit un carnet de sa poche, un crayon, lui demanda de décliner[34] son identité, attendit.

— Ce n'est pas la peine, je ne répondrai pas maintenant, dit l'homme.

L'inspecteur n'insista pas et alla rejoindre ses collègues qui questionnaient la patronne, assis à la dernière table de l'arrière-salle.

L'homme s'assit près de la femme morte, lui caressa les cheveux et lui sourit. Un jeune homme arriva en courant à la porte du café, un appareil-photo en bandoulière[35] et le photographia ainsi, assis et souriant. Dans la lueur du magnésium,

---

[28] **apport:** ce qui est ajouté; ici, les gens venus des rues.
[29] **fourgon noir:** grande voiture de la police.
[30] **se faufiler:** s'introduire adroitement.
[31] **arrière-salle:** le fond de la salle.
[32] **agrippé à:** ayant saisi avec avidité.
[33] **se vautrer:** «to sprawl».
[34] **décliner:** ici, réciter.
[35] **en bandoulière:** suspendu à son épaule par une bande de cuir ou d'étoffe.

on put voir que la femme était jeune encore et qu'il y avait du sang qui coulait de sa bouche en minces filets[36] épars et qu'il y en avait aussi sur le visage de l'homme qui l'avait embrassée. Dans la foule, quelqu'un dit:

— C'est dégoûtant, et s'en alla.

L'homme se recoucha de nouveau le long du corps de sa femme, mais un temps très court. Puis, comme si cela l'eût lassé, il se releva encore.

— Empêchez-le de partir, cria la patronne.

Mais l'homme ne s'était relevé que pour mieux s'allonger encore, de plus près, le long du corps. Il resta là, dans une résolution apparemment tranquille, aggripé de nouveau à elle de ses deux bras, le visage collé au sien, dans le sang de sa bouche.

Mais les inspecteurs en eurent fini d'écrire sous la dictée[37] de la patronne et, à pas lents, tous trois marchant de front,[38] un air identique d'intense ennui sur leur visage, ils arrivèrent devant lui.

L'enfant, sagement assis sous le porche de Mademoiselle Giraud, avait un peu oublié. Il fredonnait[39] la sonatine de Diabelli.

— Ce n'était rien, dit Anne Desbaresdes, maintenant il faut rentrer.

L'enfant la suivit. Des renforts de police arrivèrent—trop tard, sans raison. Comme ils passaient devant le café, l'homme en sortit, encadré par les inspecteurs. Sur son passage, les gens s'écartèrent en silence.

— Ce n'est pas lui qui a crié, dit l'enfant. Lui, il n'a pas crié.

— Ce n'est pas lui. Ne regarde pas.

— Dis-moi pourquoi.

— Je ne sais pas.

L'homme marcha docilement jusqu'au fourgon. Mais, une fois là, il se débattit en silence, échappa aux inspecteurs et courut en sens inverse, de toutes ses forces, vers le café. Mais comme il allait l'atteindre, le café s'éteignit.[40] Alors il s'arrêta, en pleine course,[41] il suivit de nouveau les inspecteurs jusqu'au fourgon et il y monta. Peut-être alors pleura-t-il, mais le crépuscule trop avancé déjà ne permit d'apercevoir que la grimace ensanglantée[42] et tremblante de son visage et non plus de voir si des larmes s'y coulaient.

— Quand même, dit Anne Desbaresdes en arrivant boulevard de la Mer, tu pourrais t'en souvenir une fois pour toutes. Moderato, ça veut dire modéré, et cantabile, ça veut dire chantant, c'est facile.

------

36 **filet:** émission peu abondante.
37 **dictée:** ce qu'elle leur dictait.
38 **de front:** côte à côte.
39 **fredonner:** chanter à demi-voix.
40 **le café s'éteignit:** c'est-à-dire, les lumières du café s'éteignirent.
41 **en pleine course:** en vol.
42 **ensanglanté:** recouvert de sang.

QUESTIONNAIRE

Page 13—page 15, ligne 25	Pourquoi le professeur de musique se fâche-t-elle?
	Que pensez-vous de sa méthode pédagogique?
	En quoi l'enfant est-il «difficile»?
	Pourquoi Anne Desbaresdes est-elle joyeuse en disant: «Quel enfant j'ai là»?
	Comment essaie-t-elle de calmer le professeur?
	Pourquoi pensez-vous que l'auteur décrit le passage de la vedette?
	Avec quels moyens techniques Marguerite Duras a-t-elle commencé son roman?
Page 15, ligne 26—page 17, ligne 36	Quel est l'effet immédiat sur la leçon du cri entendu dans la rue?
	Quels seront les effets subséquents des bruits qui viennent de la rue?
	Pourquoi Anne veut-elle que son fils apprenne à jouer du piano?
	Comment l'enfant finit-il par jouer la sonatine?
	Qu'est-ce que cela prouve?
	Pourquoi le professeur désapprouve-t-elle Anne?
	Que veut dire Anne quand elle répond que son enfant la «dévore»?
	Décrivez les réactions des trois personnages face aux bruits de la rue.
Page 18, ligne 1—page 19	Comment se fait la transition qui nous mène de la leçon à la rue?
	Que s'est-il passé?
	Anne est-elle curieuse?
	Pourquoi n'amène-t-elle pas l'enfant quand elle va voir ce qui s'est passé?
	Que fait l'homme? Pourquoi?
	Que savons-nous sur ce qui a eu lieu?
	Pourquoi, à la fin du chapitre, ne pouvons-nous pas savoir si l'homme pleurait?
	Que pensez-vous d'Anne?

II

Le lendemain, alors que toutes les usines fumaient encore à l'autre bout de la ville, à l'heure déjà dépassée où chaque vendredi ils allaient dans ce quartier,

— Viens, dit Anne Desbaresdes à son enfant.

Ils longèrent le boulevard de la Mer. Déjà des gens s'y promenaient, flânant.[1] Et même il y avait quelques baigneurs.[2]

L'enfant avait l'habitude de parcourir la ville, chaque jour, en compagnie de sa mère, de telle sorte qu'elle pouvait le mener n'importe où.[3] Cependant, une fois le premier môle[4] dépassé, lorsqu'ils atteignirent le deuxième bassin des remorqueurs,[5] au-dessus duquel habitait Mademoiselle Giraud, il s'effraya.

— Pourquoi là?

— Pourquoi pas? dit Anne Desbaresdes. Aujourd'hui, c'est pour se promener seulement. Viens. Là, ou ailleurs.

L'enfant se laissa faire, la suivit jusqu'au bout.

Elle alla droit au comptoir. Seul un homme y était, qui lisait un journal.

— Un verre de vin, demanda-t-elle.

Sa voix tremblait. La patronne s'étonna, puis se ressaisit.

— Et pour l'enfant?

— Rien.

— C'est là qu'on a crié, je me rappelle, dit l'enfant.

Il se dirigea vers le soleil de la porte, descendit la marche, disparut sur le trottoir.

— Il fait beau, dit la patronne.

Elle vit que cette femme tremblait, évita de la regarder.

— J'avais soif, dit Anne Desbaresdes.

---

1 **flâner:** «to stroll».
2 **baigneur:** personne qui nage.
3 **n'importe où:** «anywhere».
4 **môle:** «breakwater».
5 **bassin des remorqueurs:** «tugboat mooring»

— Les premières chaleurs, c'est pourquoi.

— Et même je vous demanderai un autre verre de vin.

Au tremblement persistant des mains accrochées au verre, la patronne comprit qu'elle n'aurait pas si vite l'explication qu'elle désirait, que celle-ci viendrait d'elle-même, une fois cet émoi passé.

Ce fut plus rapide qu'elle l'eût cru. Anne Desbaresdes but le deuxième verre de vin d'un trait.[6]

— Je passais, dit-elle.

— C'est un temps à se promener, dit la patronne.

L'homme avait cessé de lire son journal.

— Justement, hier à cette heure-ci, j'étais chez Mademoiselle Giraud.

Le tremblement des mains s'atténua. Le visage prit une contenance presque décente.

— Je vous reconnais.

— C'était un crime, dit l'homme.

Anne Desbaresdes mentit.

— Je vois . . . Je me le demandais, voyez-vous.

— C'est naturel.

— Parfaitement, dit la patronne. Ce matin, c'était un défilé.[7]

L'enfant passa à cloche-pied[8] sur le trottoir.

— Mademoiselle Giraud donne des leçons à mon petit garçon.

Le vin aidant sans doute, le tremblement de la voix avait lui aussi cessé. Dans les yeux, peu à peu, afflua[9] un sourire de délivrance.

— Il vous ressemble, dit la patronne.

— On le dit—le sourire se précisa encore.

— Les yeux.

— Je ne sais pas, dit Anne Desbaresdes. Voyez-vous . . . tout en le promenant, je trouvais que c'était une occasion que de venir aujourd'hui ici. Ainsi . . .

— Un crime, oui.

Anne Desbaresdes mentit de nouveau.

— Ah, je l'ignorais, voyez-vous.

Un remorqueur quitta le bassin et démarra[10] dans le fracas[11] régulier et chaud de ses moteurs. L'enfant s'immobilisa sur le trottoir, pendant le temps que dura sa manœuvre, puis il se retourna vers sa mère.

---

6 **d'un trait:** «in one gulp».
7 **défilé:** action de ceux qui défilent; marche à la file.
8 **à cloche-pied:** «hopping on one foot».
9 **affluer:** ici, se former.
10 **démarrer:** se mettre en marche.
11 **fracas:** bruit.

— Où ça va?

Elle l'ignorait, dit-elle. L'enfant repartit. Elle prit le verre vide devant elle, s'aperçut de sa mégarde,[12] le reposa sur le comptoir et attendit, les yeux baissés. Alors, l'homme se rapprocha.

— Vous permettez.

Elle ne s'étonna pas, toute à son désarroi.

— C'est que je n'ai pas l'habitude, Monsieur.

Il commanda du vin, fit encore un pas vers elle.

— Ce cri était si fort que vraiment il est bien naturel que l'on cherche à savoir. J'aurais pu difficilement éviter de le faire, voyez-vous.

Elle but son vin, le troisième verre.

— Ce que je sais, c'est qu'il lui a tiré une balle dans le cœur.[13]

Deux clients entrèrent. Ils reconnurent cette femme au comptoir, s'étonnèrent.

— Et évidemment on ne peut pas savoir pourquoi?

Il était clair qu'elle n'avait pas l'habitude du vin, qu'à cette heure-là de la journée autre chose de bien différent l'occupait en général.

— J'aimerais pouvoir vous le dire, mais je ne sais rien de sûr.

— Peut-être que personne ne le sait?

— Lui le savait. Il est maintenant devenu fou, enfermé depuis hier soir. Elle, est morte.

L'enfant surgit de dehors et se colla contre[14] sa mère dans un mouvement d'abandon heureux. Elle lui caressa distraitement les cheveux. L'homme regarda plus attentivement.

— Ils s'aimaient, dit-il.

Elle sursauta, mais à peine.

— Alors, maintenant, tu le sais, dit l'enfant, pourquoi on a crié?

Elle ne répondit pas, fit, de la tête, signe que non. L'enfant s'en alla de nouveau vers la porte, elle le suivit des yeux.

— Lui travaillait à l'arsenal. Elle, je ne sais pas.

Elle se retourna vers lui, s'approcha.

— Peut-être avaient-ils des difficultés, ce qu'on appelle des difficultés de cœur[15] alors?

Les clients s'en allèrent. La patronne, qui avait entendu, vint au bout du comptoir.

— Et mariée, elle, dit-elle, trois enfants, et ivrogne, c'est à se demander.[16]

---

12 **mégarde:** faute d'attention.
13 **tirer une balle dans le cœur:** «to shoot through the heart».
14 **se coller contre:** ici, «to hug».
15 **difficultés de cœur:** problèmes d'amour.
16 **c'est à se demander:** c'est curieux.

— N'empêche,[17] peut-être? demanda Anne Desbaresdes, au bout d'un temps.
L'homme n'acquiesça pas. Elle se décontenança.[18] Et aussitôt, le tremblement des mains recommença.

Enfin, je ne sais pas . . . dit-elle.

5   — Non, dit la patronne, croyez-moi, et je n'aime pas me mêler des affaires des autres en général.

Trois nouveaux clients entrèrent. La patronne s'éloigna.

— N'empêche, je crois aussi, dit l'homme en souriant. Ils devaient avoir, oui, des difficultés de cœur, comme vous dites. Mais peut-être n'est-ce pas en raison
10 de[19] ces difficultés-là qu'il l'a tuée, qui sait?

— Qui sait, c'est vrai.

La main chercha le verre, machinalement. Il fit signe à la patronne de les servir à nouveau de vin. Anne Desbaresdes ne protesta pas, eut l'air, au contraire, de l'attendre.

15   — A le voir faire avec elle, dit-elle doucement, comme si, vivante ou morte, ça ne lui importait plus désormais, vous croyez qu'il est possible d'en arriver . . . là . . .[20] autrement que . . . par désespoir?

L'homme hésita, la regarda en face, prit un ton tranchant.[21]

— Je l'ignore, dit-il.

20   Il lui tendit son verre, elle le prit, but. Et il la ramena vers des régions qui sans doute devaient lui être plus familières.

— Vous vous promenez souvent dans la ville.

Elle avala une gorgée[22] de vin, le sourire revint sur son visage et l'obscurcit de nouveau, mais plus avant[23] que tout à l'heure. Son ivresse commençait.

25   — Oui, tous les jours je promène mon enfant.

La patronne, qu'il surveillait,[24] parlait avec les trois clients. C'était un samedi. Les gens avaient du temps à perdre.

— Mais dans cette ville, si petite qu'elle soit, tous les jours il se passe quelque chose, vous le savez bien.

30   — Je le sais, mais sans doute qu'un jour ou l'autre . . . une chose vous étonne davantage—elle se troubla.[25] D'habitude je vais dans les squares[26] ou au bord de la mer.

---

17 **n'empêche:** néanmoins.
18 **se décontenancer:** devenir déconcerté.
19 **en raison de:** à cause de.
20 **en arriver là:** arriver à ce point.
21 **tranchant:** décisif.
22 **gorgée:** «mouthful».
23 **plus avant:** ici, d'une façon plus évidente.
24 **surveiller:** ici, regarder.
25 **se troubler:** s'inquiéter.
26 **square:** petit parc.

Toujours grâce à son ivresse qui grandissait, elle en vint à[27] regarder devant elle, cet homme.

— Il y a longtemps que vous le promenez.

Les yeux de cet homme qui lui parlait et qui la regardait aussi, dans le même temps.

— Je veux dire qu'il y a longtemps que vous le promenez dans les squares ou au bord de la mer, reprit-il.

Elle se plaignit. Son sourire disparut. Une moue[28] le remplaça, qui mit brutalement son visage à découvert.[29]

— Je n'aurais pas dû boire tant de vin.

Une sirène retentit qui annonçait la fin du travail pour les équipes du samedi.[30] Aussitôt après, la radio s'éleva en rafale,[31] insupportable.

— Six heures déjà, annonça la patronne.

Elle baissa la radio, s'affaira,[32] prépara des files de verres sur le comptoir. Anne Desbaresdes resta un long moment dans un silence stupéfié à regarder le quai, comme si elle ne parvenait pas à savoir ce qu'il lui fallait faire d'elle-même. Lorsque dans le port un mouvement d'hommes s'annonça, bruissant,[33] de loin encore, l'homme lui reparla.

— Je vous disais qu'il y avait longtemps que vous promeniez cet enfant au bord de la mer ou dans les squares.

— J'y ai pensé de plus en plus depuis hier soir, dit Anne Desbaresdes, depuis la leçon de piano de mon enfant. Je n'aurais pas pu m'empêcher de venir aujourd'hui, voyez.

Les premiers hommes entrèrent. L'enfant se fraya un passage[34] à travers eux, curieux, et arriva jusqu'à sa mère, qui le prit contre elle dans un mouvement d'enlacement[35] machinal.

— Vous êtes Madame Desbaresdes. La femme du directeur d'Import-Export et des Fonderies[36] de la Côte. Vous habitez boulevard de la Mer.

Une autre sirène retentit, plus faible que la première, à l'autre bout du quai. Un remorqueur arriva. L'enfant se dégagea, d'une façon assez brutale, s'en alla en courant.

---

27 **en venir à:** arriver à.
28 **moue:** «pout».
29 **mettre à découvert:** révéler dans toute sa vérité.
30 **équipe de samedi:** «Saturday shift».
31 **rafale:** «blast».
32 **s'affairer:** s'empresser.
33 **bruissant:** faisant du bruit.
34 **se frayer un passage:** s'ouvrir un chemin, un passage.
35 **enlacement:** étreinte.
36 **fonderie:** «foundry».

— Il apprend le piano, dit-elle. Il a des dispositions, mais beaucoup de mauvaise volonté,[37] il faut que j'en convienne.

Toujours pour faire place aux hommes qui entraient régulièrement très nombreux dans le café, il se rapprocha un peu plus d'elle. Les premiers clients s'en allèrent. D'autres arrivèrent encore. Entre eux, dans le jeu de leurs allées et venues,[38] on voyait le soleil se coucher dans la mer, le ciel qui flambait et l'enfant qui, de l'autre côté du quai, jouait tout seul à des jeux dont le secret était indiscernable à cette distance. Il sautait des obstacles imaginaires, devait chanter.

— Je voudrais pour cet enfant tant de choses à la fois que je ne sais pas comment m'y prendre,[39] par où commencer. Et je m'y prends très mal. Il faut que je rentre parce qu'il est tard.

— Je vous ai vue souvent. Je n'imaginais pas qu'un jour vous arriveriez jusqu'ici avec votre enfant.[40]

La patronne augmenta un peu le volume de la radio pour ceux des derniers clients qui venaient d'entrer. Anne Desbaresdes se tourna vers le comptoir, fit une grimace, accepta le bruit, l'oublia.

— Si vous saviez tout le bonheur qu'on leur veut, comme si c'était possible. Peut-être vaudrait-il mieux parfois que l'on nous en sépare. Je n'arrive pas à me faire une raison de[41] cet enfant.

— Vous avez une belle maison au bout du boulevard de la Mer. Un grand jardin fermé.

Elle le regarda, perplexe, revenue à elle.

— Mais ces leçons de piano, j'en ai beaucoup de plaisir, affirma-t-elle.

L'enfant, traqué par le crépuscule, revint une nouvelle fois vers eux. Il resta là à contempler le monde, les clients. L'homme fit signe à Anne Desbaresdes de regarder au dehors. Il lui sourit.

— Regardez, dit-il, les jours allongent, allongent . . .

Anne Desbaresdes regarda, ajusta son manteau avec soin, lentement.

— Vous travaillez dans cette ville, Monsieur?

— Dans cette ville, oui. Si vous reveniez, j'essaierai de savoir autre chose et je vous le dirai.

Elle baissa les yeux, se souvint et pâlit.

— Du sang sur sa bouche, dit-elle, et il l'embrassait, l'embrassait.

Elle se reprit: ce que vous avez dit, vous le supposiez?

— Je n'ai rien dit.

---

37 **avoir de la mauvaise volonté:** ne pas essayer sincèrment.
38 **allées et venues:** «comings and goings», «turnover».
39 **comment s'y prendre:** «how to go about it».
40 Notez qu'il s'étonne qu'une dame soit venue avec son enfant dans un café d'ouvriers.
41 **me faire une raison de:** «I can't do anything with».

Le couchant était si bas maintenant qu'il atteignait le visage de cet homme. Son corps, debout, légèrement appuyé au comptoir, le recevait déjà depuis un moment.

— A l'avoir vu, on ne peut pas s'empêcher, n'est-ce pas, c'est presque inévitable?

— Je n'ai rien dit, répéta l'homme. Mais je crois qu'il l'a visée au cœur comme elle le lui demandait.

Anne Desbaresdes gémit. Une plainte presque licencieuse, douce, sortit de cette femme.

— C'est curieux, je n'ai pas envie de rentrer, dit-elle.

Il prit brusquement son verre, le termina d'un trait, ne répondit pas, la quitta des yeux.

— J'ai dû trop boire, continua-t-elle, voyez-vous, c'est ça.

— C'est ça, oui, dit l'homme.

Le café s'était presque vidé. Les entrées se firent plus rares. Tout en lavant ses verres, la patronne les lorgnait,[42] intriguée de les voir tant s'attarder, sans doute. L'enfant, revenu vers la porte, contemplait les quais maintenant silencieux. Debout devant l'homme, tournant le dos au port, Anne Desbaresdes se tut encore longtemps. Lui ne paraissait pas s'apercevoir de sa présence.

— Il m'aurait été impossible de ne pas revenir, dit-elle enfin.

— Je suis revenu moi aussi pour la même raison que vous.

— On la voit souvent par la ville, dit la patronne, avec son petit garçon. A la belle saison tous les jours.

— Les leçons de piano?

— Le vendredi, une fois par semaine. Hier. Ca lui faisait une sortie,[43] en somme, cette histoire.

L'homme faisait jouer la monnaie dans sa poche. Il fixait[44] le quai devant lui. La patronne n'insista pas.

Le môle dépassé, le boulevard de la Mer s'étendait, parfaitement rectiligne,[45] jusqu'à la fin de la ville.

— Lève la tête, dit Anne Desbaresdes. Regarde-moi.

L'enfant obéit, accoutumé à ses manières.

— Quelquefois je crois que je t'ai inventé, que ce n'est pas vrai, tu vois.

L'enfant leva la tête et bâilla face à elle. L'intérieur de sa bouche s'emplit de la

---

[42] **lorgner:** regarder du coin de l'œil.
[43] **sortie:** ici, quelque chose à faire hors de la maison.
[44] **fixer:** regarder fixement.
[45] **rectiligne:** en ligne droite.

dernière lueur du couchant. L'étonnement de Anne Desbaresdes, quand elle regardait cet enfant, était toujours égal à lui-même depuis le premier jour. Mais ce soir-là sans doute crût-elle cet étonnement comme à lui-même renouvelé.

QUESTIONNAIRE

Page 21—page 24, ligne 19	Comment l'enfant passait-il ses journées?
	Pourquoi a-t-il peur en passant près de Mademoiselle Giraud?
	Pourquoi Anne va-t-elle au café?
	Quel est l'effet que le vin a sur elle?
	Quelles sont les questions qu'Anne et l'homme se posent à propos du crime?
	Que fait l'enfant pendant qu'ils parlent?
Page 24, ligne 20—page 28	Pourquoi Anne ne répond-elle pas aux propos de l'homme mais continue à parler d'autre chose?
	Pourquoi s'étonne-t-on de voir Anne dans ce café?
	Combien de temps pensez-vous que dure la conversation entre Anne et l'homme?
	En quelle saison a lieu l'histoire? Quel temps fait-il?
	Qu'est-ce que l'homme sait sur Anne?
	Qu'est-ce qu'il promet si Anne revient au café?
	Pourquoi Anne gémit-elle quand l'homme lui dit sa théorie sur le crime?
	Pourquoi ne veut-elle pas rentrer?
	Décrivez les rapports entre Anne et son enfant.
	Par quels moyens Marguerite Duras a-t-elle su intéresser ses lecteurs dans ces deux chapitres?

III

L'enfant poussa la grille, son petit cartable[1] brinqueballant[2] sur son dos, puis il s'arrêta au seuil du parc. Il inspecta les pelouses autour de lui, marcha lentement, sur la pointe des pieds, attentif, on ne sait jamais, aux oiseaux qu'il aurait fait fuir en avançant. Justement,[3] un oiseau s'envola. L'enfant le suivit des yeux pendant un moment, le temps de le voir se poser sur un arbre du parc voisin, puis il continua son chemin jusqu'au dessous d'une certaine fenêtre, derrière un hêtre. Il leva la tête. A cette fenêtre, à cette heure-là de la journée, toujours on lui souriait. On lui sourit.

— Viens, cria Anne Desbaresdes, on va se promener.

— Le long de la mer?

— Le long de la mer, partout. Viens.

Ils suivirent de nouveau le boulevard en direction des môles. L'enfant comprit très vite, ne s'étonna guère.

— C'est loin, se plaignit-il—puis il accepta, chantonna.[4]

Lorsqu'ils dépassèrent le premier bassin, il était encore tôt. Devant eux, à l'extrémité sud de la ville, l'horizon était obscurci de zébrures[5] noires, de nuages ocres[6] que versaient[7] vers le ciel les fonderies.

L'heure était creuse,[8] le café encore désert. Seul, l'homme était là, au bout du bar. La patronne, aussitôt qu'elle entra, se leva et alla vers Anne Desbaresdes. L'homme ne bougea pas.

— Ce sera?[9]

---

1 **cartable:** sac d'écolier.
2 **brinqueballer:** «to bounce».
3 **justement:** en effet.
4 **chantonner:** chanter à demi-voix.
5 **zébrure:** ligne.
6 **ocre:** couleur jaune-rouge-brun, comme l'argile.
7 **verser:** ici, «pour forth».
8 **heure creuse:** moment de la journée quand il n'y a pas de clients.
9 **ce sera?:** que désirez-vous?

—Je voudrais un verre de vin.

Elle le but aussitôt servi. Le tremblement était encore plus fort que trois jours auparavant.

— Vous vous étonnez peut-être de me revoir?

5 — Dans mon métier . . . dit la patronne.

Elle lorgna l'homme à la dérobée[10]—lui aussi avait pâli—se rassit puis, se ravisant,[11] se retourna sur elle-même et, d'un geste décent,[12] alluma[13] la radio. L'enfant quitta sa mère et s'en alla sur le trottoir.

— Comme je vous le disais, mon petit garçon prend des leçons de piano chez 10 Mademoiselle Giraud. Vous devez la connaître.

—Je la connais. Il y a plus d'un an que je vous vois passer, une fois par semaine, le vendredi, n'est-ce pas?

— Le vendredi, oui. Je voudrais un autre verre de vin.

L'enfant avait trouvé un compagnon. Immobiles sur l'avancée[14] du quai, ils 15 regardaient décharger le sable d'une grande péniche.[15] Anne Desbaresdes but la moitié de son second verre de vin. Le tremblement de ses mains s'atténua un peu.

— C'est un enfant qui est toujours seul, dit-elle en regardant vers l'avancée du quai.

La patronne reprit son tricot[16] rouge, elle jugea inutile de répondre. Un autre 20 remorqueur[17] chargé à ras bord[18] entrait dans le port. L'enfant cria quelque chose d'indistinct. L'homme s'approcha d'Anne Desbaresdes.

— Asseyez-vous, dit-il.

Elle le suivit sans un mot. La patronne, tout en tricotant, regardait obstinément le remorqueur. Il était visible qu'à son gré les choses prenaient un tour déplaisant.[19]

25 — Là.

Il lui désigna une table. Elle s'assit, et lui en face d'elle.

— Merci, murmura-t-elle.

Dans la salle, il faisait la pénombre fraîche d'un début d'été.

—Je suis revenue, voyez.

30 Dehors, très près, un enfant siffla. Elle sursauta.

—Je voudrais que vous preniez un autre verre de vin, dit l'homme, les yeux sur la porte.

---

10 **à la dérobée:** furtivement.

11 **raviser:** changer d'avis.

12 **décent:** ici, correct, propre.

13 **allumer:** ici, «turn on».

14 **avancée:** ici, bout; partie la plus avancée dans l'eau.

15 **péniche:** «barge».

16 **tricot:** ici, vêtement tricoté.

17 **remorqueur:** «tugboat».

18 **à ras bord:** «to the top».

19 **prendre un tour déplaisant:** «to take a disagreeable turn».

Il commanda le vin. La patronne s'exécuta[20] sans un mot, déjà lassée sans doute du dérèglement[21] de leurs manières. Anne Desbaresdes s'adossa[22] à sa chaise, s'abandonna au répit que lui laissait sa peur.

— Il y a maintenant trois jours, dit l'homme.

Elle se redressa avec effort et but de nouveau son vin.

— C'est bon, dit-elle, bas.

Les mains ne tremblèrent plus. Elle se redressa encore, s'avança légèrement vers lui qui maintenant la regardait.

— Je voulais vous demander, vous ne travaillez donc pas aujourd'hui?

— Non, j'ai besoin de temps en ce moment.

Elle eut un sourire d'une hypocrite timidité.

— Du temps pour ne rien faire?

— Rien, oui.

La patronne était bien à son poste, derrière sa caisse. Anne Desbaresdes parla bas.

— La difficulté, c'est de trouver un prétexte, pour une femme, d'aller dans un café, mais je me suis dit que j'étais quand même capable d'en trouver un, par exemple un verre de vin, la soif . . .

— J'ai essayé de savoir davantage. Je ne sais rien.

Anne Desbaresdes s'exténua encore une fois à se ressouvenir.

— C'était un cri très long, très haut, qui s'est arrêté net alors qu'il était au plus fort de lui-même, dit-elle.

— Elle mourait, dit l'homme. Le cri a dû s'arrêter au moment où elle a cessé de le voir.

Un client arriva, ne les remarqua guère, s'accouda au comptoir.

— Une fois, il me semble bien, oui, une fois j'ai dû crier un peu de cette façon, peut-être, oui, quand j'ai eu cet enfant.

— Ils s'étaient connus par hasard dans un café, peut-être même dans ce café-ci qu'ils fréquentaient tous les deux. Et ils ont commencé à se parler de choses et d'autres.[23] Mais je ne sais rien. Ça vous a fait très mal, cet enfant?

— J'ai crié . . . si vous saviez.

Elle sourit, s'en souvenant, se renversa[24] en arrière, libérée tout à coup de toute sa peur. Il se rapprocha de la table, lui dit sèchement:

— Parlez-moi.

Elle fit un effort, trouva quoi dire.

---

[20] **s'exécuter:** faire ce qu'on est supposé faire.
[21] **dérèglement:** état déréglé.
[22] **s'adosser:** s'appuyer le dos contre.
[23] **de choses et d'autres:** «of this and that».
[24] **se renverser:** ici, se pencher.

— J'habite la dernière maison du boulevard de la Mer, la dernière quand on quitte la ville. Juste avant les dunes.

— Le magnolia, à l'angle gauche de la grille, est en fleurs.

— Oui, il y en a tellement à cette époque-ci de l'année qu'on peut en rêver et en être malade tout le jour qui suit. On ferme sa fenêtre, c'est à n'y pas tenir.[25]

— C'est dans cette maison qu'on vous a épousée il y a maintenant dix ans?

— C'est là. Ma chambre est au premier étage, à gauche, en regardant la mer. Vous me disiez la dernière fois qu'il l'avait tuée parce qu'elle le lui avait demandé, pour lui plaire, en somme?

Il s'attarda, sans répondre à sa question, à voir enfin la ligne de ses épaules.

— Si vous fermez votre fenêtre à cette époque-ci de l'année, dit-il, vous devez avoir chaud et mal dormir.

Anne Desbaresdes devint sérieuse plus que le propos, apparemment, ne l'exigeait.

— L'odeur des magnolias est si forte, si vous saviez.

— Je sais.

Il quitta des yeux la ligne droite de ses épaules, la quitta des yeux.

— Au premier étage, n'y a-t-il pas un long couloir, très long, qui est commun à vous et aux autres dans cette maison, et qui fait que vous y êtes ensemble et séparés à la fois?

— Ce couloir existe, dit Anne Desbaresdes, et comme vous le dites. Dites-moi, je vous en prie, comment elle en est venue à découvrir que c'était justement ça qu'elle voulait de lui, comment elle a su à ce point ce qu'elle désirait de lui?

Ses yeux revinrent aux siens, d'une fixité devenue un peu hagarde.

— J'imagine qu'un jour, dit-il, un matin à l'aube, elle a su soudainement ce qu'elle désirait de lui. Tout est devenu clair pour elle au point qu'elle lui a dit quel serait son désir. Il n'y a pas d'explication, je crois, à ce genre de découverte-là.

Dehors, les jeux calmes de l'enfant continuaient. Le deuxième remorqueur était arrivé à quai. Dans le répit qui suivit l'arrêt de ses moteurs, la patronne bougea des objets sous le comptoir, avec ostentation, leur rappela le temps qui s'écoulait.

— C'est par ce couloir que vous disiez qu'il faut passer pour aller dans votre chambre?

— C'est par ce couloir.

L'enfant entra en courant très vite, renversa sa tête sur l'épaule de sa mère. Elle ne prit pas garde[26] à lui.

— Oh, que je m'amuse, dit-il. Il s'enfuit de nouveau.

---

25 **c'est à n'y pas tenir:** c'est insupportable.
26 **prendre garde:** faire attention.

—J'oubliais de vous dire combien je voudrais qu'il soit déjà grand, dit Anne Desbaresdes.

Il la servit de vin, lui tendit son verre, elle le but aussitôt.

—Vous savez, dit-il, j'imagine aussi qu'il l'aurait fait de lui-même un jour, même sans ses instances à elle. Qu'elle n'était pas seule à avoir découvert ce qu'elle désirait de lui.

Elle revint de loin à ses questions, harcelante,[27] méthodiquement.

—Je voudrais que vous me disiez le commencement même, comment ils ont commencé à se parler. C'est dans un café, disiez-vous . . .

Les deux enfants jouaient à courir en rond, toujours sur l'avancée du quai.

—Nous avons peu de temps, dit-il. Les usines ferment dans un quart d'heure. Oui, je crois bien que c'est dans un café qu'ils ont commencé à se parler, à moins que[28] ce soit ailleurs. Ils ont peut-être parlé de la situation politique, des risques de guerre, ou bien d'autre chose encore de bien différent de tout ce qu'on peut imaginer, de tout, de rien. Peut-être pourrait-on boire encore un verre de vin avant que vous ne retourniez boulevard de la Mer.

La patronne les servit, toujours en silence, peut-être un peu vivement. Ils n'y prirent pas garde.

—Au bout de ce long couloir—Anne Desbaresdes parlait posément[29]—il y a une grande baie[30] vitrée,[31] face au boulevard. Le vent la frappe de plein fouet.[32] L'année dernière, pendant un orage, les vitres se sont cassées. C'était la nuit.

Elle se renversa sur sa chaise et rit.

—Que ce soit justement dans cette ville que ce soit arrivé . . . ah, comment se faire à[33] cette idée! . . .

—C'est une petite ville, en effet. A peine le contingent[34] de trois usines.

Le mur du fond de la salle s'illumina du soleil couchant. En son milieu le trou noir de leurs ombres conjuguées[35] se dessina.

—Alors ils ont parlé, dit Anne Desbaresdes, et parlé, beaucoup de temps, beaucoup, avant d'y arriver.

—Je crois qu'ils ont passé beaucoup de temps ensemble pour en arriver là où ils étaient, oui. Parlez-moi.

---

27 **harcelant:** agaçant.
28 **à moins que:** «unless».
29 **posément:** sans se presser.
30 **baie:** «bay window».
31 **vitré:** transparent.
32 **de plein fouet:** «full force».
33 **se faire à:** s'habituer à.
34 **contingent:** ici, le nombre d'ouvriers qu'il faut.
35 **conjugué:** mêlé.

— Je ne sais plus, avoua-t-elle.

Il lui sourit de façon encourageante.

— Qu'est-ce que ça peut faire?[36]

De nouveau elle parla, avec application, presque difficulté, très lentement.

5   — Il me semble que cette maison dont nous parlions a été faite un peu arbitrairement, vous voyez ce que je veux dire, mais quand même en raison d'une commodité[37] dont tout le monde devrait être satisfait.

— Au rez-de-chaussée il y a des salons où vers la fin mai, chaque année, on donne des réceptions au personnel des fonderies.

10   Foudroyante, la sirène retentit. La patronne se leva de sa chaise, rangea son tricot rouge, rinça des verres qui crissèrent[38] sous l'eau froide.

— Vous aviez une robe noire très décolletée.[39] Vous nous regardiez avec amabilité et indifférence. Il faisait chaud.

Elle ne fut pas surprise, frauda.[40]

15   — Le printemps est exceptionnellement beau, dit Anne Desbaresdes, tout le monde en parlait déjà. Vous croyez quand même que c'est elle qui a commencé à le dire, à oser le dire et qu'ensuite il en a été question entre eux comme d'autre chose?

— Je ne sais rien d'autre que vous. Peut-être en a-t-il été question une seule fois
20   entre eux, peut-être en a-t-il été question tous les jours? Comment le saurions-nous? Mais sans doute sont-ils arrivés très exactement ensemble là où ils étaient il y a trois jours, à ne plus savoir du tout, ensemble, ce qu'ils faisaient.

Il releva la main, la laissa retomber près de la sienne sur la table, il la laissa là. Elle remarqua ces deux mains posées côte à côte pour la première fois.

25   — Voilà que j'ai encore bu trop de vin, se plaignit-elle.

— Ce grand couloir dont vous parliez reste parfois allumé très tard.

— Il m'arrive de ne pas arriver à m'endormir.

— Pourquoi allumer aussi ce couloir et pas seulement votre chambre?

— Une habitude que j'ai. Je ne sais pas au juste.[41]

30   — Rien ne s'y passe, rien, la nuit.

— Si. Derrière une porte, mon enfant dort.

Elle ramena ses bras vers la table, rentra les épaules, frileusement,[42] ajusta sa veste.

---

36 **qu'est-ce que ça peut faire?**: «what difference can that make?»
37 **commodité:** qualité de ce qui est commode.
38 **crisser:** «to squeak».
39 **décolleté:** rélévant le cou, les épaules.
40 **frauder:** feindre.
41 **au juste:** exactement.
42 **frileusement:** «shivering».

— Il faut que je rentre peut-être, maintenant. Voyez comme c'est tard.

Il releva sa main, lui fit signe de rester encore. Elle resta.

— Quand c'est le jour, au petit matin, vous allez regarder à travers la grande baie vitrée.

— L'été, les ouvriers de l'arsenal commencent à passer vers six heures. L'hiver, la plupart prennent le car[43] à cause du vent, du froid. Ça ne dure qu'un quart d'heure.

— La nuit, il ne passe jamais personne, jamais?

— Quelquefois si, une bicyclette, on se demande d'où ça peut venir. Est-ce de la douleur de l'avoir tuée, qu'elle soit morte, que cet homme est devenu fou, ou autre chose s'est-il ajouté de plus loin à cette douleur, autre chose que les gens ignorent en général?

— Sans doute qu'autre chose s'est en effet ajouté à sa douleur, autre chose que nous ignorons encore.

Elle se leva, se leva avec lenteur, fut levée, réajusta une nouvelle fois sa veste. Il ne l'aida pas. Elle se tint en face de lui encore assis, ne disant rien. Les premiers hommes entrèrent au café, s'étonnèrent, interrogèrent la patronne du regard. Celle-ci, d'un léger mouvement d'épaules, signifia qu'elle-même n'y comprenait pas grand-chose.

— Peut-être que vous ne reviendrez plus.

Quand à son tour il se releva et se redressa, Anne Desbaresdes dut remarquer qu'il était encore jeune, que le couchant se jouait aussi limpide dans ses yeux que dans ceux d'un enfant. Elle scruta à travers le regard leur matière bleue.

— Je n'avais pas pensé que je pourrais ne plus venir.

Il la retint une dernière fois.

— Souvent, vous regardez ces hommes qui vont à l'arsenal, surtout l'été, et la nuit, lorsque vous dormez mal, le souvenir vous en revient.

— Lorsque je me réveille assez tôt, avoua Anne Desbaresdes, je les regarde. Et parfois aussi, oui, le souvenir de certains d'entre eux, la nuit, m'est revenu.

Au moment où ils se quittèrent, d'autres hommes débouchaient sur le quai. Ceux-là devaient venir des Fonderies de la Côte, qui étaient plus éloignées de la ville que l'arsenal. Il faisait plus clair que trois jours avant. Il y avait des mouettes[44] dans le ciel redevenu bleu.

— J'ai bien joué, annonça l'enfant.

Elle le laissa raconter ses jeux jusqu'à ce qu'ils aient dépassé le premier môle à

---

43 **car**: autobus.
44 **mouette**: «seagull».

partir duquel filait, sans une courbe, le boulevard de la Mer, jusqu'aux dunes qui marquaient sa fin. L'enfant s'impatienta.

— Qu'est-ce que tu as?

Avec le crépuscule, la brise[45] commença à balayer la ville. Elle eut froid.

5   — Je ne sais pas. J'ai froid.

L'enfant prit la main de sa mère, l'ouvrit, y enfouit la sienne dans une résolution implacable. Elle y fut contenue tout entière. Anne Desbaresdes cria presque.

— Ah, mon amour.

— Tu vas toujours à ce café maintenant.

10   — Deux fois.

— Mais tu vas y aller encore?

— Je crois.

Ils croisèrent des gens qui rentraient, des pliants[46] à la main. Le vent frappait de front.

15   — Moi, qu'est-ce que tu vas m'acheter?

— Un bateau rouge à moteur, tu veux bien?[47]

L'enfant soupesa[48] cet avenir en silence, soupira d'aise.

— Oui, un gros bateau rouge à moteur. Comment t'as trouvé?[49]

Elle le prit par les épaules, le retint comme il essayait de se dégager pour courir
20 en avant.

— Tu grandis, toi, ah, comme tu grandis, comme c'est bien.

QUESTIONNAIRE

Sur quel personnage le troisième chapitre s'ouvre-t-il? D'où vient ce personnage?

Quelle est l'attitude d'Anne envers la patronne du café?

Que fait l'enfant tandis qu'Anne est dans le café?

Comment la conversation entre Anne et l'homme recommence-t-elle?

Quel est le souvenir personnel que le cri de la femme mourante évoque chez Anne?

Quand l'homme raconte comment le couple du crime s'est connu, qu'en sait-il vraiment? Y a-t-il un rapport entre ce qu'il raconte et sa propre rencontre avec Anne?

---

[45] **brise:** «breeze».
[46] **pliant:** chaise qui se plie.
[47] **tu veux bien?:** «would you like that?»
[48] **soupeser:** ici, peser les avantages.
[49] **comment t'as trouvé?:** «how did you guess?»

Décrivez de quelle manière bizarre les conversations d'Anne et de l'homme se croisent sans se rejoindre.

Quelle est la théorie de l'homme sur le crime?

Expliquez la réplique suivante: l'homme a demandé qu'Anne parle des événements qui ont dû précéder le crime, elle répond qu'elle n'en sait pas davantage et il dit alors, «Qu'est-ce que ça peut faire?».

Qu'est-ce que l'homme sait sur la maison d'Anne et sur ses habitudes?

Qu'est-ce qu'Anne regarde souvent le matin? Pourquoi pensez-vous qu'elle y repense la nuit?

Pourquoi Anne est-elle contente que son enfant grandisse?

Quels nouveaux éléments troublants sont introduits par Marguerite Duras dans ce chapitre?

IV

Le lendemain encore, Anne Desbaresdes entraîna son enfant jusqu'au port. Le beau temps continuait, à peine plus frais que la veille. Les éclaircies étaient moins rares, plus longues. Dans la ville, ce temps, si précocement beau faisait parler.[1] Certains exprimaient la crainte de le voir se terminer dès le lendemain, en raison de sa durée inhabituelle. Certains autres se rassuraient, prétendant que le vent frais qui soufflait sur la ville tenait le ciel en haleine[2] et qu'il l'empêcherait encore de s'ennuager[3] trop avant.

Anne Desbaresdes traversa ce temps, ce vent, elle arriva au port après avoir dépassé le premier môle, le bassin des remorqueurs de sable, à partir duquel s'ouvrait la ville, vers son large quartier industriel. Elle s'arrêta encore au comptoir alors que l'homme était déjà dans la salle à l'attendre, ne pouvant sans doute échapper encore au cérémonial de leurs premières rencontres, s'y conformant d'instinct. Elle commanda du vin, dans l'épouvante encore. La patronne, qui tricotait sa laine rouge derrière le comptoir, remarqua qu'ils ne s'abordèrent que longtemps après qu'elle soit rentrée et que leur apparente ignorance l'un de l'autre se prolongea plus que la veille encore. Qu'après même[4] que l'enfant ait rejoint son nouvel ami, elle dura.

— Je voudrais un autre verre de vin, réclama Anne Desbaresdes.

On le lui servit dans la désapprobation.[5] Cependant, lorsque l'homme se leva, alla vers elle et la ramena dans la pénombre de l'arrière-salle, le tremblement des mains s'était déjà atténué. Le visage était revenu de sa pâleur habituelle.

— Je n'ai pas l'habitude, expliqua-t-elle, d'aller si loin de chez moi. Mais ce n'est pas de la peur. Ce serait plutôt, il me semble, de la surprise, comme de la surprise.

---

1 **faisait parler:** les gens en parlaient.
2 **tenir le ciel en haleine:** garder le ciel dégagé de nuages.
3 **s'ennuager:** se remplir de nuages.
4 **après même:** «even after».
5 **désapprobation:** action de désapprouver.

— Ça pourrait être de la peur. On va le savoir, dans la ville, tout se sait[6] de la même façon, ajouta l'homme en riant.

Dehors, l'enfant cria de satisfaction parce que deux remorqueurs arrivaient côte à côte vers le bassin. Anne Desbaresdes sourit.

— Que je bois du vin en votre compagnie, termina-t-elle—elle rit subitement dans un éclat—mais pourquoi ai-je tant envie de rire aujourd'hui?

Il s'approcha de son visage assez près, posa ses mains contre les siennes sur la table, cessa de rire avec elle.

— La lune était presque pleine cette nuit. On voyait bien votre jardin, comme il est bien entretenu, lisse comme un miroir. C'était tard. Le grand couloir du premier étage était encore allumé.

— Je vous l'ai dit, parfois je dors mal.

Il joua à faire tourner son verre dans sa main afin de lui faciliter les choses, de lui laisser l'aise, comme il crut comprendre[7] qu'elle le désirait, de le regarder mieux. Elle le regarda mieux.

— Je voudrais boire un peu de vin—elle réclama plaintivement, comme déjà lésée.[8] Je ne savais pas que l'habitude vous en venait si vite. Voilà que je l'ai presque, déjà.

Il commanda le vin. Ils le burent ensemble avec avidité, mais cette fois rien ne pressa Anne Desbaresdes de boire, que son penchant naissant pour l'ivresse de ce vin. Elle attendit un moment après l'avoir bu et, avec la voix douce et fautive[9] de l'excuse, elle recommença à questionner cet homme.

— Je voudrais que vous me disiez maintenant comment ils en sont arrivés à ne plus même se parler.

L'enfant arriva dans l'encadrement[10] de la porte, s'assura qu'elle était encore là, s'en alla de nouveau.

— Je ne sais rien. Peut-être par de longs silences qui s'installaient entre eux, la nuit, un peu n'importe quand ensuite et qu'ils étaient de moins en moins capables de surmonter par rien, rien.

Le même trouble que la veille ferma les yeux d'Anne Desbaresdes lui fit, de même, courber les épaules d'accablement.[11]

— Une certaine nuit, ils tournent et retournent dans la chambre, ils deviennent comme des bêtes enfermées, ils ne savent pas ce qui leur arrive. Ils commencent à s'en douter, ils ont peur.

---

6 **se savoir:** devenir connu.
7 **croire comprendre:** croire.
8 **lésé:** blessé.
9 **fautif:** coupable.
10 **encadrement:** cadre.
11 **d'accablement:** «overwhelmed».

— Rien ne les satisfait plus.

— Ce qui est en train de se passer, ils en sont débordés, ils ne savent pas le dire tout de suite. Peut-être qu'il leur faudra des mois. Des mois, pour le savoir.

Il attendit un instant avant de lui parler de nouveau. Il but un verre entier de vin.

5 Pendant qu'il buvait, dans ses yeux levés le couchant passa avec la précision du hasard. Elle le vit.

— Devant une certaine fenêtre du premier étage, dit-il, il y a un hêtre[12] qui est parmi les plus beaux arbres du parc.

— Ma chambre. C'est une grande chambre.

10 Sa bouche à lui fut humide d'avoir bu et elle eut à son tour, dans la douce lumière, une implacable précision.

— Une chambre calme, dit-on, la meilleure.

— En été, ce hêtre me cache la mer. J'ai demandé qu'un jour on l'enlève de là, qu'on l'abatte. Je n'ai pas dû assez insister.

15 Il chercha à voir l'heure au-dessus du comptoir.

— Dans un quart d'heure, ça sera la fin du travail, et vous rentrerez très vite après. Nous avons vraiment très peu de temps. Je crois, ça n'a pas d'importance, que ce hêtre soit là ou non. A votre place, je le laisserai grandir avec son ombre chaque année un peu plus épaisse sur les murs de cette chambre qu'on appelle la 20 vôtre, m'a-t-il semblé comprendre, par erreur.

Elle s'adossa de tout son buste à la chaise, d'un mouvement entier, presque vulgaire, se détourna de lui.

— Mais parfois, son ombre est comme de l'encre noire, protesta-t-elle doucement.

25 — Ça ne fait rien, je crois.

Il lui tendit un verre de vin tout en riant.

— Cette femme était devenue une ivrogne. On la trouvait le soir dans les bars de l'autre côté de l'arsenal, ivre-morte. On la blâmait beaucoup.

Anne Desbaresdes feignit un étonnement exagéré.

30 — Je m'en doutais, mais pas à ce point. Peut-être dans leur cas était-ce nécessaire?

— Je le sais aussi mal que vous. Parlez-moi.

— Oui—elle chercha, loin. Parfois aussi, le samedi, un ou deux ivrognes passent boulevard de la Mer. Ils chantent très fort ou ils font des discours. Ils vont 35 jusqu'aux dunes, au dernier réverbère,[13] et ils reviennent, toujours en chantant. En général, ils passent tard, lorsque tout le monde déjà dort. Ils s'égarent courageusement dans cette partie de la ville si déserte, si vous saviez.

---

12 **hêtre**: «beech tree».
13 **réverbère**: «lamp post».

— Vous êtes couchée dans cette grande chambre très calme, vous les entendez. Il règne dans cette chambre un désordre fortuit[14] qui ne vous est pas particulier. Vous y étiez couchée, vous l'étiez.

Anne Desbaresdes se rétracta[15] et comme à son habitude parfois, s'alanguit.[16] Sa voix la quitta. Le tremblement des mains recommença un peu.

— Ce boulevard va être prolongé au-delà des dunes, dit-elle, on parle d'un projet prochain.

— Vous y étiez couchée. Personne ne le savait. Dans dix minutes, ça va être la fin du travail.

— Je le savais, dit Anne Desbaresdes, et . . . ces dernières années, à quelqu'heure que ce soit, je le savais toujours, toujours . . .

— Endormie ou réveillée, dans une tenue décente ou non, on passait outre à votre existence.

Anne Desbaresdes se débattit, coupable, et l'acceptant cependant.

— Vous ne devriez pas, dit-elle, je me rappelle, tout peut arriver . . .

— Oui.

Elle ne cessa plus de regarder sa bouche seule désormais dans la lumière restante du jour.

— De loin, enfermé comme il est, face à la mer, dans le plus beau quartier de la ville, on pourrait se tromper sur ce jardin. Au mois de juin de l'année dernière, il y aura un an dans quelques jours, vous vous teniez face à lui, sur le perron, prête à nous accueillir, nous, le personnel des Fonderies. Au-dessus de vos seins à moitié nus, il y avait une fleur blanche de magnolia. Je m'appelle Chauvin.

Elle reprit sa pose coutumière, face à lui, accoudée à la table. Son visage chavirait[17] déjà sous l'effet du vin.

— Je le savais. Et aussi que vous êtes parti des Fonderies sans donner de raisons et que vous ne pourrez manquer d'y revenir bientôt, aucune autre maison de cette ville ne pouvant vous employer.

— Parlez-moi encore. Bientôt, je ne vous demanderai plus rien.

Anne Desbaresdes récita presque scolairement, pour commencer, une leçon qu'elle n'avait jamais apprise.

— Quand je suis arrivée dans cette maison, les troënes[18] y étaient déjà. Il y en a beaucoup. Quand l'orage approche, ils grincent comme l'acier. D'y être habituée, tenez, c'est comme si on entendait son cœur. J'y suis habituée. Ce que vous m'avez dit sur cette femme est faux, qu'on la trouvait ivre-morte dans les bars du quartier de l'arsenal.

---

14 **fortuit:** ici, «casual».
15 **se rétracter:** «to draw back».
16 **s'alanguir:** «to languish».
17 **chavirer:** bouleverser, décomposer.
18 **troëne:** «privet».

La sirène retentit, égale et juste, assourdissant[19] la ville entière. La patronne véri-
fia son heure, rangea son tricot rouge. Chauvin parla aussi calmement que s'il
n'avait pas entendu.

— Beaucoup de femmes ont déjà vécu dans cette même maison qui entendaient
5   les troënes, la nuit, à la place de leur cœur. Toujours les troënes y étaient déjà. Elles
sont toutes mortes dans leur chambre, derrière ce hêtre qui, contrairement à ce que
vous croyez, ne grandit plus.

— C'est aussi faux que ce que vous m'avez dit sur cette femme ivre-morte tous
les soirs.

10   — C'est aussi faux. Mais cette maison est énorme. Elle s'étend sur des centaines
de mètres carrés. Et elle est tellement ancienne aussi qu'on peut tout supposer.
Il doit arriver qu'on y prenne peur.

Le même émoi la brisa, lui ferma les yeux. La patronne se leva, remua, rinça
des verres.

15   — Dépêchez-vous de parler. Inventez.
Elle fit un effort, parla presque haut dans le café encore désert.

— Ce qu'il faudrait c'est habiter une ville sans arbres les arbres crient lorsqu'il
y a du vent ici il y en a toujours toujours à l'exception de deux jours par an à votre
place voyez-vous je m'en irai d'ici je n'y resterai pas tous les oiseaux ou presque
20   sont des oiseaux de mer qu'on trouve crevés après les orages et quand l'orage cesse
que les arbres ne crient plus on les entend crier eux sur la plage comme des égorgés
ça empêche les enfants de dormir non moi je m'en irai.

Elle s'arrêta, les yeux encore fermés par la peur. Il la regarda avec une grande
attention.

25   — Peut-être, dit-il, que nous nous trompons, peut-être a-t-il eu envie de la tuer
très vite, dès les premières fois qu'il l'a vue. Parlez-moi.

Elle n'y arriva pas. Ses mains recommencèrent à trembler, mais pour d'autre
raison que la peur et que l'émoi dans lequel la jetait toute allusion à son existence.
Alors, il parla à sa place, d'une voix redevenue tranquille.

30   — C'est vrai que lorsque le vent cesse dans cette ville, c'est tellement rare qu'on
en est comme étouffé. Je l'ai déjà remarqué.

Anne Desbaresdes n'écoutait pas.

— Morte, dit-elle, elle en souriait encore de joie.

Des cris et des rires d'enfants éclatèrent dehors, qui saluaient le soir comme une
35   aurore. Du côté sud de la ville, d'autres cris, adultes ceux-là, de liberté, s'élevèrent,
qui relayèrent le sourd bourdonnement des fonderies.

— La brise revient toujours, continua Anne Desbaresdes, d'une voix fatiguée,

---

19 **assourdir:** rendre sourd.

toujours et, je ne sais pas si vous l'avez remarqué, différemment suivant les jours, parfois tout d'un coup, surtout au coucher du soleil, parfois, au contraire, très lentement, mais alors seulement quand il fait très chaud, et à la fin de la nuit, vers quatre heures du matin, à l'aube. Les troënes crient, vous comprenez, c'est comme ça que je le sais. 5

— Vous savez tout sur ce seul jardin qui est à peu de choses près tout à fait pareil aux autres du boulevard de la Mer. Quand les troënes crient, en été, vous fermez votre fenêtre pour ne plus les entendre, vous êtes nue à cause de la chaleur.

— Je voudrais du vin, le pria Anne Desbaresdes, toujours j'en voudrais... 10
Il commanda le vin.

— Il y a dix minutes que c'est sonné, les avertit la patronne en les servant.
Un premier homme arriva, but au comptoir le même vin.

— A l'angle gauche de la grille, continua Anne Desbaresdes à mi-voix, vers le nord il y a un hêtre pourpre d'Amérique, je ne sais pas pourquoi, je ne sais pas 15 pourquoi du tout...

L'homme qui était au bar reconnut Chauvin, lui fit un signe de tête un peu gêné. Chauvin ne le vit pas.

— Dites-moi encore, dit Chauvin, vous pouvez me dire n'importe quoi.
L'enfant surgit, les cheveux en désordre, essoufflé.[20] Les rues qui aboutissaient à 20 cette avancée du quai résonnèrent de pas d'hommes.

— Maman, dit l'enfant.

— Dans deux minutes, dit Chauvin, elle va s'en aller.
L'homme qui était au bar essaya de caresser au passage les cheveux de l'enfant —celui-ci s'enfuit sauvagement. 25

— Un jour, dit Anne Desbaresdes, j'ai eu cet enfant-là.
Une dizaine d'ouvriers firent irruption[21] dans le café. Quelques-uns reconnurent Chauvin. Chauvin ne les vit encore pas.

— Quelquefois, continua Anne Desbaresdes, quand cet enfant dort, le soir je descends dans ce jardin, je m'y promène. Je vais aux grilles, je regarde le boule- 30 vard. Le soir, c'est très calme, surtout l'hiver. En été, parfois, quelques couples passent et repassent, enlacés, c'est tout. On a choisi cette maison parce qu'elle est calme, la plus calme de la ville. Il faut que je m'en aille.
Chauvin se recula sur sa chaise, prit son temps.

— Vous allez aux grilles, puis vous les quittez, puis vous faites le tour de votre 35 maison, puis vous revenez encore aux grilles. L'enfant, là-haut dort. Jamais vous n'avez crié. Jamais.

---

[20] **essoufflé:** hors de haleine.
[21] **faire irruption:** entrer brusquement.

Elle remit sa veste sans répondre. Il l'aida. Elle se leva et une fois de plus, resta
là, debout près de la table, à son côté, à fixer les hommes du comptoir sans les
voir. Certains tentèrent de faire à Chauvin un signe de reconnaissance, mais en
vain. Il regardait le quai.

5   Anne Desbaresdes sortit enfin de sa torpeur.

— Je vais revenir, dit-elle.

— Demain.

Il l'accompagna à la porte. Des groupes d'hommes arrivaient, pressés. L'enfant
les suivait. Il courut vers sa mère, lui prit la main et l'entraîna résolument. Elle le

10   suivit.

Il lui raconta qu'il avait un nouvel ami, ne s'étonna pas qu'elle ne lui répondit
pas. Face à la plage désertée—il était plus tard que la veille—il s'arrêta pour voir
les vagues qui battaient assez fort ce soir-là. Puis il repartit.

— Viens.

15   Elle suivit son mouvement, repartit à son tour.

— Tu marches lentement, pleurnicha-t-il,[22] et il fait froid.

— Je ne peux pas aller plus vite.

Elle se pressa autant qu'elle put. La nuit, la fatigue, et l'enfance firent qu'il se
blottit[23] contre elle, sa mère, et qu'ils marchèrent ainsi, ensemble. Mais comme

20   elle voyait mal au loin, à cause de son ivresse, elle évita de regarder vers la fin du
boulevard de la Mer, afin de ne pas se laisser décourager par une aussi longue distance.

QUESTIONNAIRE

Page 38—page 41, ligne 3

Pourquoi Anne a-t-elle peur chaque fois qu'elle entre dans
le café?

Décrivez et expliquez le «cérémonial» par lequel chaque
rencontre entre l'homme et Anne commence.

Quel est le geste d'affection ou de compréhension que l'homme
fait?

Qu'a-t-il dû faire la nuit précédente?

Pourquoi joue-t-il avec son verre?

Expliquez le penchant naissant d'Anne pour le vin.

Comment l'histoire imaginée du couple du crime se rap-
proche-t-elle de plus en plus d'Anne et de l'homme?

---

22 **pleurnicher:** «to whimper».
23 **se blottir:** «to nestle».

Page 41, ligne 4—page 44

Expliquez ce que l'homme veut dire en déclarant qu'«on passait outre» à l'existence d'Anne?

Comment a-t-il connu Anne la première fois?

Montrez comment, quand Chauvin dit son nom à Anne, il fait allusion à leur première rencontre.

Que sait Anne sur lui?

Que veut dire Chauvin quand il dit «Parlez-moi encore. Bientôt je ne vous demanderai plus rien»?

Pourquoi le paragraphe qui commence «Ce qu'il faudrait . . .» (p. 42, l. 17) est-il écrit sans ponctuation?

Décrivez les bruits qui entrent dans le café de l'extérieur. Ont-ils une signification? Laquelle?

Chauvin dit que la nuit, en été, Anne est nue quand elle ferme sa fenêtre. Est-ce qu'il sait cela ou le suppose-t-il? Y voyez-vous une importance?

Comment savez-vous que Chauvin est totalement absorbé par sa conversation?

Décrivez comment le lien entre Anne et Chauvin se développe.

V

— Tu t'en souviendras, dit Anne Desbaresdes, ça veut dire modéré et chantant.

— Modéré et chantant, répéta l'enfant.

A mesure que l'escalier montait, des grues[1] s'élevèrent dans le ciel vers le sud de la ville, toutes en des mouvements identiques dont les temps[2] divers s'entre-
croisaient.

— Je ne veux plus qu'on te gronde, sans ça[3] j'en meurs.

— Je veux plus,[4] moi aussi. Modéré et chantant.

Une pelle géante, baveuse[5] de sable mouillé, passa devant la dernière fenêtre de l'étage, ses dents de bête affamée fermées sur sa proie.

— La musique, c'est nécessaire, et tu dois l'apprendre, tu comprends?

— Je comprends.

L'appartement de Mademoiselle Giraud était suffisamment haut, au cinquième étage de l'immeuble, pour que le champ de ses fenêtres donnât de très loin sur la mer. A part le vol des mouettes, rien ne s'y profilait donc aux yeux des enfants.

— Alors, vous avez su? Un crime, passionnel,[6] oui. Asseyez-vous, Madame Desbaresdes, je vous en prie.

— Qu'est-ce que c'était? demanda l'enfant.

— Vite, la sonatine, dit Mademoiselle Giraud.

L'enfant se mit au piano. Mademoiselle Giraud s'installa auprès de lui, le crayon à la main. Anne Desbaresdes s'assit à l'écart, près de la fenêtre.

— La sonatine. Cette jolie petite sonatine de Diabelli, vas-y. Quelle mesure, cette jolie petite sonatine? Dis-le.

Au son de cette voix, aussitôt l'enfant se rétracta. Il eut l'air de réfléchir, prit son temps, et peut-être mentit-il.

---

1 **grue:** «crane».
2 **les temps:** ici, «tempi».
3 **sans ça:** ici, si cela arrive.
4 **je veux plus:** c'est-à-dire, je ne le veux plus.
5 **baveur:** «dripping».
6 **passionnel:** qui concerne les passions.

— Modéré et chantant, dit-il.

Mademoiselle Giraud croisa les bras, le regarda en soupirant.

— Il le fait exprès. Il n'y a pas d'autre explication.

L'enfant ne broncha[7] pas. Ses deux petites mains fermées posées sur ses genoux, il attendait la consommation de son supplice seulement satisfait de l'inéluctabilité,[8] 5 de son fait à lui, de sa répétition.

— Les journées allongent, dit doucement Anne Desbaresdes, à vue d'œil.

— Effectivement,[9] dit Mademoiselle Giraud.

Le soleil, plus haut que la dernière fois à cette même heure, en témoignait. De plus, la journée avait été assez belle pour qu'une brume recouvrît le ciel, légère, 10 certes, mais précoce cependant.

— J'attends que tu le dises.

— Il n'a peut-être pas entendu.

— Il a parfaitement entendu. Vous ne comprendrez jamais une chose, c'est qu'il le fait exprès, Madame Desbaresdes. 15

L'enfant tourna un peu la tête vers la fenêtre. Il resta ainsi, de biais,[10] à regarder la moire,[11] sur le mur, du soleil reflété par la mer. Seule, sa mère pouvait voir ses yeux.

— Ma petite honte,[12] mon trésor, dit-elle tout bas.

— Quatre temps,[13] dit l'enfant, sans effort, sans bouger. 20

Ses yeux étaient à peu près de la couleur du ciel, ce soir-là, à cette chose près[14] qu'il y dansait l'or de ses cheveux.

— Un jour, dit la mère, un jour il le saura, il le dira sans hésiter, c'est inévitable. Même s'il ne le veut pas, il le saura.

Elle rit gaiement, silencieusement. 25

— Vous devriez avoir honte, Madame Desbaresdes, dit Mademoiselle Giraud.

— On le dit.

Mademoiselle Giraud déplia ses bras, frappa le clavier de son crayon, comme elle faisait d'habitude depuis trente ans d'enseignement, et elle cria.

— Tes gammes.[15] Tes gammes pendant dix minutes. Pour t'apprendre. Do 30 majeur[16] pour commencer.

L'enfant se remit face au piano. Ses mains se levèrent ensemble, se posèrent ensemble avec une docilité triomphante.

---

7 **broncher:** ici, «to flinch».

8 **inéluctabilité:** inévitabilité.

9 **effectivement:** en effet.

10 **de biais:** «on a slant».

11 **moire:** reflet changeant et ondulé.

12 Anne utilise cette expression comme expression tendre, mais c'est assez bizarre.

13 **quatre temps:** «four-quarter time».

14 **à cette chose près:** «with this exception».

15 **gamme:** «(musical) scale».

16 **do majeur:** «C major».

Une gamme en do majeur couvrit la rumeur de la mer.

— Encore, encore. C'est la seule façon.

L'enfant recommença encore d'où il était parti la première fois, à la hauteur exacte et mystérieuse du clavier d'où il fallait qu'il le fît. Une deuxième, une troi-
5 sième gamme en do majeur s'éleva dans la colère de cette dame.

— J'ai dit, dix minutes. Encore.

L'enfant se retourna vers Mademoiselle Giraud, la regarda, tandis que ses mains restaient abandonnées sur le clavier, mollement.[17]

— Pourquoi? demanda-t-il.

10 Le visage de Mademoiselle Giraud, de colère, s'enlaidit[18] tant que l'enfant se retourna face au piano. Il remit ses mains en place et se figea dans une pose scolaire apparemment parfaite, mais sans jouer.

— Ça alors, c'est trop fort.

— Ils n'ont pas demandé à vivre, dit la mère—elle rit encore—et voilà qu'on
15 leur apprend le piano en plus, que voulez-vous.

Mademoiselle Giraud haussa les épaules, ne répondit pas directement à cette femme, ne répondit à personne en particulier, reprit son calme et dit pour elle seule:

— C'est curieux, les enfants finiraient par vous faire devenir méchants.

20 — Mais un jour il saura ses gammes aussi—Anne Desbaresdes se fit récon-
fortante—il les saura aussi parfaitement que sa mesure, c'est inévitable, il en sera même fatigué à force de les savoir.

— L'éducation que vous lui donnez, Madame, est une chose affreuse, cria Mademoiselle Giraud.

25 D'une main elle prit la tête de l'enfant, lui tourna, lui mania la tête, le força à la voir. L'enfant baissa les yeux.

— Parce que je l'ai décidé. Et insolent par-dessus le marché.[19] Sol majeur[20] trois fois, s'il te plaît. Et avant, do majeur encore une fois.

L'enfant recommença une gamme en do majeur. Il la joua à peine plus négli-
30 gemment que les fois précédentes. Puis, de nouveau, il attendit.

— Sol majeur j'ai dit, maintenant, sol majeur.

Les mains se retirèrent du clavier. La tête se baissa résolument. Les petits pieds ballants,[21] encore bien loin des pédales, se frottèrent l'un contre l'autre dans la colère.

35 — Tu n'as peut-être pas entendu?

---

17 **mollement**: sans énergie.
18 **s'enlaidir**: devenir laid.
19 **par-dessus le marché**: en plus.
20 **sol majeur**: «G major».
21 **baller**: «to dangle».

— Tu as entendu, dit la mère, j'en suis sûre.

L'enfant, à la tendresse de cette voix-là, ne résistait pas encore. Sans répondre, il souleva une fois de plus ses mains, les posa sur le clavier à l'endroit précis où il fallait qu'il le fît. Une, puis deux gammes en sol majeur s'élevèrent dans l'amour de la mère. Du côté de l'arsenal, la sirène annonça la fin du travail. La lumière baissa un peu. Les gammes furent si parfaites que la dame en convint.

— Puis, en plus du caractère, ça lui fait les doigts, dit-elle.

— Il est vrai, dit tristement la mère.

Mais, avant la troisième gamme en sol majeur, l'enfant s'arrêta une nouvelle fois.

— J'ai dit trois fois. Trois.

L'enfant, cette fois, retira ses mains du clavier, les posa sur ses genoux et dit:

— Non.

Le soleil commença à s'incliner de telle façon que la mer, d'un seul coup, obliquement, s'illumina. Un grand calme s'empara de Mademoiselle Giraud.

— Je ne peux rien vous dire d'autre que ceci: je vous plains.

L'enfant, subrepticement,[22] glissa un regard vers cette femme tant à plaindre et qui riait. Puis il resta fixé à son poste, le dos nécessairement tourné à la mer. L'heure fléchit vers le soir, la brise qui se levait traversa la chambre, contradictoire, fit frémir l'herbe des cheveux de cet enfant obstiné. Les petits pieds, sous le piano, se mirent à danser à petits coups, en silence.

— Qu'est-ce que ça peut faire une fois de plus, une seule gamme, dit la mère en riant, une seule fois de plus?

L'enfant se retourna vers elle seule.

— J'aime pas les gammes.

Mademoiselle Giraud les regarda tous les deux, alternativement, sourde à leurs propos, découragée de l'indignation même.

— J'attends, moi.

L'enfant se remit face au piano, mais de biais, le plus loin qu'il pouvait se le permettre de cette dame.

— Mon amour, dit sa mère, une fois encore.

Les cils battirent sous l'appellation. Cependant, il hésita encore.

— Plus les gammes, alors.

— Justement les gammes, tu vois.

Il hésita puis, alors qu'elles en désespéraient tout à fait, il s'y décida. Il joua. Mais l'isolement désespéré de Mademoiselle Giraud resta un instant égal à lui-même.

---

22 **subrepticement:** furtivement.

— Voyez-vous, Madame Desbaresdes, je ne sais pas si je pourrai continuer à m'en occuper.

La gamme en sol majeur fut de nouveau exacte, peut-être plus rapide cette fois que la fois précédente, mais d'un rien.[23]

— C'est une question de mauvaise volonté,[24] dit la mère, j'en conviens.

La gamme se termina. L'enfant, dans le désintérêt parfait du moment qui passait, se releva légèrement de son tabouret[25] et tenta l'impossible, d'apercevoir ce qui se passait en bas, sur le quai.

— Je lui expliquerai qu'il le faut, dit la mère, faussement repentante.

Mademoiselle Giraud se fit déclamatoire et attristée.

— Vous n'avez rien à lui expliquer. Il n'a pas à choisir de faire ou non du piano, Madame Desbaresdes, c'est ce qu'on appelle l'éducation.

Elle frappa sur le piano. L'enfant abandonna sa tentative.[26]

— Ta sonatine maintenant, dit-elle, lassée. Quatre temps.

L'enfant la joua comme les gammes. Il la savait bien. Et malgré sa mauvaise volonté, de la musique fut là, indéniablement.

— Que voulez-vous, continua Mademoiselle Giraud, par-dessus la sonatine, il y a des enfants avec lesquels il faut être très sévère, sans ça on n'en sort pas.[27]

— J'essaierai, dit Anne Desbaresdes.

Elle écoutait la sonatine. Elle venait du tréfonds[28] des âges, portée par son enfant à elle. Elle manquait souvent, à l'entendre, aurait-elle pu croire, s'en évanouir.

— Ce qu'il y a, voyez-vous, c'est qu'il se croit permis de ne pas aimer faire du piano.[29] Mais je sais bien que ce que je vous dis ou rien, c'est la même chose, Madame Desbaresdes.

— J'essaierai.

La sonatine résonna encore, portée comme une plume par ce barbare, qu'il le voulut ou non,[30] et elle s'abattit de nouveau sur[31] sa mère, la condamna de nouveau à la damnation de son amour. Les portes de l'enfer se refermèrent.

— Recommence et bien en mesure, cette fois, plus lentement.

Le jeu se ralentit et se ponctua, l'enfant se laissa prendre[32] à son miel. De la musique sortit, coula de ses doigts sans qu'il parût le vouloir, en décider, et sournoise-

---

23 **d'un rien:** très peu.
24 **volonté:** ici, «attitude».
25 **tabouret:** «stool».
26 **tentative:** essai.
27 **sans ça on n'en sort pas:** «that's the only way to treat them».
28 **tréfonds:** tout à fait au fond.
29 **faire du piano:** apprendre à jouer du piano.
30 **qu'il le voulut ou non:** «whether he wants to or not».
31 **s'abattre sur:** «to fall upon».
32 **se laisser prendre:** «to become absorbed by».

ment elle s'étala dans le monde une fois de plus, submergea le cœur d'inconnu, l'exténua. Sur le quai, en bas, on l'entendit.

— Il y a un mois qu'il est dessus, dit la patronne. Mais c'est joli.

Un premier group d'hommes arrivait vers le café.

— Oui, il y a bien un mois, reprit la patronne. Je le sais par cœur.

Chauvin, au bout du comptoir, était encore le seul client. Il regarda l'heure, s'étira[33] d'aise et fredonna la sonatine dans le même temps que l'enfant la jouait. La patronne le dévisagea[34] bien tout en sortant ses verres de dessous le comptoir.

— Vous êtes jeune, dit-elle.

Elle calcula le temps qui lui restait avant que le premier groupe de clients atteigne le café. Elle le prévint vite, mais avec bonté.

— Quelquefois, voyez-vous, quand il fait beau, il me semble bien qu'elle fait le tour de l'autre côté, par le deuxième bassin, qu'elle ne passe pas par ici chaque fois.

— Non, dit l'homme en riant.

Le groupe d'hommes passa la porte.

— Un, deux, trois, quatre, comptait Mademoiselle Giraud. C'est bien.

La sonatine se faisait sous les mains de l'enfant—celui-ci absent—mais elle se faisait et se refaisait, portée par son indifférente maladresse jusqu'aux confins de sa puissance. A mesure qu'elle s'échafaudait,[35] sensiblement la lumière du jour diminua. Une monumentale presqu'île[36] de nuages incendiés surgit à l'horizon dont la splendeur fragile et fugace[37] forçait la pensée vers d'autres voies. Dans dix minutes, en effet, s'évanouirait tout à fait de l'instant toute couleur du jour. L'enfant termina sa tâche pour la troisième fois. Le bruit de la mer mêlé aux voix des hommes qui arrivaient sur le quai monta jusqu'à la chambre.

— Par cœur, dit Mademoiselle Giraud, la prochaine fois, c'est par cœur qu'il faudra que tu la saches, tu entends.

— Par cœur, bon.

— Je vous le promets, dit la mère.

— Il faut que ça change, il se moque de moi, c'est criant.[38]

— Je vous le promets.

Mademoiselle Giraud réfléchit, n'écoutait pas.

— On pourrait essayer, dit-elle, qu'une autre que vous l'accompagne à ses leçons de piano, Madame Desbaresdes. On verrait bien ce que ça donnerait.[39]

---

[33] **s'étirer:** s'allonger, s'étendre.
[34] **dévisager:** regarder fixement.
[35] **s'échafauder:** «to build up».
[36] **presqu'île:** «peninsula».
[37] **fugace:** fugitif, qui ne dure pas.
[38] **c'est criant:** c'est très évident.
[39] **ce que ça donnerait:** «what that would be like».

— Non, cria l'enfant.

— Je crois que je le supporterais très mal, dit Anne Desbaresdes.

— Je crains fort qu'on soit quand même obligé d'y arriver, dit Mademoiselle Giraud.

5   Dans l'escalier, une fois la porte refermée, l'enfant s'arrêta.

— Tu as vu, elle est méchante.

— Tu le fais exprès?

L'enfant contempla tout le peuple de grues[40] maintenant immobilisé en plein ciel. Au loin, les faubourgs de la ville s'illuminèrent.

10   — Je sais pas, dit l'enfant.

— Mais que je t'aime.

L'enfant descendit lentement tout à coup.

— Je voudrais plus[41] apprendre le piano.

— Les gammes, dit Anne Desbaresdes je ne les ai jamais sues, comment faire 15 autrement?[42]

QUESTIONNAIRE ⎯⎯⎯⎯⎯⎯⎯⎯⎯⎯⎯⎯⎯⎯⎯⎯⎯⎯

Quelle est l'attitude de Mademoiselle Giraud tout au début de cette leçon de musique?

Pourquoi change-t-elle rapidement?

Pensez-vous que l'enfant soit entêté ou bien qu'il ne sache vraiment pas jouer mieux?

Pourquoi est-ce qu'Anne devrait avoir honte selon Mademoiselle Giraud?

Pourquoi est-ce que le professeur fait jouer des gammes à l'enfant? Auriez-vous fait la même chose?

Pourquoi l'enfant joue-t-il pour sa mère quand il ne veut pas jouer pour Mademoiselle Giraud?

Quelle est la menace de Mademoiselle Giraud? Et quelle est sa suggestion pour l'avenir?

Quels sont les moyens de transition entre la leçon de musique et le café?

Pourquoi Marguerite Duras a-t-elle choisi de nous transporter de nouveau chez Mademoiselle Giraud? Est-ce que ce chapitre nous fait mieux comprendre les personnages? Comment?

---

40 **tout le peuple de grues:** «a whole flock of cranes».
41 **je voudrais plus:** c'est-à-dire, je ne voudrais plus.
42 **comment faire autrement?:** «what else is there to do?».

VI

Anne Desbaresdes n'entra pas, s'arrêta à la porte du café. Chauvin vint vers elle. Quand il l'eut atteinte, elle se tourna dans la direction du Boulevard de la Mer.

— Comme il y a déjà du monde, se plaignit-elle doucement. Ces leçons de piano finissent tard.

— J'ai entendu cette leçon, dit Chauvin.   5

L'enfant dégagea sa main, s'enfuit sur le trottoir, désireux de courir comme chaque fois, à cette heure-là du vendredi soir. Chauvin leva la tête vers le ciel encore faiblement éclairé, bleu sombre, et il se rapprocha d'elle qui ne recula pas.

— Bientôt l'été, dit-il. Venez.   10

— Mais dans ces régions-ci on le sent à peine.

—Parfois, si. Vous le savez. Ce soir.

L'enfant sautait par-dessus des cordages[1] en chantant la sonatine de Diabelli. Anne Desbaresdes suivit Chauvin. Le café était plein. Les hommes buvaient leur vin aussitôt servi, un devoir,[2] et ils s'en allaient chez eux, pressés. D'autres les relayaient[3] qui arrivaient d'ateliers plus lointains.   15

Aussitôt entrée, Anne Desbaresdes s'apeura,[4] se cabra[5] près de la porte. Chauvin se retourna vers elle, l'encouragea d'un sourire. Ils arrivèrent à l'extrémité la moins en vue du long comptoir et elle but très vite son verre de vin, comme les hommes. Le verre tremblait encore dans sa main.   20

— Il y a maintenant sept jours, dit Chauvin.

— Sept nuits, dit-elle comme au hasard. Comme c'est bon, le vin.

— Sept nuits, répéta Chauvin.

Ils quittèrent le comptoir, il l'entraîna au fond de la salle, la fit asseoir à l'endroit

---

1 **cordage:** corde.
2 **un devoir:** ici, automatiquement.
3 **relayer:** prendre la place de.
4 **s'apeurer:** s'effrayer.
5 **se cabrer:** ici, «to balk».

où il le désirait. Des hommes au bar regardèrent encore cette femme, s'étonnèrent encore, mais de loin. La salle était calme.

— Alors, vous avez entendu? Toutes ces gammes qu'elle lui fait faire?

— C'était tôt. Il n'y avait encore aucun client. Les fenêtres devaient êtres ouvertes sur le quai. J'ai tout entendu, même les gammes.

Elle lui sourit, reconnaissante, but de nouveau. Les mains, sur le verre, ne tremblèrent plus qu'à peine.

— Je me suis mis dans la tête[6] qu'il fallait qu'il sache la musique, vous comprenez, depuis deux ans.

— Mais je comprends. Alors, ce grand piano, à gauche, en entrant dans le salon?

— Oui.—Anne Desbaresdes serra ses poings, se força au calme.—Mais il est si petit encore, si petit, si vous saviez, quand on y pense, je me demande si je n'ai pas tort.

Chauvin rit. Ils étaient encore seuls à être attablés[7] dans le fond de la salle. Le nombre des clients au comptoir diminuait.

— Vous savez qu'il sait parfaitement ses gammes?

Anne Desbaresdes rit, elle aussi, cette fois à pleine gorge.

— C'est vrai qu'il les sait. Même cette femme en convient, voyez-vous . . . je me fais des idées.[8] Ah . . . je pourrais en rire . . .

Tandis qu'elle riait encore mais que le flot de son rire commençait à baisser, Chauvin lui parla d'autre manière.

— Vous étiez accoudée à ce grand piano. Entre vos seins nus sous votre robe, il y a cette fleur de magnolia.

Anne Desbaresdes, très attentivement, écouta cette histoire.

— Oui.

— Quand vous vous penchez, cette fleur frôle le contour extérieur de vos seins. Vous l'avez négligemment épinglée, trop haut. C'est une fleur énorme, vous l'avez choisie au hasard, trop grande pour vous. Ses pétales sont encore durs, elle a justement atteint la nuit dernière sa pleine floraison.[9]

— Je regarde dehors?

— Buvez encore un peu de vin. L'enfant joue dans le jardin. Vous regardez dehors, oui.

Anne Desbaresdes but comme il le lui demandait, chercha à se souvenir, revint d'un profond étonnement.

— Je ne me souviens pas d'avoir cueilli cette fleur. Ni de l'avoir portée.

---

6 **je me suis mis dans la tête:** j'ai imaginé.
7 **attablé:** assis à table.
8 **se faire des idées:** «to imagine things».
9 **floraison:** épanouissement.

— Je ne vous regardais qu'à peine, mais j'ai eu le temps de la voir aussi.

Elle s'occupa à tenir le verre très fort, devint ralentie dans ses gestes et dans sa voix.

— Comme j'aime le vin, je ne savais pas.

— Maintenant, parlez-moi.

— Ah, laissez-moi, supplia Anne Desbaresdes.

— Nous avons sans doute si peu de temps que je ne peux pas.

Le crépuscule s'était déjà tellement avancé que seul le plafond du café recevait encore un peu de clarté. Le comptoir était violemment éclairé, la salle était dans son ombre. L'enfant surgit, courant, ne s'étonna pas de l'heure tardive, annonça:

— L'autre petit garçon est arrivé.

Dans l'instant qui suivit son départ, les mains de Chauvin s'approchèrent de celles de Anne Desbaresdes. Elles furent toutes quatre sur la table, allongées.

— Comme je vous le disais, parfois, je dors mal. Je vais dans sa chambre et je le regarde longtemps.

— Parfois encore?

— Parfois encore, c'est l'été et il y a quelques promeneurs sur le boulevard. Le samedi soir surtout, parce que sans doute le gens ne savent que faire d'eux-mêmes dans cette ville.

— Sans doute, dit Chauvin. Surtout des hommes. De ce couloir, ou de votre jardin, ou de votre chambre, vous les regardez souvent.

Anne Desbaresdes se pencha et le lui dit enfin.

— Je crois, en effet, que je les ai souvent regardés, soit du couloir, soit de ma chambre, lorsque certains soirs je ne sais quoi faire de moi.

Chauvin proféra un mot à voix basse. Le regard de Anne Desbaresdes s'évanouit lentement sous l'insulte, s'ensommeilla.[10]

— Continuez.

— En dehors de ces passages, les journées sont à heure fixe. Je ne peux pas continuer.

— Nous avons très peu de temps devant nous, continuez.

— Les repas, toujours, reviennent. Et les soirs. Un jour, j'ai eu l'idée de ces leçons de piano.

Ils finirent leur vin. Chauvin en commanda d'autre. Le nombre des hommes au comptoir diminua encore. Anne Desbaresdes but de nouveau comme une assoiffée.[11]

— Déjà sept heures, prévint la patronne.

Ils n'entendirent pas. Il fit nuit. Quatre hommes entrèrent dans la salle du fond,

---

10 **s'ensommeiller:** assoupir.
11 **assoiffé:** celui qui a très soif.

ceux-là décidés à perdre leur temps. La radio informa le monde du temps qu'il ferait le lendemain.

— J'ai eu l'idée de ces leçons de piano, je vous disais, à l'autre bout de la ville, pour mon amour, et maintenant je ne peux plus les éviter. Comme c'est difficile.
5   Voyez, sept heures déjà.

— Vous allez arriver plus tard que d'habitude dans cette maison, vous y arriverez plus tard, peut-être trop tard, c'est inévitable. Faites-vous à cette idée.[12]

— On ne peut pas éviter les heures fixes, comment faire autrement? Je pourrais vous dire que je suis déjà en retard sur l'heure du dîner si je compte tout le chemin
10   que j'ai à faire. Et aussi, j'oubliais, que ce soir il y a dans cette maison une réception à laquelle je suis tenue[13] d'être présente.

— Vous savez que vous ne pourrez faire autrement que d'y arriver en retard, vous le savez?

— Je ne pourrais pas faire autrement. Je sais.

15   Il attendit. Elle lui parla sur le ton d'une paisible diversion.

— Je pourrais vous dire que j'ai parlé à mon enfant de toutes ces femmes qui ont vécu derrière ce hêtre et qui sont maintenant mortes, mortes, et qu'il m'a demandé de les voir, mon trésor. Je viens de vous dire ce que je pourrais vous dire, voyez.

20   — Vous avez immédiatement regretté de lui avoir parlé de ces femmes et vous lui avez raconté quelles seraient ses vacances cette année, dans quelques jours, au bord d'une autre mer que celle-ci?

— Je lui ai promis des vacances dans un pays chaud au bord de la mer. Dans quinze jours. Il était inconsolable de la mort de ces femmes.

25   Anne Desbaresdes de nouveau but du vin, le trouva fort. Ses yeux en furent embués[14] alors qu'elle souriait.

— Le temps passe, dit Chauvin. Vous êtes de plus en plus en retard.

— Quand le retard devient tellement important, dit Anne Desbaresdes, qu'il atteint le degré où il en est maintenant pour moi, je crois que ça ne doit plus
30   changer rien à ses conséquences que de l'aggraver encore davantage ou pas.

Il ne resta plus qu'un seul client au comptoir. Dans la salle, les quatre autres parlaient par intermittence. Un couple arriva. La patronne le servit et reprit son tricot rouge délaissé jusque-là à cause de l'affluence.[15] Elle baissa la radio. La mer, assez forte ce soir-là, se fit entendre contre les quais, à travers des chansons.

35   — Du moment qu'il avait compris qu'elle désirait tant qu'il le fasse, je voudrais

---

12 **faites-vous à cette idée:** acceptez cette idée.
13 **tenu:** ici, obligé.
14 **embué:** «misty».
15 **affluence:** ici, grand nombre de clients.

que vous me disiez pourquoi il ne l'a pas fait, par exemple, un peu plus tard
ou . . . un peu plus tôt.

— Vous savez, je sais très peu de choses. Mais je crois qu'il ne pouvait pas
arriver à avoir une préférence, il ne devait pas en sortir,[16] de la vouloir autant vivante que morte. Il a dû réussir très tard seulement à se la préférer morte. Je ne sais   5
rien.

Anne Desbaresdes se replia sur elle-même, le visage hypocritement baissé mais
pâli.

— Elle avait beaucoup d'espoir qu'il y arriverait.

— Il me semble que son espoir à lui d'y arriver devait être égal au sien. Je ne sais   10
rien.

— Le même, vraiment?

— Le même. Taisez-vous.

Les quatre hommes s'en allèrent. Le couple resta là, silencieux. La femme bâilla.
Chauvin commanda une nouvelle carafe de vin.   15

— Si on ne buvait pas tant, ce ne serait pas possible?

— Je crois que ce ne serait pas possible, murmura Anne Desbaresdes.

Elle but son verre de vin d'un trait. Il la laissa s'empoisonner à son gré. La nuit
avait envahi définitivement la ville. Les quais s'éclairèrent de leurs hauts lampa-
daires. L'enfant jouait toujours. Il n'y eut plus trace dans le ciel de la moindre lueur   20
du couchant.

— Avant que je rentre, pria Anne Desbaresdes, si vous pouviez me dire,
j'aimerais savoir encore un peu davantage. Même si vous n'êtes pas sûr de ne pas
savoir très bien.

Chauvin raconta lentement, d'une voix neutre, inconnue jusque-là de cette   25
femme.

— Ils habitaient une maison isolée, je crois même au bord de la mer. Il faisait
chaud. Ils ne savaient pas, avant d'y aller, qu'ils en viendraient là si vite. Qu'au
bout de quelques jours il serait obligé de la chasser si souvent. Très vite, il a été
obligé de la chasser, loin de lui, même loin de la maison, très souvent.   30

— Ce n'était pas la peine.

— Ça doit être difficile d'éviter ces sortes de pensées, on doit en avoir l'habitude, comme de vivre. Mais l'habitude seulement.

— Elle, elle partait?

— Elle s'en allait quand et comme il le voulait, malgré son désir de rester.   35

Anne Desbaresdes fixa cet homme inconnu sans le reconnaître, comme dans le
guet,[17] une bête.

---

[16] **en sortir:** résoudre le problème.
[17] **guet:** ici, «trap».

— Je vous en prie, supplia-t-elle.

— Puis le temps est venu où quand il la regardait, parfois, il ne la voyait plus comme il l'avait jusque-là vue. Elle cessait d'être belle, laide, jeune, vieille, comparable à quiconque, même à elle-même. Il avait peur. C'était aux dernières vacan-
5   ces. L'hiver est venu. Vous allez rentrer boulevard de la Mer. Ça va être la huitième nuit.

L'enfant entra, se blottit contre sa mère un instant. Encore, il fredonnait la sonatine de Diabelli. Elle lui caressa les cheveux de très près de son visage, aveuglée. L'homme évita de les voir. Puis l'enfant s'en alla.

10   — Cette maison était donc très isolée, reprit lentement Anne Desbaresdes. Il faisait chaud, vous disiez. Quand il lui disait de s'en aller, elle obéissait toujours. Elle dormait au pied des arbres, dans les champs, comme . . .

— Oui, dit Chauvin.

— Quand il l'appelait, elle revenait. Et de la même façon qu'elle partait lorsqu'il
15   la chassait. De lui obéir à ce point, c'était sa façon à elle d'espérer. Et même, lorsqu'elle arrivait sur le pas de la porte, elle attendait encore qu'il lui dise d'entrer.

— Oui.

Anne Desbaresdes pencha son visage hébété vers Chauvin, elle ne l'atteignit pas. Chauvin recula.

20   — C'est là, dans cette maison, qu'elle a appris ce que vous disiez qu'elle était, peut-être par exemple . . .

— Oui, une chienne, l'arrêta encore Chauvin.

Elle recula à son tour. Il remplit son verre, le lui tendit.

— Je mentais, dit-il.

25   Elle remit ses cheveux d'un désordre profond, revint à elle avec lassitude et compassion contenue.

— Non, dit-elle.

Dans la lumière du néon de la salle, elle observa attentivement la crispation[18] inhumaine du visage de Chauvin, ne put en rassasier[19] ses yeux. L'enfant surgit une
30   dernière fois du trottoir.

— Maintenant, c'est la nuit, annonça-t-il.

Il bâilla longuement face à la porte, puis il retourna vers elle, mais alors il resta là, à l'abri, fredonnant.

— Voyez comme il est tard. Dites-moi encore, vite?

35   — Puis le temps est venu où il crut qu'il ne pourrait plus la toucher autrement que pour . . .

---

18 **crispation:** contraction.
19 **rassasier:** satisfaire.

Anne Desbaresdes releva ses mains vers son cou nu dans l'encolure[20] de sa robe d'été.

— Que là, n'est-ce pas?

— Là, oui.

Les mains, raisonnablement, acceptèrent d'abandonner, redescendirent du cou. 5

— Je voudrais que vous partiez, murmura Chauvin.

Anne Desbaresdes se leva de sa chaise, se planta au milieu de la salle, sans bouger. Chauvin resta assis, accablé, il ne la connut plus. La patronne, irrésistiblement, délaissa son tricot rouge, les observa l'un l'autre avec une indiscrétion dont ils ne s'aperçurent pas. Ce fut l'enfant qui arriva de la porte et prit la main de sa mère. 10

— On s'en va, viens.

Déjà le boulevard de la Mer était éclairé. Il était beaucoup plus tard que d'habitude, d'une heure au moins. L'enfant chanta une dernière fois la sonatine, puis il s'en fatigua. Les rues étaient presque désertes. Déjà les gens dînaient. Lorsqu'après le premier môle le boulevard de la Mer se profila dans toute sa longueur habitu- 15 elle, Anne Desbaresdes s'arrêta.

— Je suis trop fatiguée, dit-elle.

— Mais j'ai faim, pleurnicha l'enfant.

Il vit que les yeux de cette femme, sa mère, brillaient. Il ne se plaignit plus de rien. 20

— Pourquoi tu pleures?

— Ça peut arriver comme ça, pour rien.

— Je voudrais pas.

— Mon amour, c'est fini, je crois bien.

Il oublia, se mit à courir en avant, revint sur ses pas,[21] s'amusa de la nuit dont il 25 n'avait pas l'habitude.

— La nuit, c'est loin les maisons, dit-il.

QUESTIONNAIRE

Combien de jours se sont passés depuis la première rencontre d'Anne et Chauvin?

Quelle est l'image que Chauvin évoque de sa première rencontre avec Anne?

Expliquez les phrases suivantes: Page 55, ligne 28, Anne: «Je ne peux pas continuer.» Page 55, ligne 31, Anne: «Un jour, j'ai eu l'idée de ces leçons de piano.» Page 56,

---

[20] **encolure:** «neckline».
[21] **revenir sur ses pas:** «retrace one's steps».

ligne 6, Chauvin: «...vous y arriverez [dans votre maison] plus tard, peut-être trop tard, c'est inévitable.»

Pourquoi Anne a-t-elle parlé à son enfant des femmes qui ont vécu dans sa maison dans le passé? Quelle était la réaction de l'enfant?

Quelle est l'attitude d'Anne envers son retard?

Comment Anne peut-elle déclarer, «Elle avait beaucoup d'espoir qu'il y arriverait» quand Chauvin dit que l'homme a fini par préférer la femme morte (p. 57, l. 9)?

Pourquoi Anne pense-t-elle que cela ne serait pas possible de boire moins?

Expliquez la phrase de Chauvin, «Je voudrais que vous partiez» (p. 59, l. 6).

Pourquoi Anne pleure-t-elle en rentrant?

Décrivez le développement des rapports entre Anne et Chauvin dans ce chapitre.

VII

Sur un plat d'argent à l'achat duquel trois générations ont contribué, le saumon[1] arrive, glacé dans sa forme native.[2] Habillé de noir, ganté de blanc, un homme le porte, tel[3] un enfant de roi, et le présente à chacun dans le silence du dîner commençant. Il est bien-séant[4] de ne pas en parler.

De l'extrémité nord du parc, les magnolias versent leur odeur qui va de dune en dune jusqu'à rien. Le vent, ce soir, est du sud. Un homme rôde, boulevard de la Mer. Une femme le sait.

Le saumon passe de l'un à l'autre suivant un rituel que rien ne trouble, sinon la peur cachée de chacun que tant de perfection tout à coup ne se brise ou ne s'entache[5] d'une trop évidente absurdité. Dehors, dans le parc, les magnolias élaborent leur floraison funèbre dans la nuit noire du printemps naissant.

Avec le ressac[6] du vent qui va, vient, se cogne aux obstacles de la ville, et repart, le parfum atteint l'homme et le lâche, alternativement.

Des femmes, à la cuisine, achèvent de parfaire[7] la suite, la sueur au front, l'honneur à vif,[8] elles écorchent[9] un canard mort dans son linceul[10] d'oranges. Cependant que rose, mielleux,[11] mais déjà déformé par le temps très court qui vient de se passer, le saumon des eaux libres de l'océan continue sa marche inéluctable vers sa totale disparition et que la crainte d'un manquement quelconque au cérémonial qui accompagne celle-ci se dissipe peu à peu.

Un homme, face à une femme, regarde cette inconnue. Ses seins sont de

1 **saumon:** «salmon».
2 **natif:** ici, naturel.
3 **tel:** ici, comme.
4 **bien-séant:** correct.
5 **s'entacher:** se salir.
6 **ressac:** retour violent.
7 **parfaire:** perfectionner.
8 **l'honneur à vif:** au risque de leur réputation.
9 **écorcher:** dépouiller.
10 **linceul:** «shroud».
11 **mielleux:** comme le miel.

nouveau à moitié nus. Elle ajusta hâtivement sa robe. Entre eux, se fane une fleur. Dans ses yeux élargis, immodérés,[12] des lueurs de lucidité passent encore, suffisantes, pour qu'elle arrive à se servir à son tour du saumon des autres gens.

A la cuisine, on ose enfin le dire, le canard étant prêt, et au chaud,[13] dans le répit qui s'ensuit, qu'elle exagère. Elle arriva ce soir plus tard encore qu'hier, bien après ses invités.

Ils sont quinze, ceux qui l'attendirent tout à l'heure dans le grand salon du rez-de-chaussée. Elle entra dans cet univers étincelant, se dirigea vers le grand piano, s'y accouda, ne s'excusa nullement. On le fit à sa place.[14]

— Anne est en retard, excusez Anne.

Depuis dix ans, elle n'a pas fait parler d'elle. Si son incongruité la dévore,[15] elle ne peut s'imaginer. Un sourire fixe rend son visage acceptable.

— Anne n'a pas entendu.

Elle pose sa fourchette, regarde alentour, cherche, essaye de remonter le cours de la conversation, n'y arrive pas.

— Il est vrai, dit-elle.

On répète. Elle passe légèrement la main dans le désordre blond de ses cheveux, comme elle le fit tout à l'heure, ailleurs. Ses lèvres sont pâles. Elle oublia ce soir de les farder.[16]

— Excusez-moi, dit-elle, pour le moment, une petite sonatine de Diabelli.

— Une sonatine? Déjà?

— Déjà.

Le silence se reforme sur la question posée. Elle, elle retourne à la fixité de son sourire, une bête à la forêt.

— Moderato Cantabile, il ne savait pas?

— Il ne savait pas.

Le fleurissement des magnolias sera ce soir achevé. Sauf celui-ci, qu'elle cueillit ce soir en revenant du port. Le temps fuit, égal à lui-même, sur ce fleurissement oublié.

— Trésor, comment aurait-il pu deviner?

— Il ne pouvait pas.

— Il dort, probablement?

— Il dort, oui.

Lentement, la digestion commence de ce qui fut un saumon. Son osmose à cette espèce[17] qui le mangea fut rituellement parfaite. Rien n'en troubla la gra-

---

12 **immodéré:** ici, excessivement ouvert.
13 **au chaud:** où il fait chaud; ici, au four.
14 **à sa place:** pour elle.
15 **si son incongruité la dévore:** si sa propre incongruité l'étonne.
16 **farder:** «to apply make-up».
17 **espèce:** ici, «species».

vité. L'autre attend, dans une chaleur humaine, sur son linceul d'oranges. Voici la lune qui se lève sur la mer et sur l'homme allongé. Avec difficulté on pourrait, à la rigueur, maintenant, apercevoir les masses et les formes de la nuit à travers les rideaux blancs. Madame Desbaresdes n'a pas de conversation.

— Mademoiselle Giraud, qui donne également, comme vous le savez, des 5 leçons à mon petit garçon, me l'a racontée hier, cette histoire.

— Ah oui.

On rit. Quelque part autour de la table, une femme. Le chœur des conversations augmente peu à peu de volume et, dans une surenchère d'efforts et d'inventivités progressive[18] émerge une société quelconque. Des repères[19] sont trouvés, 10 des failles[20] s'ouvrant où s'essayent des familiarités. Et on débouche peu à peu sur une conversation généralement partisane et particuliérement neutre. La soirée réussira. Les femmes sont au plus sûr de leur éclat. Les hommes les couvrirent de bijoux au prorata[21] de leurs bilans.[22] L'un d'eux, ce soir, doute qu'il eut raison.

Dans le parc correctement clos, les oiseaux dorment d'un sommeil paisible et 15 réconfortant, car le temps est au beau. Ainsi qu'un enfant, dans une même conjugaison.[23] Le saumon repasse dans une forme encore amoindrie. Les femmes le dévoreront jusqu'au bout. Leurs épaules nues ont la luisance[24] et la fermeté d'une société fondée, dans ses assises,[25] sur la certitude de son droit, et elles furent choisies à la convenance de celle-ci.[26] La rigueur de leur éducation exige que leurs 20 excès soient tempérés par le souci majeur de leur entretien. De celui-ci on leur en inculqua, jadis, la conscience. Elles se pourlèchent[27] de mayonnaise, verte, comme il se doit,[28] s'y retrouvent,[29] y trouvent leur compte.[30] Des hommes les regardent et se rappellent qu'elles font leur bonheur.

L'une d'entre elles contrevient[31] ce soir à l'appétit général. Elle vient de l'autre 25 bout de la ville, de derrière les môles et les entrepôts[32] à huile, à l'opposé de ce boulevard de la Mer, de ce périmètre qui lui fut il y a dix ans autorisé, où un homme lui a offert du vin jusqu'à la déraison.[33] Nourrie de ce vin, exceptée de la règle,

---

[18] **surenchère. . . progressive:** «by dint of a major effort and increasingly fanciful imagination».
[19] **repère:** marque, indication qui permet de se retrouver.
[20] **faille:** fente, crevasse.
[21] **au prorata:** en proportion de.
[22] **bilan:** ici, «bank statement».
[23] **dans une même conjugaison:** dans les mêmes circonstances.
[24] **luisance:** éclat.
[25] **assises:** ici, «legal basis».
[26] **à la convenance de celle-ci:** «because they fit in it (society)».
[27] **se pourlécher:** passer la langue sur les lèvres.
[28] **comme il se doit:** comme il faut.
[29] **s'y retrouver:** se trouver confortable.
[30] **compte:** ici, avantage.
[31] **contrevenir:** aller contre.
[32] **entrepôt:** «warehouse».
[33] **déraison:** manque de raison.

manger l'exténuerait.[34] Au-delà des stores[35] blancs, la nuit et, dans la nuit, encore, car il a du temps devant lui, un homme seul regarde tantôt la mer, tantôt le parc. Puis la mer, le parc, ses mains. Il ne mange pas. Il ne pourrait pas, lui non plus, nourrir son corps tourmenté par d'autre faim. L'encens des magnolias arrive toujours sur lui, au gré du vent, et le surprend et le harcèle autant que celui d'une seule fleur. Au premier étage, une fenêtre s'est éteinte tout à l'heure et elle ne s'est pas rallumée. On a dû fermer les vitres de ce côté-là, de crainte de l'odeur excessive, la nuit, des fleurs.

Anne Desbaresdes boit, et ça ne cesse pas, le Pommard[36] continue d'avoir ce soir la saveur anéantissante des lèvres inconnues d'un homme de la rue.

Cet homme a quitté le boulevard de la Mer, il a fait le tour du parc, l'a regardé des dunes qui au nord, le bordent, puis il est revenu, il a redescendu le talus, il est redescendu jusqu'à la grève. Et de nouveau il s'y est allongé,[37] à sa place. Il s'étire, reste un moment immobile face à la mer, se retourne sur lui-même et regarde une fois de plus les stores blancs devant les baies illuminées. Puis il se relève, prend un galet,[38] vise une de ces baies, se retourne de nouveau, jette le galet dans la mer s'allonge, s'étire encore et tout haut,[39] prononce un nom.

Deux femmes, dans un mouvement alterné et complémentaire, préparent le deuxième service. L'autre victime attend.

— Anne, comme vous le savez, est sans défense devant son enfant.

Elle sourit davantage. On répète. Elle lève encore la main dans le désordre blond de ses cheveux. Le cerne[40] de ses yeux s'est encore agrandi. Ce soir, elle pleura. L'heure est arrivée où la lune s'est levée tout à fait sur la ville et sur le corps d'un homme alongé au bord de la mer.

— Il est vrai, dit-elle.

Sa main s'abaisse de ses cheveux et s'arrête à ce magnolia qui se fane entre ses seins.

— Nous sommes toutes pareilles, allez.[41]

— Oui, prononce Anne Desbaresdes.

Le pétale de magnolia est lisse, d'un grain nu. Les doigts le froissent jusqu'à le trouer[42] puis, interdits, s'arrêtent, se reposent sur la table, attendent, prennent une contenance,[43] illusoire. Car on s'en est aperçu. Anne Desbaresdes s'essaye à[44] un

---

34 **exténuer:** épuiser, fatiguer.
35 **store:** «window shade», «blind».
36 **Pommard:** un vin rouge de Bourgogne.
37 **s'allonger:** ici, s'étendre par terre.
38 **galet:** caillou plat.
39 **tout haut:** ici, à haute voix.
40 **cerne:** cercle sombre autour des yeux.
41 **allez:** ici, ne vous en faites pas.
42 **trouer:** faire des trous.
43 **prendre une contenance:** «to strike a pose».
44 **s'essayer à:** essayer de faire.

sourire d'excuse de n'avoir pu faire autrement, mais elle est ivre et son visage prend le faciès[45] impudique[46] de l'aveu. Le regard s'appesantit,[47] impassible,[48] mais revenu[49] déjà douloureusement de tout étonnement. On s'y attendait depuis toujours.

Anne Desbaresdes boit de nouveau un verre de vin tout entier, les yeux mi- 5
clos.[50] Elle en est[51] déjà à ne plus pouvoir faire autrement. Elle découvre, à boire, une confirmation de ce qui fut jusque-là son désir obscur et une indigne consolation à cette découverte.

D'autres femmes boivent à leur tour, elles lèvent de même leurs bras nus, délectables, irréprochables, mais d'épouses. Sur la grève, l'homme siffle une chan- 10
son entendue dans l'après-midi dans un café du port.

La lune est levée et avec elle voici le commencement de la nuit tardive et froide. Il n'est pas impossible que cet homme ait froid.

Le service du canard à l'orange[52] commence. Les femmes se servent. On les choisit belles et fortes, elles feront front[53] à tant de chère.[54] De doux murmures 15
montent de leurs gorges à la vue du canard d'or. L'une d'elles défaille[55] à sa vue. Sa bouche est desséchée par d'autre faim que rien non plus ne peut apaiser qu'à peine, le vin. Une chanson lui revient, entendue dans l'après-midi dans un café du port, qu'elle ne peut pas chanter. Le corps de l'homme sur la plage est toujours solitaire. Sa bouche est restée entrouverte sur le nom prononcé. 20

— Non merci.

Sur les paupières fermées de l'homme rien ne se pose que le vent et, par vagues impalpables et puissantes, l'odeur du magnolia, suivant les fluctuations de ce vent.

Anne Desbaresdes vient de refuser de se servir. Le plat reste cependant encore devant elle, un temps très court, mais celui du scandale.[56] Elle lève la main, comme 25
il lui fut appris, pour réitérer son refus. On n'insiste plus. Autour d'elle, à table, le silence s'est fait.

— Voyez, je ne pourrais pas, je m'en excuse.

Elle soulève une nouvelle fois sa main à hauteur de la fleur qui se fane entre ses seins et dont l'odeur franchit le parc et va jusqu'à la mer. 30

— C'est peut-être cette fleur, ose-t-on avancer, dont l'odeur est si forte?

---

45 **faciès**: aspect.
46 **impudique**: immodeste, imprudent.
47 **s'appesantir**: s'alourdir.
48 **impassible**: insensible.
49 **revenu**: c'est-à-dire, revenu à soi.
50 **mi-clos**: fermé à moitié.
51 **en être**: être au point.
52 **à l'orange**: «with orange sauce».
53 **faire front**: faire face.
54 **chère**: nourriture.
55 **défaillir**: perdre momentanément ses forces physiques ou morales.
56 **celui du scandale**: assez longtemps pour provoquer un scandale.

— J'ai l'habitude de ces fleurs, non, ce n'est rien.

Le canard suit son cours. Quelqu'un en face d'elle regarde encore impassible-
ment. Et elle s'essaye encore à sourire, mais ne réussit encore que la grimace
désespérée et licencieuse de l'aveu. Anne Desbaresdes est ivre.

On redemande si elle n'est pas malade. Elle n'est pas malade.

— C'est peut-être cette fleur, insiste-t-on, qui écœure subrepticement?

— Non. J'ai l'habitude de ces fleurs. C'est qu'il m'arrive de ne pas avoir
faim.

On la laisse en paix. La dévoration du canard commence. Sa graisse va se fondre
dans d'autres corps. Les paupières fermées d'un homme de la rue tremblent de
tant de patience consentie. Son corps éreinté a froid, que rien ne réchauffe. Sa
bouche a encore prononcé un nom.

A la cuisine, on annonce qu'elle a refusé le canard à l'orange, qu'elle est malade,
qu'il n'y a pas d'autre explication. Ici, on parle d'autre chose. Les formes vides des
magnolias caressent les yeux de l'homme seul. Anne Desbaresdes prend une
nouvelle fois son verre qu'on vient de remplir et boit. Le feu nourrit son ventre
de sorcière contrairement aux autres. Ses seins si lourds de chaque côté de cette
fleur si lourde se ressentent de[57] sa maigreur nouvelle et lui font mal. Le vin coule
dans sa bouche pleine d'un nom qu'elle ne prononce pas. Cet événement silencieux
lui brise les reins.[58]

L'homme s'est relevé de la grève, s'est approché des grilles, les baies sont toujours illuminées, prend les grilles dans ses mains, et serre. Comment n'est-ce pas
encore arrivé?

Le canard à l'orange, de nouveau, repassera. Du même geste que tout à l'heure,
Anne Desbaresdes implorera qu'on l'oublie. On l'oubliera. Elle retourne à
l'éclatement[59] silencieux de ses reins, à leur brûlante douleur, à son repaire.

L'homme a lâché les grilles du parc. Il regarde ses mains vides et déformées par
l'effort. Il lui a poussé, au bout des bras, un destin.

Le vent de la mer circule toujours à travers la ville, plus frais. Bien du monde
dort déjà. Les fenêtres du premier étage sont toujours obscures et fermées aux
magnolias sur le sommeil de l'enfant. Des bateaux rouges à moteur voguent[60] à
travers sa nuit innocente.

Quelques-uns ont repris du canard à l'orange. La conversation, de plus en plus
facile, augmente à chaque minute un peu davantage encore l'éloignement[61] de
la nuit.

---

[57] **se ressentir de:** sentir.
[58] **briser les reins:** casser le dos.
[59] **éclatement:** rupture. Notez que l'auteur continue l'image décrit dans la note 58.
[60] **voguer:** errer.
[61] **éloignement:** distance.

Dans l'éclatante lumière des lustres,[62] Anne Desbaresdes se tait et sourit toujours.

L'homme s'est décidé à repartir vers la fin de la ville, loin de ce parc. A mesure qu'il s'en éloigne, l'odeur des magnolias diminue, faisant place à celle de la mer.

Anne Desbaresdes prendra un peu de glace au moka[63] afin qu'on la laisse en paix.

L'homme reviendra malgré lui sur ses pas. Il retrouve les magnolias, les grilles, et les baies au loin, encore et encore éclairées. Aux lèvres, il a de nouveau ce chant entendu dans l'après-midi, et ce nom dans la bouche qu'il prononcera un peu plus fort. Il passera.

Elle, le sait encore. Le magnolia entre ses seins se fane tout à fait. Il a parcouru l'été en une heure de temps. L'homme passera outre au parc tôt ou tard. Il est passé. Anne Desbaresdes continue dans un geste interminable à supplicier la fleur.

— Anne n'a pas entendu.

Elle tente de sourire davantage, n'y arrive plus. On répète. Elle lève une dernière fois la main dans le désordre blond de ses cheveux. Le cerne de ses yeux s'est encore agrandi. Ce soir, elle pleura. On répète pour elle seule et on attend.

— Il est vrai, dit-elle, nous allons partir dans une maison au bord de la mer. Il fera chaud. Dans une maison isolée au bord de la mer.

— Trésor, dit-on.[64]

— Oui.

Alors que les invités se disperseront en ordre irrégulier dans le grand salon attenant[65] à la salle à manger, Anne Desbaresdes s'éclipsera,[66] montera au premier étage. Elle regardera le boulevard par la baie du grand couloir de sa vie. L'homme l'aura déjà déserté. Elle ira dans la chambre de son enfant, s'allongera par terre, au pied de son lit, sans égard pour ce magnolia qu'elle écrasera entre ses seins, il n'en restera rien. Et entre les temps sacrés de la respiration de son enfant, elle vomira là, longuement, la nourriture étrangère que ce soir elle fut forcée de prendre.

Une ombre apparaîtra dans l'encadrement de la porte restée ouverte sur le couloir, obscurcira plus avant la pénombre de la chambre. Anne Desbaresdes passera légèrement la main dans le désordre réel et blond de ses cheveux. Cette fois, elle prononcera une excuse.

On ne lui répondra pas.

---

62 **lustre:** chandelier.
63 **moka:** café noir très fort.
64 C'est sans doute son mari qui appelle Anne.
65 **attenant:** contigu.
66 **s'éclipser:** partir, disparaître.

QUESTIONNAIRE

Page 61—page 64, ligne 29	Où sommes-nous au début du Chapitre VII?
	Décrivez la scène quand Anne arrive chez elle en retard. Comment agit-elle?
	Décrivez le dîner—les invités et leur conversation.
	Que fait Chauvin pendant le dîner?
	Pourquoi Anne se sent-elle isolée?
	Décrivez la technique narrative dans cette première partie du Chapitre VII.
Page 64, ligne 30—page 67	Pourquoi Anne continue-t-elle de boire?
	Expliquez la phrase suivante: «D'autres femmes boivent à leur tour, elles lèvent de même leurs bras nus, délectables, irréprobables, mais d'épouses» (p. 65, l. 9).
	Pourquoi y a-t-il un silence autour de la table quand Anne refuse de prendre du canard?
	Décrivez ce que peuvent être les pensées d'Anne pendant ce dîner.
	Qu'est-ce que Chauvin attend à l'extérieur?
	Que fait Anne après le repas? Que font les autres?
	Pensez-vous que la fin du chapitre ait une valeur symbolique? Justifiez votre réponse.
	Décrivez l'action du mari dans ce chapitre.
	Comment peut-on dire que le saumon et le canard sont, en quelque sorte, les «personnages» principaux du chapitre?

VIII

Le beau temps durait encore. Sa durée avait dépassé toutes les espérances. On en parlait maintenant avec le sourire, comme on l'eût fait d'un temps mensonger qui eût caché derrière sa pérennité[1] quelque irrégularité qui bientôt se laisserait voir et rassurerait sur le cours habituel des saisons de l'année.

Ce jour-là, même eu égard aux[2] jours derniers, la bonté de ce temps fut telle, pour la saison bien entendu, que lorsque le ciel ne se recouvrait pas trop de nuages, lorsque les éclaircies[3] duraient un peu, on aurait pu le croire encore meilleur, encore plus avancé qu'il n'était, plus proche encore de l'été. Les nuages étaient si lents à recouvrir le soleil, si lents à le faire, en effet, que cette journée était presque plus belle encore que celles qui l'avaient précédée. D'autant que la brise qui l'accompagnait était marine, molle, très ressemblante à celle qui soufflerait certains jours, dans les prochains mois.

Certains prétendirent que ce jour avait été chaud. La plupart nièrent—non sa beauté—mais que celle-ci avait été telle que ce jour avait été chaud. Certains n'eurent pas d'avis.

Anne Desbaresdes ne revint que le surlendemain[4] de sa dernière promenade sur le port. Elle arriva à peine plus tard que d'habitude. Dès que Chauvin l'aperçut, de loin, derrière le môle, il rentra dans le café pour l'attendre. Elle était sans son enfant.

Anne Desbaresdes entra dans le café au moment d'une longue éclaircie du temps. La patronne ne leva pas les yeux sur elle, continua à tricoter sa laine rouge dans la pénombre du comptoir. Déjà, la surface de son ouvrage avait augmenté. Anne Desbaresdes rejoignit Chauvin à la table où ils s'étaient assis les jours qui avaient précédé, au fond de la salle. Chauvin n'était pas rasé du matin,[5] mais seulement de

1 **pérennité:** permanence, longue durée.
2 **eu égard à:** par rapport à.
3 **éclaircie:** période où il fait du soleil.
4 **surlendemain:** deux jours après.
5 **du matin:** ici, ce matin.

la veille. Le visage d'Anne Desbaresdes manquait du soin qu'elle mettait d'habitude à l'apprêter avant de le montrer. Ni l'un ni l'autre, sans doute, ne le remarqua.

— Vous êtes seule, dit Chauvin.

Elle acquiesça longtemps après qu'il l'ait dite à cette évidence, tenta de l'éluder,
5 s'étonna encore de ne pas y parvenir.

— Oui.

Pour échapper à la suffocante simplicité de cet aveu, elle se tourna vers la porte
du café, la mer. Les Fonderies de la Côte vrombissaient[6] au sud de la ville. Là,
dans le port, le sable et le charbon se déchargeaient comme à l'accoutumée.

10 — Il fait beau, dit-elle.

Dans un même mouvement que le sien, Chauvin regarda au dehors, scruta
aveuglément le temps, le temps qu'il faisait ce jour-là.

— Je n'aurais pas cru que ça arriverait si vite.

La patronne, tant durait leur silence, se retourna sur elle-même, alluma la radio,
15 sans aucune impatience, avec douceur même. Une femme chanta loin, dans une
ville étrangère. Ce fut Anne Desbaresdes qui se rapprocha de Chauvin.

— A partir de cette semaine, d'autres que moi mèneront mon enfant à sa
leçon de piano, chez Mademoiselle Giraud. C'est une chose que j'ai acceptée que
l'on fasse à ma place.

20 Elle but le reste de son vin, à petites gorgées.[7] Son verre fut vide. Chauvin oublia
de commander d'autre vin.

— Sans doute est-ce préférable, dit-il.

Un client entra, désœuvré,[8] seul, seul, et commanda également du vin. La
patronne le servit, puis elle alla servir les deux autres dans la salle, sans qu'ils l'aient
25 demandé. Ils burent immédiatement ensemble, sans un mot pour elle. Anne Desbaresdes parla de façon précipitée.

— La dernière fois, dit-elle, j'ai vomi ce vin. Il n'y a que quelques jours que je
bois. . .

— Ça n'a plus d'importance désormais.

30 — Je vous en prie. . . supplia-t-elle.

— Au fond,[9] choisissons de parler ou de ne rien dire, comme vous le voudrez.

Elle examina le café, puis lui, l'endroit tout entier, et lui, implorant un secours
qui ne vint pas.

— J'ai souvent vomi, mais pour des raisons différentes de celle-ci. Toujours
35 très différentes, vous comprenez. De boire tellement de vin à la fois, d'un seul coup,
en si peu de temps, je n'en n'avais pas l'habitude. Que j'ai vomi. Je ne pouvais plus

---

6 **vrombir:** bourdonner.
7 **à petites gorgées:** «in sips».
8 **désœuvré:** qui n'a rien à faire.
9 **au fond:** ici, en effet.

m'arrêter, j'ai cru que je ne pourrai plus jamais m'arrêter, mais voilà que tout à coup ça n'a plus été possible, j'ai eu beau essayer. Ma volonté n'y a plus suffi.

Chauvin s'accouda à la table, la tête dans ses mains.

— Je suis fatigué.

Anne Desbaresdes remplit son verre, le lui tendit. Chauvin ne lui résista pas. 5

— Je peux me taire, s'excusa-t-elle.

— Non.

Il posa sa main à côté de la sienne, sur la table, dans l'écran d'ombre que faisait son corps.

— Le cadenas[10] était sur la porte du jardin, comme d'habitude. Il faisait beau, 10
à peine de vent. Au rez-de-chaussée, les baies étaient éclairées.

La patronne rangea son tricot rouge, rinça des verres et, pour la première fois, ne s'inquiéta pas de savoir s'ils resteraient encore longtemps. L'heure approchait de la fin du travail.

— Nous n'avons plus beaucoup de temps, dit Chauvin. 15

Le soleil commença à baisser. Il en suivit des yeux la course fauve[11] et lente sur le mur du fond de la salle.

— Cet enfant, dit Anne Desbaresdes, je n'ai pas eu le temps de vous le dire. . .

— Je sais, dit Chauvin.

Elle retira sa main de dessus la table, regarda longuement celle de Chauvin tou- 20
jours là, posée, qui tremblait. Puis elle se mit à gémir doucement une plainte impatiente—la radio la couvrit—et elle ne fut perceptible qu'à lui seul.

— Parfois, dit-elle, je crois que je l'ai inventé. . .

— Je sais, pour cet enfant, dit brutalement Chauvin.

La plainte d'Anne Desbaresdes reprit, se fit plus forte. Elle posa de nouveau sa 25
main sur la table. Il suivit son geste des yeux et péniblement il comprit, souleva la sienne qui était de plomb et la posa sur la sienne à elle. Leurs mains étaient si froides qu'elles se touchèrent illusoirement dans l'intention seulement, afin que ce fût fait, dans la seule intention que ce le fût, plus autrement, ce n'était plus possible. Leurs mains restèrent ainsi, figées dans leur pose mortuaire.[12] Pourtant la plainte d'Anne 30
Desbaresdes cessa.

— Une dernière fois, supplia-t-elle, dites-moi.

Chauvin hésita, les yeux toujours ailleurs, sur le mur du fond, puis il se décida à le dire comme d'un souvenir.

— Jamais auparavant, avant de la rencontrer, il n'aurait pensé que l'envie aurait 35
pu lui en venir un jour.

10 **cadenas:** serrure.
11 **fauve:** «tawny».
12 **mortuaire:** de la mort.

— Son consentement à elle était entier?

— Emerveillé.

Anne Desbaresdes leva vers Chauvin un regard absent. Sa voix se fit mince, presque enfantine.

— Je voudrais comprendre un peu pourquoi était si merveilleuse son envie qu'il y arrive un jour.

Chauvin ne la regarda toujours pas. Sa voix était posée, sans timbre, une voix de sourd.

— Ce n'est pas la peine d'essayer de comprendre. On ne peut pas comprendre à ce point.

— Il y a des choses comme celle-là qu'il faut laisser de côté?

— Je crois.

Le visage d'Anne Desbaresdes prit une expression terne, presque imbécile. Ses lèvres étaient grises à force de pâleur et elles tremblaient comme avant les pleurs.

— Elle ne tente rien pour l'en empêcher, dit-elle tout bas.

— Non. Buvons encore un peu de vin.

Elle but, toujours à petites gorgées, il but à son tour. Ses lèvres à lui tremblaient aussi sur le verre.

— Le temps, dit-il.

— Il faut beaucoup, beaucoup de temps?

— Je crois, beaucoup. Mais je ne sais rien. Il ajouta tout bas: «Je ne sais rien, comme vous. Rien».

Anne Desbaresdes n'arriva pas jusqu'aux larmes. Elle reprit une voix raisonnable, un instant réveillée.

— Elle ne parlera plus jamais, dit-elle.

— Mais si. Un jour, un beau matin, tout à coup, elle rencontrera quelqu'un qu'elle reconnaîtra, elle ne pourra pas faire autrement que de dire bonjour. Ou bien elle entendra chanter un enfant, il fera beau, elle dira il fait beau. Ça recommencera.

— Non.

— C'est comme vous désirez le croire, ça n'a pas d'importance.

La sirène retentit, énorme, qui s'entendit[13] allégrement[14] de tous les coins de la ville et même de plus loin, des faubourgs, de certaines communes environnantes, portée par le vent de la mer. Le couchant se vautra,[15] plus fauve encore sur les murs de la salle. Comme souvent au crépuscule, le ciel s'immobilisa, relativement,

---

13 **s'entendre:** ici, être entendu.
14 **allégrement:** vivement.
15 **se vautrer:** ici, s'enfoncer.

dans un calme gonflement[16] de nuages, le soleil ne fut plus recouvert et brilla libre-
ment de ses derniers feux. La sirène, ce soir-là, fut interminable. Mais elle cessa
cependant, comme les autres soirs.

— J'ai peur, murmura Anne Desbaresdes.

Chauvin s'approcha de la table, la rechercha, la recherchant, puis y renonça. 5

— Je ne peux pas.

Elle fit alors ce qu'il n'avait pas pu faire. Elle s'avança vers lui d'assez près pour
que leurs lèvres puissent s'atteindre. Leurs lèvres restèrent l'une sur l'autre, posées,
afin que ce fût fait et suivant le même rite mortuaire que leurs mains, un instant
avant, froides et tremblantes. Ce fut fait. 10

Déjà, des rues voisines une rumeur arrivait, feutrée, coupée de paisibles et gais
appels. L'arsenal avait ouvert ses portes à ses huit cents hommes. Il n'était pas loin
de là. La patronne alluma la rampe lumineuse au-dessus du comptoir bien que le
couchant fût étincelant. Après une hésitation, elle arriva vers eux qui ne se disaient
plus rien et les servit d'autre vin sans qu'ils l'aient demandé, avec une sollicitude 15
dernière. Puis elle resta là après les avoir servi, près d'eux, encore cependant ensemble, cherchant quoi leur dire, ne trouva rien, s'éloigna.

— J'ai peur, dit de nouveau Anne Desbaresdes.

Chauvin ne répondit pas.

— J'ai peur, cria presque Anne Desbaresdes. 20

Chauvin ne répondit toujours pas. Anne Desbaresdes se plia en deux presque
jusqu'à toucher la table de son front et elle accepta la peur.

— On va donc s'en tenir[17] là où nous sommes, dit Chauvin. Il ajouta: «Ça doit
arriver parfois».

Un groupe d'ouvriers entra, qui les avaient déjà vus. Ils évitèrent de les regar- 25
der, étant au courant, eux aussi, comme la patronne et toute la ville. Un chœur de
conversations diverses, assourdies[18] par la pudeur, emplit le café.

Anne Desbaresdes se releva et tenta encore, par-dessus la table, de se rapprocher
de Chauvin.

— Peut-être que je ne vais pas y arriver, murmura-t-elle. 30

Peut-être n'entendit-il plus. Elle ramena sa veste sur elle-même, la ferma,
l'étriqua[19] sur elle, fut reprise du même gémissement sauvage.

— C'est impossible, dit-elle.

Chauvin entendit.

— Une minute, dit-il, et nous y arriverons. 35

---

16 **gonflement:** «swelling».
17 **s'en tenir:** rester.
18 **assourdi:** rendu moins bruyant.
19 **étriquer:** serrer.

Anne Desbaresdes attendit cette minute, puis elle essaya de se relever de sa chaise. Elle y arriva, se releva. Chauvin regardait ailleurs. Les hommes évitèrent encore de porter leurs yeux sur cette femme adultère. Elle fut levée.

— Je voudrais que vous soyez morte, dit Chauvin.

5 — C'est fait, dit Anne Desbaresdes.

Anne Desbaresdes contourna sa chaise de telle façon qu'elle n'ait plus à faire le geste de s'y rasseoir. Puis elle fit un pas en arrière et se retourna sur elle-même. La main de Chauvin battit l'air et retomba sur la table. Mais elle ne le vit pas, ayant déjà quitté le champ où il se trouvait.

10 Elle se retrouva face au couchant, ayant traversé le groupe d'hommes qui étaient au comptoir, dans la lumière rouge qui marquait le terme de ce jour-là.

Après son départ, la patronne augmenta le volume de la radio. Quelques hommes se plaignirent qu'elle fût trop forte à leur gré.

QUESTIONNAIRE

Que pensez-vous qu'il soit arrivé le lendemain du dîner?

Où Chauvin attend-il Anne? Pourquoi?

Expliquez la dureté de Chauvin.

Expliquez le dialogue suivant (p. 71, ll. 23–24):

—Parfois, dit-elle, je crois que je l'ai inventé (l'enfant) . . .
—Je sais, pour cet enfant, dit brutalement Chauvin.

Décrivez les mains de Chauvin et d'Anne qui se touchent.

Comment l'impression que c'est la fin s'impose-t-elle lentement?

En quoi Anne et Chauvin ont-ils une idée différente de l'avenir?

Décrivez et expliquez leur baiser.

Expliquez cette phrase d'Anne (p. 73, l. 30): «Peut-être que je ne vais pas y arriver . . .»

Pourquoi les hommes dans le café évitent-ils de regarder Anne et pourquoi Marguerite Duras utilise-t-elle l'expression «femme adultère»?

Expliquez ces répliques (p. 74, ll. 4–5):

—Je voudrais que vous soyez morte, dit Chauvin.
—C'est fait, dit Anne Desbaresdes.

Questions générales

Décrivez le café et la patronne.

Comment l'expression, *clair-obscur*, pourrait-elle s'appliquer à ce roman?

Attribuez-vous une signification au temps qu'il fait pendant la durée du roman? aux bruits qu'on entend?

Que signifie le titre du roman?

Discutez les deux personnages principaux.

Quel est le rôle de l'enfant?

Discutez la construction du roman.

Discutez le style de Marguerite Duras.

Pensez-vous qu'on puisse deviner que *Moderato Cantabile* fut écrit par une femme sans savoir que Marguerite Duras en est l'auteur?

Bibliographie Sélective

Berger, Yves, «Marguerite Duras» dans Bernard Pingaud, éd., *Ecrivains d'aujourd'hui*. Paris: Editions Bernard Grasset, 1960.

Brée, Germaine, «Quatre Romans de M. Duras», *Cahiers Renaud-Barrault*, No. 52 (décembre 1965). Cet article est une traduction de l'introduction écrite pour l'édition américaine de Marguerite Duras, *Four Novels* (New York: Grove Press, 1965).

Duvignaud, Jean, «Le Clair-obscur de la vie quotidienne», *ibid*. Ce numéro des *Cahiers* est consacré à Marguerite Duras.

Guicharnaud, Jacques, «Woman's Fate: Marguerite Duras», *Yale French Studies*, No. 27 (1961).

Hell, Henri, «L'Univers romanesque de Marguerite Duras», dans Marguerite Duras, *Moderato Cantabile*. Paris: 10/18, 1958.

Picon, Gaëtan, «Les Romans de Marguerite Duras», *Mercure de France* (juin 1958).

Recovering 9/11 in New York

Recovering 9/11 in New York

Edited by

Robert Fanuzzi and Michael Wolfe

CAMBRIDGE
SCHOLARS

PUBLISHING

Recovering 9/11 in New York,
Edited by Robert Fanuzzi and Michael Wolfe

This book first published 2014

Cambridge Scholars Publishing

12 Back Chapman Street, Newcastle upon Tyne, NE6 2XX, UK

British Library Cataloguing in Publication Data
A catalogue record for this book is available from the British Library

ISBN (10): 1-4438-5343-7, ISBN (13): 978-1-4438-5343-9

TABLE OF CONTENTS

LIST OF FIGURES

ACKNOWLEDGEMENTS

We wish to take to thank so many people who helped to make possible our 2011 conference, "Making Meaning of 9/11 Ten Years After" and now this book. Our gratitude goes first to Rev. Donald J. Harrington, C.M. As president of St. John's University at the time, he generously supported our desire to study and commemorate events that struck our own university community so very deeply. We also thank Dr. Julia A. Upton, R.S.M., whose support as provost took so many forms, including a splendid paper on spirituality and 9/11. Dr. Jeffrey Fagen, dean of St. John's College of Liberal Arts and Sciences, along with all the wonderful people in the Office of the Dean and the Graduate Division, provided invaluable help with the planning and then holding of our conference. We also wish to express our appreciation to all the people who contributed to our conference conversation by way of papers, panel discussions, or posing questions as audience members. It was a memorable experience for all. This book represents a permanent legacy of that experience for which we would like to thank Carol Koulikourdi, her staff at Cambridge Scholars Press, and Ross Wolfe who lent his considerable skills in photo editing to this collection. Like so many other families in New York, St. John's lost many dear friends and alumni on that terrible day in September. This book is offered in remembrance of them.

INTRODUCTION

ROBERT FANUZZI AND MICHAEL WOLFE

The impulse to turn fields of battle and wartime violence into hallowed ground is deeply ingrained in American culture. From this impulse has sprung stirring national memorials and commemorative sites like Gettysburg National Park and Pearl Harbor National Memorial. The Oklahoma City National Memorial and Museum offers eloquent testimony to the fact that even as Americans find themselves threatened by stateless terrorist groups and paramilitary organizations that attack without declarations of war, the tradition of transforming sites and moments of violence into markers of national purpose continues to this day.

In 2012, a portion of the National 9/11 Memorial and Museum opened, turning a section of Lower Manhattan previously known colloquially as "Ground Zero" into a national memorial. And yet despite this formal designation, the mission statement of the National 9/11 Memorial and Museum includes language that suggests a shift in the way we remember and memorialize national tragedies. Committed to "demonstrating the consequences of terrorism on individual lives and its impact on communities at the local, national, and international levels", this mission statement reserves a special place for reflection on local impacts of terrorist violence in metropolitan New York rather than simply folding them into larger, more sweeping invocations of national identity and national resolve.

While not polemical in rhetoric or purpose, the Mission Statement of the National 9/11 Memorial and Museum acknowledges a reality that nearly every witness, participant, and commentator on the 9/11 World Trade Center attacks have reiterated from nearly the first 9/11 moments: that the attack that occurred in Lower Manhattan cannot easily be incorporated into a nationalist narrative of war and patriotic resolve. To be sure, a U.S. President did venture to that very spot and effectively launch a "global war on terror" that altered the course of military policy in the United States, transformed the national security state, and authorized intelligence-gathering capabilities that have forever changed the relationship between the federal government and its citizens. But none of these national and international repercussions seems to have determined the forms that the remembrance of 9/11 and its victims have taken in and around the New York area. A tension remains—a creative tension, we maintain—between the national traditions and languages for commemorating the dead and local responses to 9/11. What do Americans living in New York, New Jersey, and Connecticut know and remember about 9/11 that cannot be nationalized or adopted for nationalist ends? Even while they recover their lives and their memories in the wake of the terrorist attacks, they seem determined to recover 9/11 for New York.

Perhaps the residents and commuters of the New York metropolitan area, like many Americans, express their discontent with the foreign, domestic, military, and intelligence policies that emerged from 9/11 by implanting a local character in their commemorations and anniversaries. More intriguing is the possibility that the language and rituals of national remembrance and purpose cannot overcome the methods and strategies that New Yorkers use to deal with tragedy. So perhaps the reason is New York itself. Here we are, more than a decade removed from a national calamity that turned New York and the World Trade Center into patriotic symbols, and the gulf between New York and America might well be just as it was depicted on that famous 1976 *New Yorker* magazine cover by Saul Steinberg. New Yorkers, we all know, do things differently and want different things; they may live in the United States but they live and breathe New York. Did 9/11 change any of that?

This collection of essays offers documentary, clinical, critical and academic evidence about the distinctive way that citizens of the New York metropolitan region recovered from and memorialized the 9/11 World Trade Center attacks. The verdict is in and, as you would expect, they did it their way. Indeed, the essays and photos that we collect in this volume suggest that the 9/11 attacks put in motion a local counter-impulse to the national tradition of battlefield memorials and memorialization. In place of national rituals and languages for remembering the attacks is a distinctly experiential, quotidian pattern of ritualization and recovery that captures more than anything the ebb and flow of modern life in metropolitan New York, now amplified by the scale and gravity of the event to heroize and record for posterity. The convergence of these two aims—to hallow and to live on from moment-to-moment—has created a distinctive archive that we present in this volume, and at the same time, critique.

The language and rituals of post-9/11 recovery we assemble here are indeed unique and rich with meaning and contradiction. They may gesture toward national conventions of memorialization and invoke national traditions of heroism but they just as quickly ground that gesture in a setting or cultural practice that announces its local character—its New York or Jersey accent, if you will. Abiding throughout the gestures, rituals, and idioms that we document in this volume is the will to honor metropolitan New York, a homeland that cannot be replaced or subsumed.

Just as powerful in this impulse is a claim of propriety that can be ascribed to this locality—that the World Trade Center attacks will always be a special tragedy for those who live and work in New York, a municipal calamity that temporarily or permanently separated commuters from family members, blew a gaping hole in our beloved skyline, and yes, totally screwed up commuter patterns and work lives in Lower Manhattan for years to come. To recreate and document this perspective is to return to that fleeting instant before the words "America Under Attack" appeared on every television screen, and the World Trade Center attacks became a national tragedy; when they still were just felt and lived by people who lived or came daily to work in New York. To be sure, the outpouring of sympathy and support from communities around the United States in the aftermath of the terrorist attacks did make 9/11 a national event in the best possible way, but the ties of nationalism can be difficult to maintain and harder to quantify. The ties of New Yorkers and of commuters to their communities in the aftermath of the 9/11 attacks, however, are remarkably easy to document and observe, even though they have rarely been acknowledged in a book form.

The book that has become *Recovering 9/11* dates to a conference called "Making Meaning of 9/11: Ten Years After," held at the St. John's University Lower Manhattan campus on the tenth anniversary of the 9/11 attacks. Located exactly one block from the site still known as "Ground Zero," the St. John's University campus had served as an emergency services center for first responders and victims in the weeks directly after the attacks. A more fitting site for a New York-focused 9/11 conference could not be found, as the university was literally part of that old ten-year history. Charged with that history and its proximity to the emerging World Trade Center, the conference "Making Meaning of 9/11" let in a fresh air of inquiry and invention during a week that saw a virtual tidal wave of commemorative events, anniversaries, media specials and publications. Collectively, those efforts had produced a virtual incantation of the words, "remember," "rebuild," and "recover" that informed and inspired few. In an atmosphere charged with familiar expectations and clichés, we were delighted to find that all the efforts of national leaders and commentators to capture the meaning of the 9/11 attacks were easily matched and in some cases surpassed by the eloquence of everyday acts and the strength of civic spirit. These acts and spirit were found in classrooms, in restaurants, in ambulances, on street corners. They were embodied by municipal memorial committees, illegal immigrant workers, and yes, first responders. As our conference participants recorded and presented these negotiations with a ten year-old catastrophe, we came to the realization that they represented a set of cultural practices that had charged and changed New York City and its surrounding area with the spirit of post-9/11 recovery. To the extent that they continue to this day, these cultural practices constitute both an important chapter in New York's metropolitan history and a reminder to us all of the value of public history—that is, the potential of witnesses and participants to make their own meanings of a climactic event in recent United States history from their resources and first-hand experience.

The ambition to present the evidence of New Yorkers' post-9/11 recovery in this book goes hand-in-hand with the impulse to critique the nationalization of this tragedy that, particularly in the direct aftermath of 9/11, stifled creative and truthful ways to think about the impact of the World Center attacks on New York. As readers will discover, they also have only passing relevance to the professional, scholarly, and colloquial languages that the contributors to this volume used to document the post-9/11 recovery and commemorations in greater New York. In order to accentuate and articulate the distinct value of these languages, we also embrace for this volume the critical languages of literary history and cultural studies, which are represented in several essays on the representation of 9/11 near the end of the book. Though hardly blunt instruments, these literary and cultural critiques of 9/11 representation do the important work in this volume of hacking away at the nationalist mythos and ideologies that inhibit our responses to the World Trade Center Attacks. In doing so, they allow reflection on the preceding discoveries and documentation produced by the volume's other contributors—social workers, clinicians, cultural anthropologists, educators, and architectural critics, writers, and those who simply bore witness.

Taken together, the multi-disciplinary perspectives included in "Recovering 9/11" attest at once to the complexity of this topic and the challenge of presenting the evidence of a city post-crisis. Indeed, this collection differs in a number of important respects from the otherwise prodigious list of publications on 9/11 and its aftermath. The vast majority of titles on this subject, regardless of approach, appeared in the two to three years immediately following the attacks; many are compilations of journalistic pieces, eye-witness memoirs, or essays with a focus on international affairs or Homeland Security. These include, for example, anthologies and collections such as Phil Scranton's *Beyond September 11:*

An Anthology of Dissent (London: Pluto Press, 2002), Eric Hershberg's *Critical Views of September 11: Analyses from around the World* (New York: New Press, 2002) and Fletcher Haulley's *Critical Perspectives on 9/11: Critical Anthologies of Nonfiction*, (New York: Rosen Publishing Group, 2005). Especially notable are two works from Routledge: Ken Booth's and Tim Dunne's *Terror in Our Time*, dealing with international security issues, and Ann Kenniston's and Jeanne Follansbee Quinn's *Literature after 9/11*, which mobilizes a wide variety of theories and discourses to describe the impact of the World Trade Center attacks on literature. *Recovering 9/11* assembles an equally broad and variegated set of approaches—literary, social science, historical, pedagogical, and aesthetic—but focus this knowledge on descriptions and experiences of local impacts that are as broad and variegated as the approaches themselves. It takes a longer, more rounded perspective on the events surrounding 9/11 in the interest of documenting a project of ongoing recovery rooted in the communities and lives of people in the New York metropolitan area.

For these reasons, we are confident these essays will bring renewed interest and critical reflection to the problem of measuring recovery and resilience in the metropolitan area even while memories, gestures of commemoration, and even everyday lives remain unsettled. In this ambition, the book follows a trail brazed by the best critics of 9/11 representation and contemporary memorialization, which include Marita Sturken, Erika Doss, Kristin Haas, and David Simpson, all of whom investigate the conflicted relationship of U.S. citizens to vernacular and monumental structures of commemoration. What they investigate at the national level we document at the local.[1]

Together, the contributors to *Recovering 9/11* all share a commitment —much discussed at the ten-year anniversary conference—to use our distrust of nationalist representation and manipulative uses of commemoration to generate an interdisciplinary, socially-engaged form of scholarship capable of connecting commentators and scholars more sensitively and intimately with the experiences of people who lived or came to work in New York. In this respect, the contributors were guided not merely by an

---

[1] See Martina Sturken, *Tourists of History: Memory, Kitsch, and Consumerism from Oklahoma City to Ground Zero* (Durham, N.C.: Duke University Press, 2007); Erika Doss, *Memorial Mania: Public Feeling in America* (Chicago, Ill.: University of Chicago Press, 2010); Kristin Anne Haas, *Carried to the Wall: American Memory and the Vietnam Veterans Memorial* (Berkeley: University of California Press, 1998); David Simpson, *9/11: The Culture of Commemoration* (Chicago, Ill.: University of Chicago Press, 2006).

intellectual mission to record a local impact but by a methodology shared by the writers, clinicians, educators, and professionals assembled here: to know their subjects as they really live, and to bring back first-hand knowledge. Indeed, the sensitive and reflective approach of contributors to *Recovering 9/11* brings an immediacy not often found in academic writing precisely because its essays take up directly the lives and efforts of people who have long labored to make meaning of the World Trade Center attacks: the quilt makers, social workers and psychologists, the first-responders, teachers, clinical psychologists, displaced workers, and all the compassionate, anonymous New Yorkers who document the tragedy in countless creative ways. In doing so, these essays give academics and clinical professionals an opportunity to model a publicly-engaged scholarship that regards the people of a community—in this case, metropolitan New York—as partners and even protagonists in creating paradigms and structures for commemoration.

But while the essays in this collection resist the "nationalization" of the World Trade Center attacks in Lower Manhattan and recover the uniqueness of local responses, they also resist the temptation to totalize those responses into a romanticized concept of "New Yorkers' spirit." On the contrary, they help us to elaborate upon the disparate factors of class, race and ethnicity, profession, and educational attainment that shape life in the complex communities that radiate in, around and beyond the New York metropolitan area. These disparities are on display within the New York classroom that attempts to discuss 9/11, within the New Jersey communities that locally memorialize it, and even within volunteers and professionals we collectively heroize as "first responders." They remind us that 9/11 did nothing to tame the fractious spirit of a region and a city that has always juxtaposed creation with destruction, memory with futurity, and modernity with neighborhood tribalisms. In the years after the completion of the National 9/11 Memorial and Museum focalized the commemorative activities of people in New York, we might well look back at the disparate scenes and occasions for 9/11 commemoration that are recorded here as a unique period in which the warring impulses of New York had free reign to generate both discord and consensus in a bid to deal with calamity.

The collection is comprised of sixteen essays by experts drawn from across a wide range of scholarly and professional fields. Part One, "Local Expressions of 9/11", investigates the question of how people across the New York metropolitan region have remembered and commemorated the events of September 11th. This section documents the outpouring of human and local responses to 9/11 in familiar places like the spontaneous writing that covered public wall surfaces throughout the city and the spectral image of the Twin Towers memorialized in the signage of local small businesses that operated in the shadow of the city's huge finance district. The need for New Yorkers to come together to affirm their unity and sense of community as well as to begin to mourn their loss, also engaged them more fully with the national pastime, as post-9/11 events turned both Yankee Stadium and the New York Mets' Citi Field into secular cathedrals for the assembled throngs.

Part Two, "Memorializing 9/11", gathers together essays that consider diverse ways of remembering the World Trade Center site after 9/11. In doing so, they intervene in the highly charged, contested efforts of various local and national constituencies to control the making of meaning *in situ* after the attacks. In one essay, the forgotten stories of service workers, many undocumented, who perished in the attacks provide a powerful corrective to the monumental scale of 9/11 memorials. Their place in the story of the famous "Windows on the World" restaurant joins those told about the World Trade Center as a tourist destination, a nexus of competing political and economic interests and contested politics, international in dimension, and, finally, as a site of ruin. The impact of the World Trade Center also became manifest in commuter communities throughout suburban New Jersey, where in the years following 9/11, modest, yet moving memorials took form for loved ones and neighbors who never returned home from work on that fateful day. These layered memories complicate, perhaps even render impossible, the complex negotiations to memorialize September 11th in a manner that achieves some fixed form or stable consensus.

The essays in Part Three, "Responding to 9/11", engage directly with the emotional and psychological aftermath of the attacks, approaching the questions of healing and teaching from a variety of institutional, professional, and non-professional perspectives. The spontaneous urge to help began minutes after American Airlines Flight 11 struck the North Tower at 8:46 a.m., and continued in the horrifying hours, days, and weeks that followed. Eventually, the bravery and sacrifice of first responders gave way to the arduous efforts of clinicians, religious ministers, and teachers to help people recover. Is their intervention a story of triumph and enlightenment? Emphasizing the resilience of witnesses, family members of victims, and first responders but also the vulnerability of professionals, this section brings together various professional perspectives to critically assess the effectiveness of recovery efforts, including those that take place in the classroom. Classroom discussion, at times, yields real conflict about the ability of students and teachers to make meaning of the World Trade

Center in the face of media-driven representations of 9/11 and prevailing suspicion or ignorance of the Muslim world.

The volume concludes with a selection of essays that grapples with the challenge of "Representing 9/11." Contributors to this section evaluate contemporary novels and films that have risked engagement with deep narrative traditions to translate the recent memory of public events into resonant stories and imaginative language. No representation, not even the 2007 documentary recounting Philippe Petit's dramatic and triumphal tightrope walk in 1974 between the Twin Towers of the World Trade Center, allows us to retreat to the simpler time before these towers were national symbols. We are invited to glimpse instead the making of the tenuous connection between New York City's landmark skyscrapers and national symbolism before and after the destruction of the towers. The contributors' incisive critiques of post-9/11 American fiction question whether "representing 9/11" can or should ever become a literary genre or branch of national literature, given the contradictions that exist between the national meaning, public history, and the private and increasingly complex international lives of New Yorkers affected by the World Trade Center attacks. The historical example of nineteenth-century American literature, which, in the aftermath of the United States Civil War, also struggled with the patriotic, national meaning of the war's human toll, provides a cautionary tale. Can we better understand the burden of expectation that we have placed on literature, on memorials, on media representations and on professionals by thinking more broadly—historically and nationally—about our capacity to remember? We close this book with the invitation to consider this question in light of the attempts of residents of the New York metropolitan area to make their own distinctive, unique contribution to this ongoing national effort.

PART ONE:

LOCAL EXPRESSIONS OF 9/11

CHAPTER ONE

REVISITING THE HEARTBEAT OF NEW YORK

JOANNE ROBERTSON-ELETTO

In this essay, I revisit a piece written more than a decade ago, entitled "Listening to the Heartbeat of New York: Writings on the Wall" (2003), to discuss the lens and interpretive stance I used to view the literacy events that followed the attack on the Twin Towers on 9/11. I explore the layers of meaning accumulated over the past ten years as I again experience and become entangled with the images of life interrupted, buried, and frozen in time. The reflexive and transactional nature of constructing and negotiating meaning become revealed as new themes emerge, such as the role of spontaneous writing, the resiliency of purpose, and the permanency of the written word, as well as the new literacy events that continue to take place in the "footprints of the Twin Towers."

Fig. 1.1 The World Trade Center after the Attack
(Photo courtesy of a New York City firefighter}

Introduction
"Strong spirits never break"

It is over a decade later, and once again I am asked to tell the story. As before, I strive for accuracy of representation when describing the literacy events that occurred in Lower Manhattan during the weeks following 9/11. I am mindful that reader and text are never separate entities, and for the second time I find myself entangled with the visual images and writings as I process them anew.[1] I realize that while documenting and interpreting the artifacts in 2001, I was concurrently experiencing history. The discovery of their story was, and continues to be, a discovery of my own.[2]

Therefore, as I re-visit "Listening to the Heartbeat of New York," I acknowledge the personal nature of my interpretations of the photographs, images, and messages left on the walls. A "born and bred" New Yorker, I make no claims to objectivity. I believe that writing plays a powerful role in the mediation of human experience. My goals for this piece are heuristic. That is, I strive to enable readers to appreciate the ways writing was purposefully used in response to the terrorist attacks of 9/11, and woven into the very fabric of daily life. As before, collected writings are interspersed throughout the narrative to give them voice. Here is an example of the message inscribed on a flag honoring police officers who died on September 11th.

To all the boys. Heaven has one hell of a team.

God Bless America

We didn't ask for this fight but we will finish it now.

I am not surprised to find new dimensions to the original "heartbeat." For the way I view the world has been transformed. Consequently, new themes emerge from the original artifacts. I now appreciate the role of spontaneous writing as a system of communication to maintain personal and cultural identity in a time of uncertainty. They wrote to honor, grieve,

---

[1] John Dewey and Arthur Bentley, *Knowing and the Known* (Boston, Mass.: Beacon, 1949) and Louise Rosenblatt, *The Reader, the Text, and the Poem* (Carbondale: Southern Illinois Press, 1978).

[2] Norman K. Denzin,"The Art and Politics of Interpretation" in *Collecting and Interpreting Qualitative Materials,* edited by Norman K. Denzin and Yvonna S. Lincoln (Thousand Oaks, Cal. : Sage, 1998), pp. 313-44; and Susan Krieger, *Social Science and the Self: Personal Essay as Art Form* (New Brunswick, N.J.: Rutgers University Press, 1991).

and remember. They wrote to give purpose to their lives. They wrote to sustain themselves. They wrote to express feelings that might otherwise go unexpressed. They, and I, wrote to know who we were.

We will not be intimidated. We will be strong in love.

Senseless, BUT NOT IN VAIN. We love you all. God Bless.

Ten Years Ago

The air was still toxic and smoke-filled when the university called us back. I was teaching "Literacy and Research," a graduate methods course, and most of my students were novice teachers. We had just completed our first class the weekend before 9/11. Now, just three weeks later, I was driving through Lower Manhattan on my way to the Varick Street campus. It was in close proximity to the smoldering ruins of Ground Zero. Immediately I was struck by the signage posted everywhere. There appeared to be no free standing wall space devoid of a written plea, prayer, or message. Makeshift banners hung from fire escapes, notes clung to fences, pictures and messages were affixed to walls, fences, and lamp posts. Just like the mythological Phoenix, writing had been reborn from the ashes.

Fig. 1.2 Typical Sidewalk Memorial Constructed Near Ground Zero

Hate the enemy—the enemy is hate.

The spirit of the World Trade Center is giving us the energy to rebuild this great city. Thank you!

We will not be defeated! Our thoughts and prayers are with you.

I could see the desperation in the way every resource was summoned into action. The public, private, past, and present intersected in sidewalk memorials. Vibrant faces smiled back at me, forever frozen in time. Transfixed by the photos, I could not gaze away. This could have been my twenty-eight year-old son, who was working near that area. He could see the towers collapse from his office windows. On that day, he walked from Lower to Midtown Manhattan to find his uncle. I remember those agonizing hours when I could not reach him. All cell phone service had been cut off.

Sylvia Grider writes about ways memorials enable people to "come to grips" and feel less hopeless in a numbing situation they cannot change. She writes that "placing a memento at a shrine is an act as sacred and comforting as lighting a candle in a church altar."[3] And, as long as a loved one's photo remained in that place, they were not truly lost or missing. Here is an example of a letter found in the subway commenting on the reactions that placing such mementos induced.

> My name is Marc, and my friend Joey worked on the 105th floor of No 1 WTC. After 9/11 I put his "missing" flyer all over the streets of this changed city, choosing spots as if I were painting graffiti, looking for the best light, the easiest places to see my friend's face. At 26th and Lex, next to the Armory, strangers were nice to me saying, "I hope you find your friend." I just thanked them and kept looking for more places where Joey's smile would catch people's eyes.

Surprisingly, most of the students were there when I arrived for our second class. They were determined to complete the coursework despite it all. We talked for a long time about the ways we could accomplish this, in light of all we had just experienced. Our lives were in crisis, and a "business as usual" mindset was antithetical to everything I believed as a teacher. So, I took a chance. I asked the students to share their impressions about the profusion of written messages posted around the university, and how they might relate to the constructs of literacy, situated practice, and

---

[3] Sylvia Grider, "Spontaneous Shrines: A Modern Response to Tragedy and Disaster," *New Directions in Folklore* 5 (2001): 1-10, p. 2.

ethnography, all listed on their syllabus. Together, we conceived a more mindful approach for our scholarship that semester. We would assume the stance of qualitative researchers, and actually venture outside the following week to record and photograph the self-generating and organic literacy event that was occurring just around the corner. We would face our fears, learn to look more closely, and use our sociocultural theory of literacy to inform our observations about the text generation in Lower Manhattan. Two students who expressed trepidation, but wanted to participate in our ethnographic exploration, began to search cyberspace for additional postings.

Even heroes cry, from the ashes we will become even stronger.

We will fight and win in your honor!

Looking Through Smeared Lenses

I remember how our eyes began to tear during that first day outside. The air quality was poor, but in an effort to normalize routines city officials had not informed the public. I felt protective of my students and very inadequate to support or even protect them should something happen. We were all emotionally fragile. Terror had come into our lives accompanied with a sense of vulnerability. So, naturally I would second-guess my plan. A police officer stationed there, perhaps sensing our mood or curious about the intent of our actions, wanted to know why we were taking photographs and writing notes. Afterwards, he seemed satisfied, and shared that they referred to the area as "The Dead Zone." However, there was one section of this zone that was teeming with activity, and that place was Nemo's. Here, only footsteps away from our campus, was the place I would document New Yorkers' and others' private and collective expressions of sadness, resiliency, solidarity, and community. These sentiments come through poignantly in this icon and message received from an anonymous sender via America Online on December 4, 2001.

A candle loses nothing by lighting another candle.
( ) This candle was lit on the 11th of September, 2001—
Please pass it on to your friends & family, so that it
[] may shine all across America.
[]
[]
[]
[]

Nemo's clothing store was transformed into a respite station for the exhausted, yet tireless, firefighters, police officers, and medical personnel in search, recover, and containment efforts at Ground Zero.[4] There, they could get a hot meal, take a needed rest, recharge, and talk with other first responders. Placed in front of Nemo's were plywood panels, pens, and post-it notes, which they encouraged us to use to "tell our story" to the world. As panels became filled to capacity, they were immediately replenished. I wondered what would happen to them, as they were not removed but just stacked behind one another. I tried to quickly copy down as many of the notes as possible, without making judgments. This moment could not be lost. I wanted to preserve the messages to describe the impact of 9/11 upon our cultural sensibilities and affirmation as a people. So, I scrupulously gathered them up, like the petals of a wilting flower. But I was far from detached, and naïve to think I could be. Throughout the entire process of reading, writing, and experiencing the messages, I was emotionally engaged. The messages became living, breathing entities with palpable heartbeats that resonated with my own, as in this one.

And yet, look at all this LIFE.

Fig. 1.3 Nemo's Respite Station Close to Ground Zero

---

[4] As I drafted this essay in May 2012, it was also the tenth anniversary of the day they stopped search and rescue efforts at Ground Zero. In 2013, parts of the plane's fuselage were recovered in Lower Manhattan.

Fear of them! Fear of us!

Looking at my analysis more than a decade later, I only captured as Jacques Derrida would describe "traces and erasures" of the mosaic of thoughts.[5] He points out that no element can function as a sign without referring to another element which might not be observable. For me, that element was discourse. It shaped both the tone of the writings, and the social practices that contributed to their import.[6] A broader conceptual framework of semiotics, a linguistic-based social theory, is therefore the lens through which I focus this analysis. For, literacy practices are always situated within broader social and ideological contexts.[7] Language, and language use, is essential to the development of thinking and of self.[8] It shapes our thought, and our thoughts shape culture. After 9/11, writing was spontaneously used to develop, confirm, situate, and represent to others personal and national feelings of identity.

Look! You only caused us to unite. Our country is now stronger than ever.

It's no(t)w our war!

Every time I have Irish money, I'll think of you.

No one takes away the spirit and courage of NY & the USA.

I Pray.

---

[5] Jacques Derrida, *Positions,* translated by Alan Bass, (Chicago, Ill.: The University of Chicago Press, 1981).
[6] James Paul Gee, *An Introduction to Discourse Analysis: Theory and Method* (New York: Routledge, 2005).
[7] David Barton, *Literacy: An Introduction to the Ecology of Written Language* (Malden, Mass.: Blackwell Publishing, 1994 [2007])
[8] Mikhail Bahktin, "Discourse in the Novel," in *The Dialogic Imagination*, edited by Michael Holquist and translated by Caryl Emerson, (Austin: University of Texas Press, 1981), pp. 259-422; and Lev S. Vygotsky, *Mind in Society: The Development of Higher Psychological Processes,* edited by Michael Cole, Sylvia Scribner, Ellen Soubermann, and Vera John-Steiner, (Cambridge, Mass.: Harvard University Press, 1978).

Fig. 1.4 One of the Many Plywood Panels Filled with Notes and Messages

As if on a pilgrimage, people came to Nemo's to see what had been written, as seen above in two selections, or to add a note of their own. In doing so, knowledge was constructed, re-constructed, mediated, and expressed. So many collective feelings filled the small space of the post-it notes. I am reminded of Ferdinand de Saussure's writings about "langue et parole," and the arbitrary nature of the written word. The surface structure of the messages was simplistic, but their deep structure was not.[9] The brief jottings only alluded to the massive grief, shock, and terror that lay beneath the surface of our public sensibilities. As Norman Denzin recently stated, "the global is always local."[10] We didn't realize the historical

[9] Ferdinand de Saussure, *Course in General Linguistics*, translated by Roy Harris, (New York: The Philosophical Library Inc., 1959 [1998]).
[10] Norman Denzin's introductory remarks at the Eighth International Congress of Qualitative Inquiry, May 17, 2012, Champaign-Urbana, Illinois.

significance, but the photographs and writings we collected documented
the ways a sense of solidarity and brotherhood evolved, despite the
disruption, disconnection, and devastation of 9/11. As I look at the past
through the lens of the present, I wish I had noticed the placement of the
postings. Did one note lead into another? Were contrary thoughts
expressed? Instead of fragments, I wish I had seen the whole.

Fig. 1.5 My Students Reading the Notes Posted Outside Nemo's

All Gave Some, Some Gave All. For Engine Company 4.

Flags may change, but we all wear the common flag of humanity, and so
we must show our patriotism as humans, as beings, as existing entities.

I was born here. I grew up here. I moved to Chicago but you always
remained a part of me and now I know why—this is still the most special
place on earth. I am so proud of you taking care of each other and getting
through with style. I miss you and love you more than ever.

I was moved by the postings, and the journal entries my students wrote
in response to 9/11.Their personal reflections, scribed immediately after
our walks outside, were a window into their thinking and my own. Writing
became a way to revisit our self-identity, to question our belief systems,

and to discover those undercurrents of thinking that might have pushed to the boundaries of our consciousness. Here are some examples.

> Losing one of my best friends has changed/shaped my life forever. Talking about HOPE I don't see that right now. I only see SADNESS! I had to make the flyer for Jenn so I see that side of how people let their emotions out. At the time of the flyers I put my heart to the side and let my mind take over. To write MISSING was the hardest part to describe her. But I feel the worst part is seeing her constantly around the neighborhood with MISSING on top. Is this my friend—are these my words—is this real?

> …We must look to see what this representation means. Do we know of others' pain in other lands? Do they have these words on the wall? Did we care before it was 'no(t)w our war?" Yes, there is hope abounding out there on the walls. But for me, it is about what is not being said—or hasn't been reflected upon before.

> I found the quotes to be very moving and powerful. They helped me to feel safe, to know that I was not alone with my feelings. Many people share the same fears and concerns. It is what joins us together as a people and as Americans.

> Reading the writing from the WTC makes you see the stories. Individuals come to life even though you have never met them. The writing and reading have been a healing process. Listening to the eulogies, the power of storytelling at memorials has given life to lives that have been lost.

> …While so many people posted their thoughts and feelings on the wall for all to read, I couldn't find the right words for myself to post. I felt more comfortable reading others' words and connecting to complete strangers who were feeling similar emotions to myself.

As my students and I experienced, processed, and analyzed the 9/11 writings together, we engaged in a self-reflexive, interpretive, and interactive process that enabled us to reflect critically upon our experiences and to be truly present in the moment. We were heartsick and drowning in fear. Writing was the gift we gave ourselves. Sharing our stories, like the writers who posted in Lower Manhattan, was the way we resisted, reinvented, and reclaimed our lives.

Rachel Naomi Remen writes about story: "Often in crisis we stumble on our wholeness and our real power…Trapped though it may be, it can be called upon for guidance, direction, and most fundamentally comfort. It can be remembered. Eventually, we may come to live by it."[11] Telling our stories, Remen suggests, helped us to heal and find our bearings in unsettled times.

America—'Like a Rock'
America = Unity Unity = Life
I feel so SAD. There's an emptiness in my soul. WE WILL SURVIVE.
THANK YOU ALL FOR HELPING.

Art, Emotion, and Critical Literacy Development

Young children are also meaning makers, who form theories of the world and their place in it based upon their experiences and interactions with the significant others in their lives. David Elkind describes them as our "emotional compatriots," a fact he claims adults often neglect to acknowledge.[12] 9/11 was difficult for us all, but particularly so for children. As a teacher, I observed how they drew their way to understandings of terrorism. Popular symbols they used to portray their emotions were hearts, stars, flags, angels, planes, and towers. There were so many representations of hearts, some broken in half, others personified with smiling faces and encouraging messages. The Twin Towers were drawn with a broken heart and angel wings. Many children drew angels hovering over or walking near the towers after the explosions. Their symbolic representations show the transformative power of their thinking in response to horror, grief, or sadness. They envisioned a more peaceful reality. Instead of terrorists, children drew a city of angels.

Over and over, students in the elementary grades drew the same image, that is, the plane hitting and shearing the first tower, billowing black smoke, fire plumes, and erupting explosions. The intersection of art and emotion was revealed in their re-enactments of this exact moment. Their color choice, often black, white, and red, expressed both the stark reality of the event and their fear. I believe that as they drew, and processed their thoughts on paper, they refined and broadened their understandings about what 9/11 meant for them and their families. Art was the outlet that allowed them to share their feelings freely, without worrying about the

---

[11] Rachel Naomi Remen, *Kitchen Table Wisdom: Stories That Heal* (New York: Riverhead Books, 1996), pp. 105-6.
[12] David Elkind, *Images of the Young Child: Collected Essays on Development and Education* (Washington, D.C.: National Association for the Education of Young Children, 1993).

structure and mechanics of written language. Drawing was a part of the healing process.

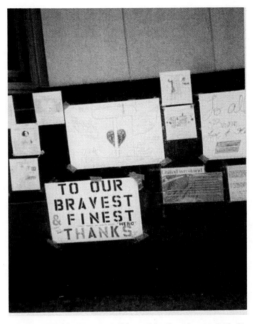

Fig. 1.6 Broken-Hearted Twin Towers, Ringed in Smoke at their Base, Sprout Angel Wings and a Halo

In turn, their letters and pictures had a restorative effect on those who received them. A young police woman told me they displayed the children's work all over the station, and that they provided them with a sense of comfort and encouragement. She added, "We're always reading the children's letters, they warm up the place and make us laugh. You need that you know." Reading and viewing these heartfelt and pieces enabled officers to ground themselves and transcend the horror of the moment.

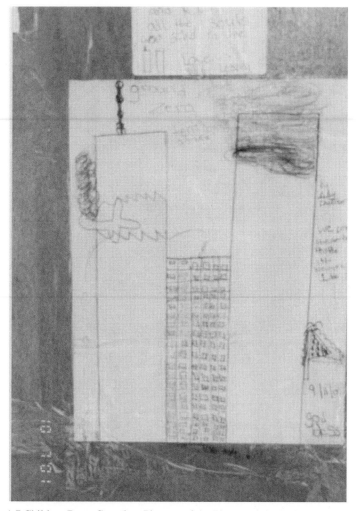

Fig. 1.7 Children Drew Countless Pictures of the Plane and the Twin Towers)

Do not give up trying to save people. (Third grader)

Dear Rescue Workers, I hope that you find more people. Every night I pray for the people who got hart [hurt] and that you find more people. God Bless America. Love, Meghan (First grader)

I'm not scared because you rescue workers protect everyone. (Second grader)

Fig. 1.8 and 1.9 Hearts Like these Decorated a Police Station near Ground Zero

America is a good cahte [country].

Dear New York. I hope you feel better.

(Children's notes on hearts)

Memorial Day 2011

It was a summer of anticipation. Soon, it would be the tenth anniversary of 9/11, and makeshift memorials were erected around Battery Park. Instantly, I am reminded of Canal and Varick Streets. Now, however, I expect to see writing used to negotiate and mediate this milestone event. People gather to read and unite with and through the written word. Anderson and MacCurdy describe the therapeutic components of reading and writing in the following terms:

> As we manipulate the words on the page, as we articulate to ourselves and others the emotional truth of our pasts, we become agents in our own healing, and if those to whom we write receive what we have to say and respond to it as we write and rewrite, we create a community that can accept, gloss, inform, invent, and help us discover, deepen, and change

what we have become as a consequence of the trauma we have experienced.[13]

Fig. 1.10 Makeshift Memorial at Battery Park, May 2011

September 11, 2012

I watched families enter Memorial Plaza to say good-bye one more time. "I Will Remember You" played softly in the background. They were the first to visit "Reflecting Absence," two massive pools with cascading waterfalls, situated within the footprints of the Twin Towers. Many carried roses to place by their loved one's inscription.[14] They walked hand-in-hand with their children and grandchildren, many too young to remember 9/11 or perhaps not even born yet. I noted the ways people touched the names. In a gentle ritual, transcending time and space, they were able to

---

[13] Charles M. Anderson and Marian M. MacCurdy, *Writing and Healing Towards an Informed Practice* (Urbana, Ill.: National Council of Teachers of English, 2000), p. 7.

[14] The names of the nearly 3,000 individuals killed on September 11th in New York City, Washington, D.C., Pennsylvania, and in the February 1993 World Trade Center bombing are inscribed around the edges of the pools.

experience their departed one's presence. Many created pencil etchings to commemorate the day and take with them. I appreciate the power of the written word, and its potential to restore memories and connect the disconnected. Its permanency provides comfort and closure (of sorts). For the history of 9/11 still remains unfinished.

Final Thoughts

As an educator, I know that our nation's students have few opportunities to engage in the types of spontaneous writing presented in this narrative. For current analytical and mechanical models of literacy instruction focus only upon those writing genres that appear on state assessments. Consequently, students are taught the five paragraph essay. They learn to persuade and summarize with objectivity so as to score well on the test. They are not asked to reflect upon their feelings, memories, or life experiences. This self-reflexive writing, which can afford them of an understanding across the disciplines, is sorely disregarded. Writing from the heart, as portrayed in this piece, enables them to learn about themselves and the world. Nevertheless, the system we call school still depreciates its significance in the curriculum.

In the same line of thought, our youngest literacy learners benefit from the integration of the visual arts with the literacy curriculum, to support their cognitive, emotional, and social development. Unfortunately, the arts have been pushed to the periphery of education in the early childhood, primary, and elementary years, despite its numerous benefits to enhance teaching and learning. Art is a symbol system through which children give representation to their ideas, concepts, and emotions. To deny them this symbolic form through which to communicate is to silence their voices and deny ourselves the opportunity to observe what they really know and want to learn.

Fig. 1.11 The View from World Trade One, "Freedom Tower"
(Photo courtesy of construction worker)

We believe in life. We are living for life. (anonymous)

Postscript

I thought it appropriate to come full circle when concluding this chapter. I began with an image of destruction at Ground Zero. I conclude with a picture of construction at the Freedom Tower, sent from a construction worker's iPhone. The tower approaches completion as I write. I know that beneath its shiny and finished outer facade are messages that have been etched into the steel beams by those who worked there. For this is our human nature. We write to know who we are, we write to declare our existence, and we write to leave our mark for the future, just as President Barack Obama did with his inscription on the 104th floor beam of World Trade Center, lifted into place on August 2, 2012:

We remember. We rebuild. We come back stronger.

CHAPTER TWO

PARK SLOPE, BROOKLYN, IN THE AFTERMATH OF 9/11

JEROME KRASE

Introduction

The partial title of the conference where this essay originated, "Making Meaning," is an interesting phrase for any subject. For the past, present, and future images that still surround the collective horror of what became globally known as "9/11", it is especially challenging. There have been other terrible events of national significance in Manhattan, such as the retreat of George Washington and the Continental Army in 1776 as well as the Draft Riots of 1863. Each historical event has its own unique meaning and interpretation. When we talk about how meaning is made, we must first ask, where does it come from? Who or what makes meaning? For the British Crown and American Loyalists alike, Washington's retreat was a "victory," and one need not contemplate long how the interpretation of the Civil War Draft Riots differed for recent Irish immigrants and their innocent victims, New York's black residents at the time.

When we walk around New York City, we are surrounded by all kinds of signs that seem to be trying to tell us something about yesterday, today, and tomorrow. To me, the meaning of the signs that we see around us during the course of our daily lives comes directly from our store of knowledge that has been informed by our personal experiences. Semiology is simply defined as the study of those signs. Being a visual semiotician, I am fascinated by the signs and symbols that are thought to convey meaning to me and other viewers. In my work, I try to show how ordinary people change the meaning of places and spaces merely by changing what those places and spaces look like. As a common example of this phenomenon, we can think about how changing the signage on a shopping street makes it a different kind of place. Thinking about city neighborhoods in this way, we can understand how, after 9/11, the sidewalks and other common objects became canvasses or spaces for exhibiting our feelings. For more than half a century I have paid very close attention to the most mundane of neighborhood landscapes.[1] In that process, I have recorded how even the most powerless persons have been able to transform seemingly uninhabitable areas of global cities. During two of my excursions abroad, I have photographed how, despite abject poverty, migrant workers living in the informal townships of Cape Town, South Africa, as well as those in abandoned neighborhoods of Beijing, China, created homes and communities for themselves and their families. These inspiring sights support my conviction that the tragedy of September 11, 2001 offers us another example of how ordinary people can change, indeed sanctify, the meanings of ruthlessly profaned places. In this cleansing process, they helped us to heal our psychic wounds with small but immensely effective visual statements that can divert our eyes from more painful memories.

Ground Zero Sacred and Profane

Even the disrespectful helped us to revive and recover. For example, not very long after the creation of Ground Zero, street vendors, most of them immigrants from West Africa, surrounded the horror created by Osama bin Laden with a colorfully irreverent outdoor market. In this morbid *suk*, hordes of "disaster" tourists further diminished their global stature and thumbed their noses at Al Qaeda by grabbing up "We love NYC more than ever" and left-over "NYC Blackout" T-shirts from lines of folding tables.

Many visitors continue today to have their photos taken, smiling and standing near the edge of the guarded precipice as if it were just another version of the Grand Canyon—wrought not by terrorists alone but by the hand of Whomever. To some of them it seems that 9/11, like the caldera of Santorini or the Vesuvian lava flow that preserved Pompeii, happened so that they would have another place to vacation. Few of those tourists ever heard or read the words of Minoru Yamasaki, the designer of the disappeared World Trade Center:[2]

---

[1] Jerome Krase, "Polish and Italian Vernacular Landscapes in Brooklyn," *Polish American Studies* 54 n. 1 (1997): 9-31, and *idem*, "Navigating Ethnic Vernacular Landscapes Then and Now," *Journal of Architecture and Planning Research* 19 n. 4 (2002): 274-81.

[2] http://www.greatbuildings.com/buildings/World_Trade_Center.html   Accessed

I feel this way about it. World trade means world peace and consequently the World Trade Center buildings in New York...had a bigger purpose than just to provide room for tenants. The World Trade Center is a living symbol of man's dedication to world peace...beyond the compelling need to make this a monument to world peace, the World Trade Center should, because of its importance, become a representation of man's belief in humanity, his need for individual dignity, his beliefs in the cooperation of men, and through cooperation, his ability to find greatness.

A few more of the gawkers might try to make some sense of Yakov Smirnoff's mural painting "hanging" high above the site—"America's Heart"—including a special message that reflected his belief in the human condition: "The human spirit is not measured by the size of the act, but by the size of the heart."

Fig. 2.1 Sidewalk shrine, 2001.

Only the most well-read among them would see the semiotic connection between the splintered wooden cross and the crucified Geremio that represented the fate of blue collar workers in Pietro Di Donato's *Christ in Concrete* (1939) and the twisted steel girder crucifix that stands for the equal sacrifices made by blue, pink, and white-collar workers alike who also died on 9/11 for simply being on the "job."

July 29, 2013.

Fig. 2.2 Missing persons at the entrance to Dizzy's, 2001.

Fig. 2.3 Ground Zero *suk*, 2002.

Fig. 2.4 Flag and heart at Ground Zero, 2002.

In general, I don't like big buildings and my preference is for human-scale urban spaces. My own research interests in architecture have focused on the vernacular, which includes the ways that ordinary people alter the meanings and intended uses of works, especially those of high-minded and

Fig. 2.5 Twisted girder cross at Ground Zero, 2002.

powerful architects.[3] I have long observed and photographed how ordinary persons create, perhaps distort, the intended meanings of space. The most powerful instance of this in New York City is Ground Zero. The World Trade Center was created for the express purpose of making money. On September 11, 2001, it was destroyed by fanatics and not long after was fought over by designers, developers, and politicians. It is not less painful to consider that 9/11 easily lends itself to semiotic analysis. There were no

---

[3] Jerome Krase review of Jean La Marche. "The Familiar and the Unfamiliar in Twentieth-Century Architecture," *Visual Studies* 19 n. 2 (2005): 195-99.

accidents made in the selection of the Twin Towers in New York City, and the Pentagon Building in Washington, D.C., as the primary venues and specific targets of the terrorists' assault. These were the almost mythic capitals of American financial and political power. They figuratively symbolized the U.S.A.

Memory and Meaning

As with the "sneak attack" by Imperial Japan on Pearl Harbor on December 7, 1941, 9/11 will be forever remembered as "[A] date which will live in infamy." In 1941 and beyond, American audiences were treated to weekly newsreels at every movie theater that helped moved the country to mobilize quickly and passionately against enemies both foreign and domestic. With similar but greater immediate effect, the electronic mass media in 2001 treated us to thousands of hours of images of the crashes, burning, and ensuing collapse of the towers, followed soon thereafter by frantic and often tragically misdirected military and domestic campaigns. The incessant repetition of these images not only increased the horror of the terrorist attacks but inadvertently magnified the power of Al Qaeda by increasing the psychic injury.

The meaning of events, large and small, is always personal, as are our own little connections to the big times and big spaces that we sometimes call "history." Speaking about such biographical reconstruction, Wolfram Fischer referred to the work of Alfred Schuetz, as well as that of Peter L. Berger and Thomas Luckmann, to argue that all our knowledge of the world, including our scientific knowledge, is self-selected.[4] Our understanding of 9/11 is a social reconstruction from our everyday lives. Most members of my generation can recite where they were and what they were doing when they heard about the assassination of President John F. Kennedy at 12:30 p.m., Central Standard Time, on Friday, November 22, 1963, in Dallas, Texas. I was in the Army and walking while out of

---

[4] Wolfram Fischer, "Biographical Reconstruction as Applied Knowledge or Professional Competence?", paper presented at the Joint Conference of the Research Network "Biographical Perspectives on European Societies" European Sociological Association, and the Faculty of Social Sciences, (Georg Simon Ohm University of Applied Sciences, Nuremberg, 2010); Albert Schuetz, "Common-sense and Scientific Interpretation of Human Action," in Alfred Schuetz, *Collected Papers. Vol. 1, The Problem of Social Reality* (The Hague: Martinus Nijhoff, 1971), pp. 3-47; and Peter L Berger and Thomas Luckmann, *The Social Construction of Reality: A Treatise in the Sociology of Knowledge* (New York: Doubleday, 1966)

uniform down the steep hill from the Defense Language Institute of the Presidio of Monterey, California, when I heard someone shout "Kennedy was shot!." My first reaction was "who's Kennedy"? And then realizing he was the President, I turned and raced back to the barracks where we were put on Red Alert.

In the fall of 2001, I was still teaching full-time at Brooklyn College and had scheduled an ethnographic field trip for my graduate sociology class to Battery Park City during that semester to observe an example of a "modern urban community." Our meeting point was at the subway entrance to the U.S. Customs Building near the north bridge entrance to the World Financial Center. The only time I had been inside one of the Twin Towers above the first floor was when I was treated to dinner at Windows on the World where my host had mistakenly thought I might prefer sitting closer to the window.

Almost every day of the week I sit in Dizzy's, which bills itself as a "finer diner," and read the papers from 7 to 9 a.m. As I was leaving on that fateful day, someone came through the door and calmly said he heard that a plane had hit one of the Twin Towers. Everyone assumed it was a small plane that had gone off course. I slowly walked up the block to my house and turned on the television as the second airplane was shown crashing into the second of the Twin Towers. My wife Suzanne was working full-time at Brooklyn Hospital, which is located near the Manhattan and Brooklyn Bridges, a short ambulance ride from the World Trade Center. I immediately called her office to give her a heads up that the hospital should expect a rush of patients coming over the bridges from Manhattan he told me later that day that she and other members of the staff had already gone to the roof after the first crash and watched in horror as the second plane hit. She and most of the other staff stayed at the hospital until late in that evening, but sadly the anticipated crowd of injured workers never came. Survivors were few.

In the fall of 2001, my daughter Kathryn started work every day at 9:00 a.m. at the Children's Aid Society at 150 Williams Street, a short walk away from what came to be called Ground Zero. On the morning of September 11, 2001, she delayed her trip by subway in order to help her sister, Kristin, who had some post-delivery problems after the birth of her second child. The first plane hit the North Tower (WTC 1) at 8:46 a.m. My niece and nephews, Suzanne, John, and Peter, worked in finance in Manhattan and experienced history via frantic phone calls from people in the burning buildings and unforgettably horrible views from their south-facing office windows. My friend Michael's law office was close by at 30 Vesey Street; he later told me that he thought he saw "debris" falling from the Towers before realizing that what was falling were people. Another niece, Carolyn, lived in Battery Park City across the street from the World Trade Center. Millions of people like us can recount their various personal relations to places far and near.

Communication and Grief

Beyond the 24/7 television coverage of the event, the Internet provided another immediate and continuous connection to the horror. However, telephone communication in New York City was at first disrupted by the attack and then overwhelmed by a flood of calls. In the early evening of 9/11, I received the following message from my niece Elizabeth:

> Subj: Is Everyone Safe????
> Date: 9/11/01 5:37:29 PM Eastern Daylight Time
> From: (Liz)
> To: (Uncle Johnny), (Uncle Jerry), (Kristen Krase), (Katherine Krase), (Aunt Maryann), (Aunt Suzanne)
> I don't know where everyone works. Can someone please check in with me and let me know our family is all safe and accounted for? Thank you. Love Liz

I could read the fear in her words and immediately sent her a short note that my family members were all okay. Anticipating more queries from relatives, friends, and colleagues, early the next day I thought it was prudent to send out my own message to everyone in my AOL address book and to all my professional association list services. Here is what I wrote:

> We live in Brooklyn but the smoke from the fires and dust from the debris coated the neighborhood and we had to close all the windows and people were wearing dust masks on the street. My family is fine but there is so much horror. I spent the day with my three daughters and two grandsons. My wife worked at one of the hospitals receiving some of the bodies and triaged patients. I and my daughters went to the local hospital to give blood but there were so many people who came to contribute their blood that we were told to come back the next day. I have asked everyone to give blood and say prayers. I will go into the college today and see if I can do something meaningful. I'm worried about intergroup problems in the city and especially at the university where students had been at each other's throats over Middle Eastern issues.

Then, later in the afternoon, I added this note:

I decided to play squash today as I usually do on Wednesday mornings and forgot that when I take the subway there is a point en route which has[d] such a wonderful view of the NYC skyline and the twin towers. As we approached the Smith and Ninth Street Station which reputedly is the world's highest subway station I moved to the window and almost simultaneously, and in total silence, people got out of their seats and moved to one side of the car. It was the most quiet time I have ever heard on a NYC subway car. I will not take a picture of any of this as I've already seen too much.

I must note here that I had publicly vowed not to photograph scenes of the tragedy itself. Admittedly this is a rather odd response for a visually-oriented social scientist and ethnographer. I remained true to my promise and only some time later in 2002 did I take a photo out of the, still dirty, windows of the Manhattan-bound F train in order to capture what was now the "new view" of Lower Manhattan

Fig. 2.6 The "new view" of Lower Manhattan from the F train after 9/11.

Eerily, the smears on the grimy glass that I caught through my lens emulated what once was the ugly massive plume of grey-black smoke that had wafted across the water, over Brooklyn Heights and then made its way slowly up the slope of Brooklyn. By the time it arrived on my block, the cloud had lightened in color and it menacingly hovered for several days over my brownstone and occasionally deposited an assortment of paper debris onto the streets, sidewalks, and especially into the backyards. One of my closest neighbors found, much to their sorrow, a check from the high-powered investment bank and brokerage business, Cantor-Fitzgerald. Cantor Fitzgerald's offices were located on the 101st to the 105th floors, just above the spot where the first airplane, American Airlines Flight 11, crashed into The North Tower. As a consequence, they lost more than six hundred employees, the most of any World Trade Center tenant.

In response to my message, I received hundreds of responses expressing various degrees of sympathy and support. I was shocked however at the number of people who added a "but" to their notes of condolence. In the days after the attacks, I began to notice that the views of America, especially by Europeans, had not radically changed since the United States had been regarded as an "ugly" but well-intentioned superpower in the 1960s.[5] I naturally assumed that there would be immediate and unequivocal sympathy, if not support, for the United States from my international colleagues. Their ample expressions of concern for me and my family were too often accompanied by qualified expressions of compassion, however.

As we all know, academics have an annoying tendency to give some kind of informed, supposedly objective and emotionless opinion about historical events, and this one was no exception. I was saddened by the implication in more than a few e-mail responses that the actions of my own country abroad, such as its support for oppressive regimes when it suited the national interest, had diminished my own claim to victimhood. Some of the most detailed of those many sobering messages reminded me that people around the world are keenly aware of, and sensitive to, American foreign policy, especially our military adventures.

Shortly after 9/11, I flew to Ireland to deliver the keynote address at the annual meeting of the Sociology Association of Ireland, in Tralee. Many of the conference attendees expressed surprise that I made the trip so soon after the tragedy. We New Yorkers think of Ireland as another borough, so I expected unrestrained commiseration at the conference.

---

[5] Eugene Burdick and William Lederer, *The Ugly American* (New York: W.W. Norton, 1999).

Besides many warm welcomes, we also received the candid observation by one of my hosts that, in a way, the U.S.A. had it coming. At this point, we had a hard time maintaining the pose of grateful guests.

As time passed after 9/11, one could hear in discussions among colleagues and read remarks that American foreign policy, at least indirectly, had caused those planes to crash into the Twin Towers as some form of "divine retribution." In spring 2002, I was on a "9/11" Panel at a meeting of the Multicultural Education Society of Europe and the Americas in Padua, Italy. I introduced my photo essay, "Park Slope in the Aftermath of the World Trade Center Tragedy", by reading aloud, for the first time, the words of my 9/12 e-mail message. Unexpectedly, tears came to my eyes as I relived that day. I remembered, then from a great distance, that after watching the planes crash on television and then calling my wife and daughters, I went upstairs to help my elderly in-laws to close all the windows in their apartment, thinking that perhaps I would not be returning to see them again. Choking smoke already filled the streets of the neighborhood and panicked rumors soon circulated of poisonous vapors in the mix as well as possible follow-up attacks. When I left my in-laws secured, I walked quickly a few blocks over to my daughter Kristin's house where her two younger sisters, Karen and Kathryn, had already instinctively gathered. We all stayed in her similarly closed up apartment with her and my three-year-old and one-month-old grandsons, Spencer and Leander, and waited, watching the Towers fall again and again, without admitting, to each other at least, that "The End" might be near.

Although the visible expression of my personal pain moved many of the listeners in Padua, there were again too many others who took what I described as a terrible tragedy as an opportunity to "explain" why it had happened; to rationalize why 3,000 people died in a few minutes of my life and effectively in front of my eyes. Perhaps this is a stretch but my colleagues discussed 9/11 then in much the same way that some Americans talked about the "collateral damage" in Belgrade, Baghdad, Gaza, Lebanon, Tel Aviv, Dresden, or even Nagasaki and Hiroshima: "Terrible, but after all didn't they have it coming?"

Individual perceptions of one's own victimization are also interesting phenomena. For example, when I had gone upstairs in my brownstone to tell my elderly mother in-law to close the windows on the morning of 9/11, her response to me was an Italian-American version of the very Brooklyn Yiddishism *"Oy Vey ist mir!"*, or "Why do these things always happen to me?" Over the course of her eighty some odd years, she had drawn a very small circle of empathy around herself. It seems that for millions of people around the globe, we all-too-powerful Americans fall well outside of their circles of empathy. Also, they honestly believed that because of what had been done in our name in the past in places like Vietnam, we are not entitled to their sympathy. I continue today to mourn for the 3,000 who died in the U.S.A. on 9/11. But in order to grieve in good faith, I also must lament for the tens, if not hundreds, of thousands of civilian victims of America's misguided military adventures abroad that carelessly used our first 3,000 victims as an excuse for the subsequent pursuit of meaningless vengeance.

I am a volunteer in a wonderful high school mentoring program called ACE, which stands for Architecture, Construction and Engineering. In 2002, the multicultural students of my ACE mentor team, my young fellow New Yorkers, chose as their project the rebuilding of the World Trade Center site, and also to create there a fitting memorial. At the prodding of one of the professional architect mentors, they sought to actualize *in situ* Frank Lloyd Wright's mile-high skyscraper, along with a few site-specific accoutrements such as radar and anti-aircraft missiles. Their simply elegant memorial was a polished absolutely black granite cube that would also reflect the images of 9/11's less recognized victims or terrorism—anyone who looked at it. We also went on a field trip to the Queens Museum to view the "The Panorama of the City of New York" that was created by Robert Moses for the 1964 World's Fair. The almost ten thousand square foot architectural model includes all pre-1992 structures in the five boroughs and, at the time, the World Trade Center towers were gently wrapped in a red, white and blue bow. In later years, our ACE students also received an opportunity to appraise the efforts of the world-class architects, such as Daniel Libeskind, to fashion a suitable replacement for the voids left at Ground Zero.

Today we can see the new World Trade Center, known as Freedom Tower, fill some of the space but never replace what was there before. A few commentators on post-9/11 New York see culture wars—jihads and Crusades—define (and perhaps redefine) the landscape of the powerful. Others offer their stern opinions on the pressing need for a new aesthetic of security. Some observers see the new 104-story skyscraper as a powerful expression of our commitment never to surrender to terror, and I agree that it is. But to me, the most powerful expressions will always be those of ordinary people—friends, family, and neighbors—who did modest things on the days following 9/11. I would argue that as texts to be read, my neighbors' efforts were far more transformative.[6]

---

[6] Jerome Krase, *Seeing Cities Change: Local Culture and Class* (Aldershot, U.K.: Ashgate, 2012).

Fig. 2.7 Queens Museum Panorama, 2002.

Park Slope

In the wake of the horrible recurring images of the destruction of the
World Trade Center that bombarded me on television and in the press, I
looked for and found some comfort in the power of ordinary people to
transform the routes of my daily excursions symbolically into memorial
streetscapes. Although I had the opportunity, I did not initially photograph
scenes of the tragedy. It was years later before I even ventured near the
site. Except for those of Ground Zero and the Queens Museum of Art, the
images that follow of immediate, visceral human responses to our own
grief and that of others are a small selection from among the three hundred
photos I took shortly after 9/11. Every year, in the first or second week
after the commemoration of 9/11, I have taken one or another of my
cameras with me and retraced my steps to re-photograph the area. As the
years have gone by, I have seen more clearly what is and is not visible in
the vernacular landscapes of my home territory. Intellectually, I have
always understood how a *camera obscura* works, but this practice of
scanning and rescanning the same locations in search of what is less and
less in evidence on the surface has convinced me that the camera which
creates our visual memory remains a far more miraculous invention.

Fig. 2.8 A 9/11 benefit sidewalk sale, 2001.

Fig. 2.9 Most patriotic block, 2001.

Fig. 2.10 Car window, "God Bless America," 2001.

Fig. 2.11 Two Hens Bakery Window Display, 2001.

Fig. 2.12 Lemonade stand for families of 9/11 victims, 2001.

Fig. 2.13 Louie G's prayers, 2001.

Fig. 2.14 Johnny Mack's Bar and Restaurant window display, 2001.

Fig. 2.15 Improvised FDNY, NYPD, and EMS memorial, Bartel Pritchard Square, 2001.

CHAPTER THREE

THE ICONOGRAPHY OF THE TOWERS

JASON STEINHAUER

Fig. 3.1 New York State license plate, December 1, 2005

Introduction

This story begins in 2005, when I noticed the Twin Towers on a van in
Long Island City. Two weeks later, I saw them on an electrician's truck in
Midtown Manhattan. It was a storage truck in Lower Manhattan after that,
followed by a take-out menu in Harlem later that night. Soon I was seeing
them on newspaper dispensers, building facades, trash bags, and store
windows. In every borough, everywhere I turned, the towers were there.

Over the course of a generation, from the 1970s to the early 2000s, the iconography of the towers had quietly proliferated throughout the city. Small businesses, restaurants, city agencies and companies had independently incorporated the towers into their branding in order to signify "New York-ness" and communicate authenticity. As a result, their likeness marked hundreds of New York storefronts, awnings, commercial vehicles, and ephemera by the time the towers came crashing down. This phenomenon, in turn, reflected a larger story of how the World Trade Center, when it stood, was marketed across the globe as a symbol of an affluent and powerful New York full of possibility and opportunity. While that may seem obvious in retrospect, the fact that these commercial representations of the towers existed for three decades without recognition suggests that the story of the Twin Towers' ascendance as a New York City brand icon occurred largely unnoticed—at least by me. It was only once I had grown accustomed to not seeing them in the sky that I began to notice them on the ground.

The irony, of course, is that we had grown accustomed not to see the towers in the sky, even when they stood. Despite their size, the buildings managed to pass largely unnoticed by many New Yorkers. Before 9/11, I rarely thought of them, and in this I am not unique. Sociologist Miriam Greenberg recalls that "before that fateful day, [the towers] weren't venerated…by most New Yorkers, who had little reason to even visit them."[1] Unless one worked in the financial industry or services supporting them—or was a tourist—the towers were largely outside New Yorkers' frame of consciousness.[2] Conspicuous when first built, considered "oversized and inhumane," as scholar Tony Hiss recalls,[3] "politely, quietly, unhurriedly—a new round of slow, soft changes took hold."[4] The towers were absorbed into the city. After a while, we stopped noticing—at least actively.

---

[1] Miriam Greenberg, "The Limits of Branding: The World Trade Center, Fiscal Crisis and the Marketing of Recovery," *International Journal of Urban and Regional Research* 27 n. 2 (2003): 413.

[2] *Ibid*. Greenberg repeats the widely-held belief—perhaps true, perhaps mythical—that only the 50,000 people who worked there and tourists frequented the towers. Most other New Yorkers had no reason to go there, save when they played tourist. I visited the World Trade Center once while showing an out-of-town guest around Manhattan. The line for the Windows on the World restaurant was so long we decided to come back another time. We never did.

[3] Tony Hiss, "The New York Region Had Found a Centering Point," *New York Times*, September 16, 2001. Accessed via ProQuest Historical Newspapers: http://search.proquest.com/docview/431871289?accountid=12084.

[4] *Ibid*.

Then, suddenly, they were gone. All we could notice was their absence. Christoph Lindner, now Professor of Media Studies at the University of Amsterdam, recalls how visitors made pilgrimages to Brooklyn Heights post-9/11 to experience that absence, "to gaze upon an urban view that no longer existed."[5] Writing in 2006, he contends that, "in this abstract sense the Twin Towers of the World Trade Center have not entirely disappeared from the New York skyline. Rather, haunting the contemporary imagination, the two skyscrapers continue even now to exert a spectral presence over the city."[6] Even more than Lindner recognized, the towers' spectral presence lingered through the prevalence of their imagery—imagery that is now disappearing as quietly and unhurriedly as it arrived. The van in Long Island City awakened me to a loss I did not even know I was experiencing, and allowed me to commemorate the loss of the towers in my own particular way.

Fig. 3.2 Delancey Street, January 6, 2006

---

[5] Christoph Lindner, "New York Vertical: Reflections on the Modern Skyline," *American Studies* 47 n. 1 (2006): 32.
[6] *Ibid.*

Documenting the Towers

It startled me to notice so suddenly the towers on delivery trucks and neon signs. Post-9/11, I associated the World Trade Center with sadness, nostalgia, and a childhood memory of driving over the Brooklyn Bridge at night and seeing the tips of the lit towers poke their heads above the skyline. Noticing the towers on grocery bags and strip club marquees now made me laugh, smile, and engaged my curiosity. The towers not only formed part our collective consciousness but also our collective environment. How had I not noticed this before? Had anyone noticed? What did this mean—if anything?

In February 2005, I began to document the curious places I saw them: from the Playpen strip club on Eighth Avenue to the Harlem Car Service on 116th Street. They often caught me off-guard. Walking in Chinatown one night, I wound up face-to-face with their silhouettes in a store window on Delancey Street. Walking on the Upper West Side, I looked up to find them on a pet store awning. The spontaneity of the encounters, coupled with the fact that I was a poor graduate student, led me to use my cell phone camera to take the pictures. I contacted several photographers on Craigslist for assistance, and even met with one. But when I could not guarantee that any galleries or publishers would be interested in the end result, he chose to pass on the venture. He took one photograph: a shopping bag for Ralph's Discount City he'd seen in an apartment on the Upper East Side.

Thus with my primitive LG camera phone, I documented representations of the Twin Towers across New York from 2005 to 2007. They were everywhere: in the West Village, on the Caliente Cab Company façade, in Midtown, and on the Midtown Electric Company truck. They were on the menu for the Veg-City Diner, on the Sean Coakley Plumbing and Heating van, at the entrance to the Blue Note Jazz Club, and on the satellite dish for Metro Vision. They were at the entrance to the city bus. They were at the exit from the Lincoln Tunnel. In neon and in paint—on vans, trucks, and buses—the towers' likeness was in every borough and on a wide variety of local businesses.

Once I had captured more than fifty images, I brought the collection (a.k.a, my phone) to Mary Panzer, author of several books on photography and a former professor of mine. We met over coffee in Hell's Kitchen. Her first reaction was to laugh. "These are delightful!" she said, as she squinted at each one. It was good that someone had (a) noticed them and (b) documented them, however crudely. She then confessed that she was not sure what to make of them, if there was anything to be made. She suggested I contribute them to an archive, which I later did: the September 11 Digital Archive, which was acquired by the Library of Congress.[7] After that, I thought little about the images. Life went on. I bought several new cell phones. I moved to Washington, D.C. Five years passed. It was only when the ten-year anniversary of 9/11 came that I was inspired to re-examine them.

Fig. 3.3 Ralph's Discount City shopping bag, April 23, 2005. Photograph by Stefano Giovannini. Used with permission.

---

[7] The September 11 Digital Archive was organized by the American Social History Project at CUNY Graduate Center and Center for History and New Media at George Mason University. It was admitted to the Library of Congress collections in 2003, and ceased collecting in 2004. In 2006, I emailed my collection to a CUNY Graduate Center staff member, who forwarded it to a colleague at the Center for History and New Media, who added the images into the archive. They may be viewed at http://911digitalarchive.org/repository.php?collection_id=12438.

Upon re-examination, the collection formed a quirky and gritty pastiche of working-class New York: delis, juice bars, dry cleaners, delivery trucks, buses, commercial vans, strip clubs, jazz clubs, a Chinese importer/exporter, even garbage bags. The World Trade Center, the ostentatious symbol of capitalism, had been appropriated by salt-of-the-earth local businesses. What a charming irony, I thought: the Korean dry cleaner and the Spanish-language newspaper both adopted the monstrous hub of finance to market their modest operations.

The use of this imagery by dozens of unconnected local businesses led me to think this must have *some* significance. It seemed it could be a simple matter of packaging. If packaging strives to get customers to notice a product amid other similar products, the World Trade Center made a sensible choice. The towers were visible and recognizable; few landmarks stood out like they did. In a crowded landscape of more than 200,000 small businesses[8], the instantly recognizable towers could help a storefront get noticed, as for example, the Landmark Cleaners on the Upper West Side. Packaging also conveys a message of authenticity. Small business success depends, in part, on forming a niche within a community and having an identity tied to a sense of place. This attracts and retains a loyal, local clientele.[9] Consumers derive satisfaction from supporting local businesses that feel authentic to a community, as opposed to patronizing corporate chains stores with no local roots. Thus it would not be coincidental, then, that businesses with New York-centric names such as Midtown Electric Company, CitiStorage, Uptown Juice Bar, Metro Drug Store, and New York City Beauty Supply would incorporate the towers into their branding. The World Trade Center communicated authenticity through its image, quickly announcing "New York" to customers and residents. And upon further inspection, it was not solely the iconography

---

[8] This number comes from a study sponsored by the Citizens Budget Commission and the Federal Reserve Bank of New York, "Encouraging Small Business Success in New York City and Northern New Jersey: What Firms Value Most," Federal Reserve Bank of New York. Accessed August 2011, http://www.newyorkfed.org/regional/smallbiz_survey.pdf.   Crain's puts the number of New York small businesses at slightly over 190,000. Accessed July 2013.   http://mycrains.crainsnewyork.com/stats-and-the-city/2011/small-business /number-of-small-businesses.

[9] One theory is that customers seek an experience beyond products when making purchases. A local company that offers authenticity has a marketing edge. See Microsoft's Office Live Small Business webpage, "Authenticity Gives Small Businesses the Edge." Accessed August 2013. http://ask.officelive.com/smallbusiness/blogs/team/archive/2009/03/20/authenticity -gives-small-businesses-the-edge.aspx.

of the towers that communicated that message, but the New York City skyline as a whole with the towers as the prominent feature. Nothing visually "said" New York as much as the skyline, and nothing visually "said" the skyline quite like the Towers. The towers without the skyline would solely be two undistinguishable rectangles. And the skyline without the towers—when they stood—would be incomplete, as they were the dominant feature of it. The towers and skyline seemed to be inextricably bound in communicating brand authenticity for scores of New York business.

Fig. 3.4 Petstore, Upper West Side

Fig. 3.5 Uptown Juice Bar, Harlem

Fig. 3.6 CitiStorage, Lower Manhattan

Fig. 3.7 Midtown Electrical Company, Midtown.

Perspectives on the Skyline

The skyline and its skyscrapers representing New York were not new phenomena, however. Indeed, they have communicated "New York-ness" for nearly one hundred years. Scholars, critics, and writers—from Roland Barthes and Ayn Rand to historian Thomas Bender—have articulated the power of New York's "hyphenated silhouette" to serve as an authentic, "emblematic expression of the vertical city."[10] The skyline has served as shorthand for the city's evolution, progress, commerce, capitalism, greed, arrogance, and sublimity since it came into prominence. What, if anything, was unique to the World Trade Center story?

Fig. 3.8   Landmark Cleaners, January 14, 2006

To begin to find out, I consulted with the New-York Historical Society, Museum of the City of New York, and the New York Public Library to investigate what past advertising and ephemera of New York businesses revealed about their associations with the skyline or particular landmarks. The collections offered some evidence; however as a specialist at the New York Public Library admitted, ephemera research can be a needle-in-a-haystack proposition. Individual commercial ephemera are not catalogued by graphic description except in very few cases, and there are limited means to identify particular items that might include a graphic view of the skyline or particular building.[11] So acting on a hunch, I

---

[10] Lindner, *op. cit.*, p. 31.

[11] Emails from the New York Public Library (NYPL) Manuscripts Specialist and Rare Book Division to the author, April 7, 2012 and April 17, 2012. NYPL collections that contain iconography of the World Trade Center include the Joe Baum papers, the Eric Lipton World Trade Center research files, and the Milstein Division of U.S. History, Local History and Genealogy.

decided to search eBay for New York ephemera that featured the skyline or emblematic New York buildings. I found hundreds of letterheads, advertisements, stationery, and pamphlets from New York businesses dating to the early twentieth century. Many incorporated the skyline into their marketing. In 1921, the City of New York Insurance Company letterhead featured the downtown skyline viewed from the Hudson. In 1922, letterhead from Hardy & Hart featured skyscrapers of Lower Manhattan viewed from the harbor, with the Statue of Liberty in the foreground. The New York City Standard Guide from 1917 also featured Lady Liberty, with Lower Manhattan skyscrapers in the distance.[12]

Common to these early representations were views of the skyline from the water, with either the Hudson River or New York Bay, along with the Statue of Liberty, included. These perspectives mimic those of the prints, postcards, and photographs in the New York Public Library's digital gallery from the late nineteenth and early twentieth century. They present Lower Manhattan to the viewer as if standing on the shores of New Jersey or steaming on a vessel mid-Hudson River. Indeed, as Thomas Bender has written, "The most common and striking perspective on New York's tall buildings from the 1890s through 1930 was the view of the skyline across the water."[13] This prevailing imagery re-creates the majesty of approaching New York by boat and seeing the full breadth of commerce extend before you. Its authenticity rests in creating the feeling of a sensational arrival into this land of opportunity. It communicates a message of possibility, not through one or two buildings but by a stunning assemblage of them. As Bender writes, "The city, in such views, is a mountain range; the ensemble is perceptually more important than the individual peaks."[14]

The erection of the Empire State Building in the 1930s added a significant new peak to the ensemble, and makes for an interesting comparison to the World Trade Center. With the Empire State come attempts to embody the distinctive New York character of the skyline graphically by centering on one structure. In her article "The Empire State Building: The Construction and Aging of a Metaphor," written in 1987, Lynn Francis asserts that for a time, the Empire State did serve as

---

[12] Items retrieved from E-Bay searches for "New York ephemera", "New York skyline", "Empire State Building ephemera", "World Trade Center ephemera." Accessed April 6, 2012. http://www.ebay.com.

[13] Thomas Bender, *Unfinished City: New York and the Metropolitan Idea* (New York: The New Press, 2002), p. 48.

[14] *Ibid.*

symbolic shorthand for New York.[15] Francis shows, however, that the narrative surrounding the Empire State's construction imposed limits on how it could function as an icon. Rising one year after the great stock market collapse, the Empire State's construction was celebrated with a public relations campaign fronted by former New York Governor and presidential candidate Al Smith, who served as president of the Empire State Company. He framed the Empire State as a symbol of the workingman's triumph in the face of economic adversity, and commissioned Lewis Hine from 1930 to 1931 to photograph the workers nobly performing feats of construction high above the city. The construction workers were patriots. The act of construction "was elevated to a civic act and the building was seen as an act of faith in the city and the nation."[16] Our archives still communicate this mythic narrative. The Museum of the City of New York's online photograph collection returns 230 images of the Empire State. Thirty percent of them celebrate the construction or completion of the building, and 70 percent of them depict the Empire State within its first decade.[17] Roughly half of the New York Public Library's 266 digitized images of the Empire State depict its excavation, construction or completion, including those from Lewis Hine's now famous book "Men at Work," published in 1932.[18] The erection of the building was the achievement; that it remained largely vacant and failed as a dirigible docking station were inconsequential.

This narrative had immediate consequences for how the Empire State could function as a representative icon. As Francis points out, the Empire State, lacking tenants and commercial use, quickly became a tourist attraction. The flowery language surrounding its rise evolved into a romantic and whimsical understanding of its significance. Tourist literature described the landmark as a monument, an Eighth Wonder of the World to revere and make pilgrimage to. It was not a site of commerce and industry. The Empire State Building came to "be" New York on tourist maps, New York City guidebooks, and the occasional lifestyle ad, but not

---

[15] Lynn Francis, "The Empire State Building: The Construction and Aging of a Metaphor," *Journal of American Culture* 10 n. 2 (1987): 83-90, p. 83.

[16] *Ibid.*, p. 85.

[17] Museum of the City of New York online collections. Accessed July 7, 2013 http://collections.mcny.org. Numbers tallied by the author.

[18] New York Public Library (NYPL) digital gallery. Accessed April 23, 2012 and July 7, 2013, http://digitalgallery.nypl.org, and NYPL's "Lewis Wickes Hine: The Construction of the Empire State Building, 1930-1931." Numbers tallied by the author. Accessed July 7, 2013.
http://www.nypl.org/research/chss/spe/art/photo/hinex/empire/empire.html.

as a commercial symbol.[19] Interestingly, the Museum of the City of New York's digitized ephemera that feature the Empire State are almost entirely tourist postcards, as if to corroborate Francis's conclusions.[20] As her article title suggests, the Empire State Building was already an artifact soon after its construction. It ceased to symbolize progress. Optically, the building's distinction as the tallest in the world inspired imagery that paid homage to its height: aerial views from high above the city or sharp-angle perspectives looking upward from the streets. Yet it never functioned as a symbol of commercial possibility. At best it was an icon of whimsy and recreation. And gradually graphic depictions of the skyline of the 1930s and 1940s reverted back to the view of the early century: from the water, viewing an assemblage of buildings, the Empire State a part of the ensemble. A 1940s Metropolitan New York City map produced by Calso Gasoline depicts the Empire State and Chrysler buildings as if approaching them from the Hudson. Photographs revert to capturing the skyline from the river or far west side streets. The iconography of the Empire State, while it proliferated on guidebooks and city maps, never proliferated in the marketing of New York's working class businesses.

Why, though, did the World Trade Center? Writing in the late 1980s, Francis sensed the branding ascendance of the towers and the optical shift away from midtown and back toward Lower Manhattan.[21] What Francis sensed is uncovered in Miriam Greenberg's post-9/11 study on the marketing of the World Trade Center, later incorporated into her book titled *Branding New York: How a City in Crisis Was Sold to the World*. That the World Trade Center came to be the iconic spokesman of New York was not an accident, nor solely a matter of slow soft changes, as Hiss politely phrases it. The towers' ascendancy as New York's brand icon came about through a tactical marketing campaign—and directly informed those charming World Trade Center logos I stumbled upon with my cell phone camera.

---

[19] Throughout her article, Francis delineates numerous representations of the Empire State on guidebooks, maps, and city tourism ephemera.

[20] Museum of the City of New York online collections. Accessed July 7, 2013, http://collections.mcny.org.

[21] Francis points out on page 89 where the two viewpoints overlapped. She points to the *I Love New York Travel Guide* that placed the Empire State on the front cover and a view of Lower Manhattan, including the Twin Towers and the Chrysler Building, from the vantage point of Liberty Island, on the inside flap. She also uncovers an ad for Rémy Martin Cognac that represented a view, artistically rendered, of a collection of New York's most distinctive buildings with the Empire State and the Chrysler Buildings framing the Twin Towers.

Fig. 3.9 Exit from the Lincoln Tunnel, February 9, 2006

The Towers as Icon

Roland Barthes writes of the Eiffel Tower:

> As a universal symbol of Paris, it is everywhere on the globe where Paris is
> to be stated as an image; from the Midwest to Australia, there is no journey
> to France that isn't made, somehow, in the Tower's name, no schoolbook,
> poster or film about France which fails to propose it as the major sign of a
> people and of a place.[22]

What Barthes writes of the Eiffel Tower and Paris could be said for the
World Trade Center and New York from the late 1970s through the early
2000s. The image of the World Trade Center could not be detached from
the identity of the city. It was introduced into nearly every visual
representation of New York. Its meanings and effects echoed widely and
loudly. The Empire State Building never achieved this semiotic significance.
The Empire State was lauded as a construction triumph, celebrated for its
rise, and then revered as a tourist destination. The towers transcended
tourism: they became the universal symbol for New York in marketing,

---

[22] *Ibid.*, p. 86. Originally in Roland Barthes, *The Eiffel Tower and Other
Mythologies*, translated by Richard Howard, (Berkeley: University of California
Press, 1979).

film, advertising, travel, cartography, businesses, and city agencies.

Ironically, the towers' early days were the exact opposite of the Empire State's. Not only were their aesthetics excoriated at the time of construction, they were deemed a fiscal and urban planning disaster, not as a savior. When the towers were completed in 1977 for a price of $900 million, they were five years behind schedule and $500 million over budget.[23] Many argued that the construction and operation of the towers had contributed to the city's spiraling fiscal crisis of the mid-1970s.[24] With the city plunged into debt, the towers were not a symbol of the resilient American spirit but a money pit of corruption. No patriotic public relations campaign trumpeted their construction.[25] Only a strategic marketing effort centered on the completed World Trade Center rebranded them as the visual shorthand for New York.

To rescue the city from its fiscal and image crisis of the 1970s, New York City and State economic development agencies looked to recast the city's global image, attract tourism, and revive the local economy. As Greenberg recalls, the popular image of New York at that time depicted it as a crime-ridden urban jungle. Alongside apocalyptic visions of a city descending into chaos arose two expensive corporate office towers. Edward Sorel's 1975 mock horror movie poster in *New York Magazine* of "The Towering Insanity" captures the prevailing sentiment that the towers symbolized greedy capitalists pushing the city closer toward the brink of bankruptcy.[26] In response, city leaders joined forces with business leaders to re-package New York as a global brand. "In this effort the new trade towers were seized upon as the perfect, unambiguous logo for a globally resurgent Big Apple," Greenberg writes.[27] City leaders and marketing professionals devised a campaign to change the public perception linking the towers to the fiscal crisis by separating the interior of the buildings, still largely empty and losing money, from their exterior.[28]

---

[23] Greenberg, *op. cit.* p. 391.

[24] *Ibid.*, p. 392.

[25] *Ibid.*, p. 390. Greenberg theorizes that the focus on the architectural symbolism of the skyscrapers detracted from the foresight of the Port Authority's eventual effort to develop a broad-based public relations campaign to sell the towers to the public. Outcry from critics and activists far outweighed the marketing that promoted the project.

[26] *Ibid.*, pp. 389-392. Edward Sorel's "Towering Insanity" was originally published in *New York Magazine*, December 30, 1975.

[27] Greenberg, *op. cit.*, p. 396.

[28] *Ibid.*

Fig, 3.10 Operation Sail Logo. New York City Municipal Archives. Used with permission.

In 1975-6, the Port Authority hired an ad agency at the cost of $225,000 to create a marketing campaign that depicted the World Trade Center's roof as an escape from the woes of the streets below. The Port Authority took out ads in business and travel magazines that associated tourist entertainment with financial travel to Lower Manhattan. The City Visitor Bureau launched its first nationwide 'Big Apple' campaign, in which the towers starred on posters, pamphlets, and guides. The city planned a bicentennial celebration called 'Operation Sail' to bring thousands of boats down the Hudson and past the new Lower Manhattan skyline. And finally, the now-famous 'I Love NY' campaign was launched, with downtown nightlife around the World Trade Center at its heart.[29] In this context, images of the World Trade Center were mass-marketed repeatedly on behalf of Manhattan at-large. The perception of the towers, and the city, became that of a business and entertainment destination that could be enjoyed from a vantage point high above the streets. As Francis sensed in 1987, "The idea of hard work and industry has been replaced by an emphasis on fun and excitement, the idea of

---

[29] Full details of the marketing campaigns launched by the city and private firms are detailed in *ibid.*, pp. 393-404.

building up the city has been replaced by the desire to escape it."[30] This was no accident. The towers were the ideal poster children for this marketing campaign.

Through the 1980s and 1990s, the city joined with corporate partners to feature the towers—often complemented with the Statue of Liberty—in images, postcards, videos, maps, guides, and meeting planners.[31] From 1992-1999, scores of television and film productions were situated in a wealthy New York, usually signified by an establishing shot with the World Trade Center in the background. The website "World Trade Center in Movies" lists no fewer than 450 films of the 1980s and 1990s that featured the World Trade Center. Ninety of the films featured the towers on the film poster, and more than 100 included the towers in the opening credits.[32] Released around the world, these films reinforced the direct visual shorthand between New York and the World Trade Center. Through the conscious selection of city officials to work with developers and private marketing firms, the World Trade Center ascended to become the city's brand icon as the Twin Towers' likeness circulated the globe in thousands of commercials, Hollywood films, TV sitcoms, New York ephemera, images, magazine covers, and tourist literature. "They were pictured so often, and marketed so strategically, that to people around the world they became like a brand logo for an affluent New York City, and a preeminently powerful United States."[33] The towers became synonymous with New York in every medium where New York was visually represented.

That the Korean dry cleaner and the Spanish-language newspaper each integrated the towers into their logos now seems entirely predictable. For a generation of the city's inhabitants, the World Trade Center towers' "New York-ness" had subliminally become inevitable. Much like the view from the boat in the harbor at the turn of the twentieth century, the view towards the towers at the turn of the twenty-first century was of New York's sense of possibility, wealth, commercial activity, luxury, entertainment, and sublime escape from the streets below. To appropriate that view was to participate fully in the authentic New York experience, and an affluent, modern, and successful America. For immigrants in particular, this has long been the strong allure of New York. "In the imagination of many immigrant and ethnic American writers," Lindner reminds us, "the New

---

[30] Francis, *op. cit.*, p. 88.
[31] Greenberg, op. cit., p. 405.
[32] "World Trade Center in Movies." Accessed April 2012. http://wtcinmovies.tripod.com.
[33] Greenberg, *op. cit.*, p. 413.

York skyline also functions as a powerful symbol of social opportunity. New York, now filtered through the immigrant gaze, represents no longer an encoding of capital but instead a space of unbound possibility."[34] The towers represented that unbound possibility worldwide, resonating with those who owned and operated businesses in the 1980s and 1990s.

It was not solely immigrants who adopted the towers brand but New York businesses of all types, as well as city agencies such as the Metropolitan Transit Authority and the New York Police Department. The towers' symbolic meanings were numerous: "the magic and energy of New York, freedom, prosperity, civilization, ingenuity, modernity, urbanity, capitalism, arrogance, top-down globalization, and king-of-the-hill notions of power" among them.[35] Unlike the Empire State Building, the World Trade Center embodied a host of associations based on how it was strategically marketed. The towers could be shorthand for any number of New Yorks; their authenticity held up for numerous audiences, both local and foreign. And if any skepticism remains on how the mass visualization of the towers actively or subliminally influenced those who branded local businesses, recall the Chinese store window on Delancey Street I stumbled upon in 2005. The logo in the window almost identically mirrored that of the "Operation Sail" logo from a 1976 brochure. The towers found their way into the windows, menus, and store signs in every borough because they were in the sub-consciousness of every New Yorker. As such, businesses took on a remarkable capacity to appropriate this seemingly impersonal, corporate logo in order to signify their New York authenticity.

Scholar Elliott Weiss has examined authenticity and packaging in the kosher food industry. "What matters," Weiss writes, "is not whether the package convinces that this or that product is authentic. Rather, it is the prevalence of such packaging which serves as a diagnosis for a said phenomenon."[36] So whether we actively believed the Korean dry cleaner was more New York than its competition down the street due to its World Trade Center window sign is less important than recognizing the phenomenon of local businesses, police stations, jazz bars, and supermarkets using the skyline and Twin Towers to brand themselves and communicate their "New York-ness" during this era. Apart from its

---

[34] Lindner, *op. cit.*, p. 5.

[35] Jane Caputi, "Guest Editor's Introduction 'Of Towers and Twins, Synchronicities and Shadows: Archetypal Meanings in the Imagery of 9/11'", *Journal of American Culture* 28 n. 1 (2005): 1.

[36] Elliot Weiss, "Packaging Jewishness: Novelty and Tradition in Kosher Food Packaging," *Design Issues* 20 n. 1 (2004): 61.

business function, affiliation with place is the defining feature of the local business. No stronger affiliation with place could be visualized than through the use of this quintessential skyline dominated by the Twin Towers, at least in the era in which they stood. The towers reinforced "New York-ness" to the people and businesses that collectively constituted the city. As the city's most defining visual and commercial feature, they were groomed to be its natural spokesmen. As such, for a time they were everywhere, even when we weren't noticing.

Fig. 3.11 Manhattan Avenue, October 30, 2005

Coming Down Again

With the loss of the World Trade Center came a "loss of something less tangible but apparently no less profound: that of the Twin Towers as symbol," says Greenberg.[37] We lost part of New York that had been mass-burned into our minds—and with it sustained a blow to our collective psyche and confidence. This is perhaps why they were selected as a target. The loss of World Trade Center in one day destroyed a city brand that had been built over twenty-five years. In the wake of the attacks, movies,

---

[37] Greenberg, *op. cit.*, p. 386.

commercials, businesses and the city had to negotiate this trauma—to choose whether to edit out the now tragic symbol, or leave it where it stood. Many kept the towers as they were. The blockbuster film *Spider-Man*, however, when released in 2002 opted to remove the towers from a featured scene in the film and the film poster. In a later scene, though, the camera shows a fleeting glimpse of the Twin Towers reflected in the eyes of Spider-Man's mask.[38] Once again, the absence of the towers—and how their likeness remains spectrally present—is the new narrative shaping the legacy of the buildings.

But was it only me who suddenly noticed the towers on the ground once their absence from the sky had sunk in? Well, of course, I wasn't. In 2003, a Hell's Kitchen-based writer named Charles Forbes contributed a column to "ThinkandAsk.com", a non-profit news website in New York. Forbes recalled that in 2001 the Playpen strip club, pressured by the city-enforced sanitization of Times Square, changed its marquee from a sultry female performer to that of the skyline featuring the Twin Towers. A few months later the 9/11 attacks occurred. Forbes surmised that it was no coincidence that the outcry against the Playpen ceased in the ensuing months. It was not that residents had grown more tolerant of pornography; rather, they had come to notice the towers on the marquee and did not wish to see them come down again. Forbes came to this realization during New York's blackout in August 2003. "After wandering this dark city with friends, I stumbled upon The Playpen marquee. Lifeless and wilted without power, the Twin Towers were nothing more than gray hollow tubes against a black city skyline. This sign, I realized, was an image I could not live without."[39]

Just as I noticed the towers still standing, they began to disappear. A souvenir store on Fifth Avenue that had featured them on their awning became a construction site. *Hoy*, the Spanish-language newspaper, installed new paper dispensers and changed their logo. And in 2007 the Playpen finally succumbed when the strip club that had opened as a vaudeville theater in 1916 was torn down to make way for condominiums. Even the "Think & Ask.com" website, which has the New York skyline as its masthead, features an aerial view of the skyline with the Empire State Building at its center, harkening back to the perspective of the 1940s. An era was closing, one when two tall rectangles had defined the skyline and claimed to be the exclusive authentic representations of New York.

---

[38] See *Spider-Man* entry on http://wtcinmovies.tripod.com/chrono.html. Accessed April 2012.

[39] Charles Forbes, "'Twin Towers' Icons Transend [sic] Commercial Appeal, Memorialize 9-11," *Think & Ask*, September 2003. Accessed April 2012. http://www.thinkandask.com/news/neon.html.

Fig. 3.12 The Playpen strip club, March 16, 2005.

That the towers had become the branding icon for the city perhaps only became comprehensible once the actual towers had disappeared. It certainly was for me. The story compelled me to photograph it for two years, ponder it for five years, and commemorate it here. Perhaps I did so because I was seeking closure. Perhaps I saw the towers again only because in my heart and in my head, I was still looking for them. Tracing them throughout the city, marking where they stood and, ultimately, where they were disappearing, allowed me to experience the loss gradually, more manageably, and devoid of the shocking horror of their actual destruction. In essence, this was my own private commemoration, cementing to me that yes, indeed, the World Trade Center was gone. Its demise became fully comprehensible only through this process of documentation. But after all, isn't that what commemorations really are? Aren't they ways to mark with dignity and formality rupture points when what had been was changed to what is now? Only then can they provide us ways to find meaning and comfort. We are still struggling to cope with our profound losses. As Weiss writes, "the stronger the loss the more it is overcompensated with commemorations."[40]

---

[40] Weiss, *op. cit.*, p. 49

CHAPTER FOUR

ORDINARY THEOLOGIES, EXTRAORDINARY CIRCUMSTANCES: BASEBALL AT THE INTERSECTIONS OF FAITH AND POPULAR CULTURE

CARMEN NANKO-FERNÁNDEZ

How the sacred stones lie strewn at every street corner! (Lam. 4:1)

Breaking My Scholarly Silence

For ten years, I have held my scholarly and theological tongue on matters concerning the events and aftermath of September 11, 2001. My response to that day, which reruns annually with unusual clarity in my mind, is not unlike that of the friends of Job, who responded to his extraordinary suffering first by weeping aloud, tearing their cloaks and throwing dust into the air over their heads, and then as they sat on the ground and for seven days and nights "none of them spoke a word to him" (Job 2:11-13).

Job's friends travel each from their own place to offer sympathy and comfort to their distressed companion. Like one in five Americans, I too know at least one person directly affected at one of the three sites. However, as a New Yorker living in diaspora in Washington D.C., I found and continue to find myself resonating simultaneously with the experiences of both Job and his friends. Working as director of campus ministry at a college three miles from the U.S. Capitol, I spent that day in pastoral crisis mode: praying here, comforting there, trying to stop hysterical parents from racing into the streets to retrieve their children from local schools and first-year students from jumping in their cars to drive up the New Jersey Turnpike. At the same time, my heart was home in New York worrying about the whereabouts of my Westchester County firefighter brother and the safety of my sister who bore witness to the tragedy from her workplace in Astoria, Queens. The ensuing days and weeks and months and even years of mourning, remembering, collective suffering and high-level anxiety—at least for the part of me that identifies as a theologian—merited the response of Job's friends, a profound silence "for they saw how great was his suffering."

Theologians seek to articulate, signify and make meaning from within faith communities. Biblical scholar Fernando Segovia points to the particularity of perspective that each theologian brings to this enterprise. He writes "[a]t a fundamental level I have used my life story as a foundation for my work as a critic in biblical studies, as a theologian in theological studies, and as a critic in cultural studies...I have relied on both the individual and the social dimensions not as binary oppositions but as interrelated and interdependent."[1] As a matter of full disclosure, I am a theological migrant worker who was born and raised in the Bronx, resides in Washington D.C. and since 2004, teaches in Chicago. I self-identify as an Hurban@´ theologian—Hispanic and urban—for it these two perspectives that I explicitly bring to the endeavor of sifting through and making sense of a slice of our post-9/11 reality.[2] My home is and always will be New York and that locus significantly shapes my lenses as a theologian. I am Latin@´ and that informs my scholarship and reveals the communities of thought and accountability which form and ground my attempts to articulate and make meaning out of the ongoing experience

---

[1] Fernando F. Segovia, *Decolonizing Biblical Studies: A View from the Margins* (Maryknoll, N.Y.: Orbis Books, 2000), p. 155.

[2] This essay employs Spanglish as both an intentional writing strategy and as a metaphor for the hybridity constituted by the Hispanic presence in the United States. Spanglish is one of many terms used to describe the fusion of Spanish and English in daily communication. It is manifest in this chapter through the following conventions. First, words and expressions in Spanish are not italicized or translated unless they appear as such in direct quotations; at times sentences include both languages. Second, I created @´, the "at" symbol (el aroba) with an acute accent mark. I borrow the use of @ from others because it conveniently combines the "o" and "a" into one character that is gender inclusive. I add the acute accent (@´) to accentuate the fluidity of language, culture and identity. I develop these themes in my book *Theologizing en Espanglish: Context, Community and Ministry* (Maryknoll, N.Y.: Orbis, 2010). For more on my use of the term Hurban@´, see Carmen Nanko-Fernández, "Creation: A Cosmo-politan Perspective," in *In Our Own Voices: Latino/a Renditions of Theology*, edited by Benjamin Valentin, (Maryknoll, N.Y.: Orbis, 2010), pp. 41-63. This expression highlights the intentional use of Latin@´ sources as well as a distinctive urban focus.

emanating from 9/11. Like Job and his friends, I am embedded, implicated, impacted, and engaged in this tragic and complicated mess.

For Latin@´ theologians, lo cotidiano, our daily lived experience, serves as *locus theologicus*—situated places and grounds for doing theology. These situated places of our theologizing, with their rhythms and disruptions of ordinary living, root our reflections even as they call for the critical assessments necessary for convivencia. Convivencia in this sense is a negotiated living together as comunidad. It is predicated upon careful analysis of the complexity of our living with the hope that we will be able to live together justly and well.[3] From this Latin@´ perspective, boundaries between what constitutes the sacred as opposed to the secular are blurred if not fluid. The daily makes no clear-cut distinctions among sources of hope or comfort; nor does it delineate which rituals facilitate mourning or encourage survival. The "faith(s) of the people" find expression in multivalent practices that need not be explicitly religious. At the same time, these popular manifestations may communicate particular theologies and elicit a range of interpretations. After more than decade, it seems only appropriate to unpack some of these ordinary theologies employed to make sense of these events and critically sort through their contested and ongoing legacies situated at the intersections of faith and popular culture. In this case, a site for interrogations of the daily, its disruptions and reconfigurations, is through a slice of life which has the moniker of "the national pastime"—baseball.

This look back at baseball, through Latin@´ lenses, reveals a curious intersection of faith and popular culture that overlays a deeper, older, and more complex interrelationship between the sport and religion. A look back through Latin@´ lenses suggests a complicated, nuanced, and at times contested intersection where baseball represents a slice of our globalized vida cotidiana, our daily living, where the boundaries of sacred and secular are erased, and where international victims and alternately documented immigrants are othered into a conveniently post-mortem U.S.

---

[3] Nanko-Fernández, *Theologizing en Espanglish,* p. xviii. I intentionally use the Spanish term comunidad here instead of the English community. I draw on a distinction made by Puerto Rican scholar Juan Flores who observes that the Spanish term accentuates the two constitutive parts, común, i.e., what do we share in common and unidad, i.e., what binds us beyond our "diverse particular commonalities." Intentional critical reflection on and attention to both of these aspects of community I propose is necessary for negotiating convivencia, a just living together. See Juan Flores, *From Bomba to Hip-Hop: Puerto Rican Culture and Latino Identity* (New York: Columbia University Press, 2000), p. 193.

American identity.[4] A look back through Hurban@' lenses finds in baseball a locus for ordinary theologizing.

The "Church of Baseball" Post-9/11

In many ways, baseball is a sport of the daily, with its 162 game schedule, extensive postseason, and even its preseason. Therefore, the interruption of play in the days following the attacks was nearly unprecedented. The week long pause was the first significant interruption in the sport's history since World War I shortened the 1918 season by a month.[5] When the ordinary is disrupted, interrupted, and even ruptured, any intimation of familiar quotidian rhythms is welcome, so MLB resumed play on September 17th, though not in New York.

In September of 2001, the New York Mets were in the hunt for a wild card playoff slot when security concerns moved their home games for the 17th-19th to Pittsburgh.[6] Therefore neither team was in New York when the regular season resumed with the Yankees already on their scheduled road trip. Five days later, after much deliberation, baseball returned to New

---

[4] I use the term "alternately documented" to refer to those immigrants living and working in the United States who do not have federally-designated documents for residency or employment. They are not "undocumented" because many if not all have documentation for various aspects of their existence that are not recognized by the U.S. government. The term "illegal" is ethically problematic when referring to human beings and does not accurately reflect the status of these immigrants. Furthermore, the term is often used in a derogatory manner that inscribes verbal and physical violence.

[5] The War Department issued a draft compliance extension for major league baseball players in return for an abbreviated season. The military draft deadline was set for September 2 and in turn the regular season ended by Labor Day. See Robert Elias, *The Empire Strikes Out: How Baseball Sold U.S. Foreign Policy and Promoted the American Way Abroad* (New York: The New Press, 2010), Kindle edition, p. 82. During World War II, all baseball games were canceled on the occasion of the Normandy invasion by Allied forces, June 6, 1944, D-Day (*Ibid.*, p. 135).

[6] The reason given by the Mets for shifting their home games to Pittsburgh was as follows: "Out of respect for the tragic events of last Tuesday at the World Trade Center and the Pentagon in Washington, D.C., the Mets have moved the games originally scheduled with the Pirates at Shea from September 17th-September 19th to PNC Ballpark in Pittsburgh." "Mets Plan Special Night as Baseball Returns to NYC." Accessed July 2013. http://www.gameops.com/features/essay-writers/mets-911.

York City at Shea Stadium in Queens on September 21ˢᵗ and continued at
Yankee Stadium into November with the World Series.

From the Beginning...

The relationship between baseball and religion can be traced back to the
earliest chronicling of the sport by invested businessman, entrepreneur and
showman, Albert Goodwill Spalding. In 1911, he authored *America's
National Game*, which includes a chapter that specifically addresses the
relationship. He writes:

> It cannot be claimed for Base Ball that it is essentially religious, either as to
> its features or its objects. During the history of the evolution and
> development of the pastime, magnates, managers, even players, have been
> known who were not conspicuous examples of personal piety. So far as the
> sport has developed any religious side whatever, it can be said of it that,
> thus far it has avoided sectarian bias or control...[7]

Spalding was so intent on securing a provenance for the sport that he
situated it within an historical transnational ball throwing tradition, which
included the following piece of possibly contrived ecclesial trivia: "it is a
remarkable fact that the ecclesiastics of the early Church adopted this
symbol (ball-tossing) and gave it a very special significance by meeting in
the churches on Easter Day, and throwing up a ball from hand to hand, to
typify The Resurrection."[8] In other sections of the book, he affirms that the

---

[7] Albert G. Spalding, *America's National Game: Historical Facts Concerning the
Beginning, Evolution, Development and Popularity of Base Ball* (New York:
American Sports Publishing Company, 1911), p. 439. Available also online at
http://archive.org/details/cu31924029949579. Accessed July 30, 2013. The
"endorsements" of baseball by the Catholic Archbishop of Baltimore, Cardinal
Gibbons, as a fan, juxtaposed with player/Presbyterian evangelist Billy Sunday is
an intriguing example of Spalding's ecumenical reach, pp. 439-43.
[8] *Ibid.*, p. 18. Spalding provides no source for his contention. However, it is worth
noting that in the Baseball Hall of Fame in Cooperstown hangs a replica of an
illumination from the *Cantigas de Santa María*. The image depicts young men
tossing a ball in the air while others play with a stick and ball. Scholars tend to
interpret this as one of several examples of daily life in medieval Spain at the time
of Alfonso X (1221-1284). The ball and bat in the image raise intriguing
possibilities about baseball's precursors. See the image and commentary on the
Canticles of Mary at "La cultura manuscrita (manuscritos de lujo de la corte de
Alfonso X)," in Capítulo 3: La hegemonía cristiana en la península (siglos XIII-
XV), Español 3349/Culturas hispánicas I: de la España musulmana a la época

sport will respect the sanctity of Sundays—if that is enshrined in local law or custom. This attention reflects a concern of the churches:

> Sporting spectacles on weekends stole attention from church activities. Juxtaposed to the mysteries of metaphysics, baseball's rational ordering through its rules and statistical cornucopia posed a threat to religion similar to the advance of materialist and capitalist values. Perhaps some ministers feared the potential for this compulsive sport to satisfy the emotional and spiritual needs of their parishioners in competition with the established religion.[9]

It comes as no surprise then to hear the phrase "church of baseball" made famous in the movie *Bull Durham*. It is a metaphor that speaks in some ways to how the sport, with its rituals, traditions, sacred spaces and mechanisms for belonging, has functioned over the past century and a half. Religion scholar David Chidester spells it out: "Like the church, with its orthodoxy and heresies, its canonical myths and professions of faith, its rites of communion and excommunication, baseball appears in these terms as the functional religion of America."[10]

Baseball as Pastoral Ministry in the Aftermath of 9-11

In light of the events immediately following the 9/11 attacks in New York, a function of church glaringly absent in Chidester's description—namely, the pastoral role of care and ministry—became particularly manifest in the postures and actions of New York's two MLB franchises. In the aftermath of the tragedy, there emerged a ministerial identity in association with the sport, its professional athletes, and its stadiums. The vocabulary with which baseball came to understand and claim its role bore striking resemblance to the traditional functions of pastoral care, specifically sustaining and healing as well as performing the more recent functions as

---

colonial, Department of Latin American and Iberian Cultures, Columbia University. Accessed July 30, 2013.
http://www.columbia.edu/cu/spanish/courses/spanish3349/03edadmedia/arte_manu scrito.html.
[9] Stefan Szymanski and Andrew Zimbalist, *National Pastime: How Americans Play Baseball and the Rest of the World Plays Soccer* (Washington, D.C.: Brookings Institute Press, 2005), p. 21.
[10] David Chidester, "The Church of Baseball, the Fetish of Coca-Cola and the Potlatch of Rock 'n' Roll: Theoretical Models for the Study of Religion in American Popular Culture," *Journal of the American Academy of Religion* 64 n. 4 (1996): 748.

articulated especially in the scholarship of African-American, liberationist, womanist and feminist theologians: surviving, empowering, and transforming.

First, these functions were carried out in the physical space of the stadiums. Yankee Stadium in the Bronx became the site of an interfaith prayer service at the request of Mayor Rudy Giuliani, who likened the space to a cathedral and sought an open arena because people were afraid of being outdoors.[11] The use of stadiums as homes for worship was not new; the "house that Ruth built" by 2001 had already housed Billy Graham crusades, one of the largest wedding ceremonies sponsored by the Unification Church,[12] and two papal masses.[13] Commenting on this aspect of stadium life, author Neil Sullivan writes: "When popes say Mass in New York, Yankee Stadium can become a church. At a mass on October 2, 1979, John Paul II urged the faithful to meet their obligations to the poor and all those in need—a poignant appeal at a time when the Yankees thrived and the Bronx suffered."[14]

In Queens, Shea Stadium became a site for disaster relief, with Mets personnel, especially manager Bobby Valentine, directing the efforts. This use of the facility provided yet another reason for the Mets to play their homestand in Pittsburgh, not Queens, after the resumption of play. One MLB reporter recalls, "There was an eerie sensation at PNC Park that night when the Pirates played the New York Mets. The series actually was supposed to be played in New York, but it was moved to Pittsburgh because Shea Stadium was being used as a staging area for the cleanup from the tragedy."[15] Upon their return to Shea the, Mets found "supplies

---

[11] Interview with Rudy Guiliani, at "9/11 Remembered: Day of Prayer," YES Network.
http://web.yesnetwork.com/media/video.jsp?content_id=18988991&topic_id=&tcid=vpp_copy_18988991&v=3.
[12] The official name of the Unification Church is The Holy Spirit Association for the Unification of World Christianity.
[13] Mark Pattison, "Papal Masses at Baseball Stadiums Not New to U.S. Catholics," *Catholic News Service.* April 17, 2008. Accessed July 2013.
http://www.catholicnews.com/data/stories/cns/0802087.htm. For a detailed study of papal masses at Yankee Stadium, see William R. Whitmore, "The Vicar of Christ and the House that Ruth Built: Papal Masses at Yankee Stadium" (Senior Thesis, Princeton Theological Seminary, 2013).
[14] Neil J. Sullivan, *The Diamond in the Bronx: Yankee Stadium and the Politics of New York* (New York: Oxford University Press, 2001), pp. xi-xii.
[15] Jim Street, "Emotions Flowed as Games Returned," September 9, 2002. Accessed July 30, 2013.

stack[ing] up in the parking lot and exhausted relief workers [a]sleep in the corridors where pitchers and shortstops usually roam. The manager of the Mets, Bobby Valentine, [was] in constant motion, on an endless mission to help the hurting."[16]

As is evident from the example of Valentine, these pastoral functions were carried out by players and coaches. Reflecting on his flurry of activity, Valentine explained, "It was almost impossible to go to sleep...How many funerals can you go to? How many times can you hold a hand and look into empty eyes that show you nothing but a broken heart?"[17] Echoing similar sentiments, Yankee shortstop Derek Jeter queried: "What do you say?...It was pretty uncomfortable at the beginning, but then they started opening up and telling us how much they appreciated us coming. But you don't understand why at the time...I think after that we had a better appreciation of what we represented."[18] The engagement between team members and rescuers, recovery workers, survivors, loved ones keeping vigil awaiting news, and all those experiencing the profound grief of sudden and violent loss appears to go beyond the expectations that accompany celebrity status. The responses of these athletes-turned-pastoral-agents reveal their own discomfort and awkwardness, as well as a sense of their own inadequacies in dealing with those most seriously affected by the tragedy. Journalist Michael Lopresti makes a pastoral connection: "They were all there trying to find the right words to help; clergy, counselors, and Yankees."[19]

At the same time, there was a growing realization that what these athletes do and say matters. For example, ballplayers began wearing caps associated with city workers who were first responders and part of the rescue and recovery work. In place of their own caps, the Mets wore not only the NYPD, FDNY, but the Port Authority police, EMS, Department of Sanitation, Canine Unit, among others. The team went so far as to replace their uniform caps in this manner throughout the last weeks of the

---

http://mlb.mlb.com/news/article.jsp?ymd=20020909&content_id=124585&vkey=news_mlb&fext=.jsp&c_id=null.

[16] Mike Lopresti, "New York Athletes, Coaches Remember 9/11," *USA Today*, September 1, 2011. Accessed July 30, 2013. http://www.usatoday.com/sports/story/2011-08-31/New-York-athletes-coaches-remember-911/50208244/1.

[17] *Ibid.*

[18] *Ibid.*

[19] *Ibid.*

season, in defiance of MLB uniform policy.[20]   This act of resistance and
solidarity bound them in a unique way to the local context. Their act of
wearing these caps in the course of each game inscribed a level of
interactivity and intimacy. It is worth noting that the Mets sought to wear
the caps on the tenth anniversary but their request was denied by Joe Torre
in his role as Executive Vice President for Baseball Operations. Ironically,
Torre, a former Met manager, was the Yankee manager in 2001. In 2011,
the threat of substantial fines for violating uniform policy kept the Mets in
check.[21]

Post-9/11, a pastoral dimension inserted itself into the master narrative
of the national pastime to assert that baseball is more than just a
distraction; it can be a force for local and national recovery and healing. It
emerged as a means to retrieve a less traumatic and more stable immediate
past, reestablish a more comforting status quo, provide a semblance of
order and restore a sense of normalcy with a familiar daily routine. The
expectation that sport, particularly New York baseball, would surface as a
source of inspiration was not a surprise, considering the proximity of the
tragic events to the post season. With both New York teams in contention
that year, and the Yankees' string of four consecutive championships as a
precedent, the possibility of baseball rising to inspirational proportions
was not farfetched. While for some, the return to sport and the new rituals
that accompanied that return were interpreted as acts of resilience, the
persistent memory of ballplayers as comforters, counselors and pastoral
care providers deserves more attention, as does the impact on the players
themselves.

Thrust into public pastoral ministry, these athletes and their coaches
expanded the role of sport beyond that of restoring a sense of normalcy or

[20] See for example, Tim Kurkjian, "Wearing Hats Symbolic Gesture by Mets,"
ESPN New York, September 11, 2011. Accessed September 12, 2011.
http://espn.go.com/new-york/mlb/story/_/id/6957532/new-york-mets-symbolic-
gesture-united-people-sept-11. Al Yellon, "MLB Forbids Mets To Wear New York
Tribute Caps," *Baseball Nation,* September 11, 2011. Accessed July 30, 2013.
http://mlb.sbnation.com/2011/9/11/2419367/mlb-forbids-mets-nypd-nyfd-tribute-
caps. Andrew Keh, Andrew, "A 9/11 Gesture Curtailed," *New York Times,*
September 11, 2011. Accessed July 30, 2013.
 http://bats.blogs.nytimes.com/2011/09/11/a-911-gesture-curtailed/. It is also worth
noting that the commemoration of the tenth anniversary at Citi Field focused more
on city workers than the military.
[21] "Joe Torre: MLB Denial of Mets' 9/11 First Responder Caps 'A Unanimity
Thing'," *CBS New York,* September 12, 2011. Accessed July 30, 2013,
http://newyork.cbslocal.com/2011/09/12/joe-torre-mlb-denial-of-mets-911-first-
responder-caps-a-unanimity-thing/.

providing escape in troubling times. Communications scholar Robert Brown posits that escapism would involve avoidance of the source of pain but the evidence shows that baseball as well as NFL football attempted to address the tragedy in various ways, communicating a variety of influential messages directly and indirectly. Brown captured the pastoral element in his citing of a *USA Today* commentary by Erik Brady on the one year anniversary of 9/11. Brady writes, "Ballparks became home to sacramental ceremony. It seemed natural to salute and sing and cry and then settle in for a game that meant exactly nothing and everything all at once."[22] However, while he did not substantially develop these themes in his own essay, there was yet another dimension beyond care and worship—an evangelism of sorts. Brown acknowledges that besides "messages to re-enforce unity amongst Americans and remind everyone that life must go on. There were also not so subtle messages of supporting the war against terrorism."[23]

Two Windows on the Post-9/11 World

There exists an intimate relationship between baseball and U.S. national identity. In their book, *The Faith of Fifty Million*, church historian Christopher Evans and biblical scholar William Herzog observe that "Within the popular imagination of Americans, baseball embodied the soul of the nation, distinctively historical yet uniquely transcendent."[24] This transcendent character becomes embedded in the sacral language with which sport—and baseball especially—is extolled, "what some describe as sacred mythology that reinforces symbols of our national identity—that we are 'one nation under God'."[25] This aspect upholds an innate patriotism that was also part of the not so subtle messages communicated in the aftermath of the attacks. At the same time, conveniently ignored in the master narrative of U.S. baseball is a global dimension that is not

---

[22] Erik Brady, "Continuity of Sports Helped Heal the Times," *USA Today*, September 11, 2002. Accessed July 30, 2013.
http://www.usatoday.com/sports/sept11/2002-09-10-ccover_x.htm. Cited in Robert S. Brown, "Sport and Healing America," *Society* 41 (November/December 2004): 37-41.

[23] *Ibid.*

[24] Christopher H. Evans and William R. Herzog II. "Introduction: More than a Game: The Faith of Fifty Million," in *The Faith of Fifty Million: Baseball, Religion and American Culture*, edited by Christopher H. Evans and William R. Herzog II (Louisville, Ken.: Westminster John Knox Press, 2002), pp. 2-3.

[25] *Ibid.*

necessarily derivative of U.S. experiences. Béisbol is part and parcel of other national identities, particularly in Latin America. Cuba and the Dominican Republic are iconic in this regard as is Puerto Rico, where the memory of Roberto Clemente Walker remains a source and exemplar of cultural pride. This global dimension also remained underappreciated in narratives and commemorations of 9/11. One exception was in the color commentary by Bobby Valentine on ESPN's Sunday Night Baseball coverage of the September 11, 2011 Mets-Cubs game. Former Met manager Valentine alluded to this global reality when he acknowledged the diversity of the sport in terms of its players, its fan base and its global presence. He reflected that in this sense, baseball resembled all who lost their lives at the World Trade Center. One could look at baseball and see the world's sport mirroring our community. However in most commemorative events, international and alternately documented victims were subsumed under the category of "American lives lost." The irony, of course, is that in daily life alternately documented individuals were designated "others" and in death they were othered yet again, only this time identified post-mortem as U.S. "Americans."

This nexus between baseball and national identities is best viewed through two windows of interpretation. The focus first can be framed by the re-signifying of the seventh-inning stretch with the singing of *God Bless America* and the second focus is found in the poem "Alabanza: In Praise of Local 100," by Nuyorican poet Martín Espada.

God Bless America:
Re-signifying the Seventh-Inning Stretch

Herzog and Evans explore baseball in its manifestation as "a sacred symbol of American identity," whose status as national pastime "continues to be perceived as an enduring symbol of America's unique past—and among some people a sign of hope for a better future."[26] In his consideration of baseball as a civil religion, Evans notes that the sport is "permeated with a zealous patriotism that connected the exclusive claims of American uniqueness to world redemption."[27] The historic intersection of American exceptionalism and U.S. imperial impulses is found in the earliest chronicle of the sport. Spalding boasts:

---

[26] *Ibid.*, p. 2.
[27] Christopher H. Evans, "Baseball as Civil Religion: The Genesis of an American Creation Story," in *The Faith of Fifty Million*, pp. 29-30.

Base Ball [sic] has won its right to be denominated the American National Game…Ever since its establishment in the hearts of the people…Base Ball has "followed the flag." It has "followed the flag"…to Alaska…to the Hawaiian Islands…to the Philippines, to Porto Rico and to Cuba, and wherever a ship floating the Stars and Stripes finds anchorage today, somewhere on a nearby shore the American National Game is in progress.[28]

In his hyperbolic invention of baseball's creation myth, Spalding ensures a patriotic root by tying its foundational story to a Union General in the Civil War; lest he alienate a potential market, he places its play in Union and Confederate camps. The military connection is the key to the promotion of the sport, as Spalding writes:

While the game did not originate in the Army or Navy, these important departments of our government were the media through which the sport, during the Civil War, was taken out of its local environments—New York and Brooklyn—and started upon its national career. The returning veterans, "when the cruel war" was "over," disseminated Base Ball throughout the country and then established it as the national game of America.[29]

Internationally, baseball as a manifestation of U.S. neocolonialism cannot be ignored. Journalist Marcos Bretón observes that:

Almost all the nations and territories producing Latin players today have been invaded by U.S. troops in the last century: the Dominican Republic, Cuba, Puerto Rico, Mexico, Panama, and Nicaragua. And if it wasn't an invasion by American troops, it was American business that organized the sport.[30]

These historical underpinnings are essential to understanding the significance and lack of subtlety in the messages communicated long after the 2001 postseason ended. In the days following the tragedy, Major League Baseball imposed on its teams the singing of *God Bless America* at

---

[28] Spalding, *op. cit.*, p. 14.

[29] *Ibid.*, p. 366.

[30] Marcos Bretón and José Luis Villegas, *Away Games: The Life and Times of a Latin Baseball Player* (Albuquerque: University of New Mexico Press, 1999), p. 83. This book puts a face on the role of baseball in the Dominican Republic and its relationship with the United States through the story of shortstop Miguel Tejada. It is worth noting that in the case of Mexico, baseball may have also arrived via the railroad. See Alan M. Klein, *Baseball on the Border: A Tale of Two Laredos* (Princeton, N.J.: Princeton University Press, 1997).

the seventh-inning stretch, in place of *Take Me Out to the Ball Game* or other local standards. However, after 2001 few teams retain the practice on a daily basis, though the New York Yankees and the Los Angeles Dodgers are two that do. Some teams resort to the piece during weekend play or on national holidays. At Yankee Stadium, this Irving Berlin composition has acquired a status equal to the National Anthem. Fans are instructed to rise and remove their caps. The hymn is tied directly to those who are in military service, as the troops are explicitly mentioned.[31] The expectation is that all will comply, so much so that in 2008 the aggressive response of uniformed off-duty police towards a spectator who needed to use the restroom during the airing of the Kate Smith recording resulted in the filing of a law suit ultimately won by the aggrieved party. One blogger commenting on the chain of unfortunate events posted:

> Perhaps it's not surprising that the Yankees, a franchise that seems to embody the worst traits of the imperial culture, have a fan-base drawing heavily from a cohort of people who really enjoy compelled conformity… during the month following 9-11, the team had received "hundreds of e-mails and letters" from fans complaining that others in attendance were not displaying sufficient "respect" during the mid-inning nationalist benediction.[32]

Whether intentional or not, these choices on the part of sports teams impart a theological message that intricately ties the divine to a particular national and even martial agenda. The ramifications of this are not lost on religious leaders. Consider the words of Will Willimon, presiding bishop of the North Alabama Conference of the United Methodist Church:

> American Christians may look back upon our response to 9/11 as our greatest Christological defeat. It was shattering to admit that we had lost the theological means to distinguish between the United States and the

---

[31] "Please stand for a moment of silent prayer for the men and women serving our country at home and around the world." Words such as these precede singing or playing a recording of *God Bless America*. In Yankee Stadium, a Kate Smith version is usually played. It is curious to note that at Shea Stadium on the day baseball resumed, the seventh-inning anthem was *New York, New York* sung by Liza Minnelli from atop the visitors' dugout. See "Mets Plan Special Night as Baseball Returns to NYC." Accessed July 30, 2013.
http://www.gameops.com/features/essay-writers/mets-911.

[32] William N. Grigg, "The Civil Religion and the Seventh-Inning Stretch." *Pro Libertate Blog,* July 7, 2009. Accessed July 30, 2013.
http://freedominourtime.blogspot.com/2009/07/civil-religion-and-seventh-inning.html.

kingdom of God. The criminals who perpetrated 9/11 and the flag-waving boosters of our almost exclusively martial response were of one mind: that the nonviolent way of Jesus is stupid. All of us preachers share the shame; when our people felt very vulnerable, they reached for the flag, not the Cross.[33]

Questions remain, however. How did and does the church of baseball actively participate through its rituals in perpetuating this relationship? Who is excluded in this primarily and narrowly constructed Judaeo-Christian set of lenses? Evans suggests that "baseball symbolizes an American faith that the world could be subjugated by the superior values of the United States. Baseball symbolized not only American uniqueness, but in its own way reinforced a message that God was on our side."[34]

The paradox of the national pastime and its legacy of American exceptionalism are illuminated by the reality that currently baseball is dependent on what amounts to migrant labor. Ballplayers born outside of the fifty U.S. states currently constitute over 28 percent of MLB rosters and almost 50 percent of the minor leagues.[35] What then does this reality suggest for the identity of a nation whose self-understanding is tied in part to a flawed myth?

Alabanza: In Praise of Local 100

Following 9/11, Nuyorican poet, Martín Espada penned a poem that, in his own words, was both a form of mourning as well as a poem of praise. Its focus was the loss of life in the restaurant at the top of the World Trade Center, Windows on the World, which lost seventh-nine workers, forty-three of whom belonged to Local 100 of the Restaurant Employees Union and fifteen of those workers were alternately documented.[36] If not for the

---

[33] Will Willimon, "How Evangelical Leaders Have Changed Since 9/11." *Christianity Today*, September, 5, 2011. Accessed July 30, 2013.
http://www.christianitytoday.com/ct/2011/september/howleaderschanged.html?star
t=5.%20Accessed
[34] Evans, *op. cit.*, pp. 30-31.
[35] "Opening Day rosters feature 241 players born outside the U.S.," *MLB Press Release*, April 1, 2013. Accessed July 30, 2013.
http://mlb.mlb.com/news/article.jsp?ymd=20130401&content_id=43618468&vkey
=pr_mlb&c_id=mlb.
[36] Laurie Jurs, "Community Columnist: Remember Everybody from the 9/11 Tragedy," *Green Valley News and Sun*, September 10, 2011. Accessed July 30, 2013.

advocacy work of the Tepeyac Association in Lower Manhattan, many other alternately-documented workers who died that day would remain unknown, forgotten and unclaimed, forever "disappeared" in the eyes of their families.[37]

Espada is intentional in inserting this forgotten piece of the story by reminding us of the over ninety nations that lost citizens that day. In an interview, he recalled that, "For me, the poem is also saying remember those who died on 9/11, but particularly remember that there were kitchen workers who died on 9/11, and that there were immigrants who died on 9/11. And that interrupts the flow of patriotic discourse."[38]

Early in Espada's poem there appears a baseball reference:

> *Alabanza*. Praise the cook's yellow Pirates cap
> worn in the name of Roberto Clemente, his plane
> that flamed into the ocean loaded with cans for Nicaragua,
> for all the mouths chewing the ash of earthquakes.[39]

In a number of ways, invoking the name of Roberto Clemente challenges the claims of American exceptionalism that haunt baseball and sadly too often cloud our memorializing of 9/11. While Clemente is certainly remembered for his athletic feats, it was his untimely death that made his name synonymous with community service in baseball circles.

---

http://www.gvnews.com/opinion/letters_to_editor/community-columnist-remember-everybody-from-the-tragedy/article_ad9313d0-dc03-11e0-ba38-001cc4c002e0.html.

[37] "It was thanks to the efforts of Magallan and Tepeyac that it was discovered that more than 100 undocumented immigrants—deliverymen, waiters, cleaners, cooks—had been killed at the World Trade Center. Otherwise, probably no one, aside from their families and friends, would've ever known or cared." Albor Ruiz, "Time is Right to Revive Post-9/11 Attack Solidarity," *New York Daily News,* May 4, 2011. Accessed July 30, 2013. http://articles.nydailynews.com/2011-05-04/local/29523635_1_undocumented-immigrants-attacks-families . For more about the Tepeyac Association, see Alyshia Gálvez, *Guadalupe in New York: Devotion and the Struggle for Citizenship Rights among Mexican Immigrants* (New York: New York University Press, 2009).

[38] "On 9/11 and the Politics of Language: An Interview with Martín Espada," *Solidarity*, September/October, 2011. Accessed July 30, 2013. http://www.solidarity-us.org/node/3350.

[39] Martín Espada, "Alabanza: In Praise of Local 100," in *Alabanza: New and Selected Poems 1982-2002* (New York: W. W. Norton and Company, Inc., 2003), p. 231. Espada writes that this poem is "for the 43 members of Hotel Employees and Restaurant Employees Local 100, working at the Windows on the World restaurant, who lost their lives in the attack on the World Trade Center."

Clemente died off the coast of Puerto Rico in a plane crash while on a humanitarian mission delivering supplies to victims of an earthquake in Nicaragua. His advocacy for social justice, his struggle against racism and colonialism, and even the pastoral care dimension in his own life as a healer and comforter back home in Puerto Rico are often lost in the domestication of Clemente's image. The reference to Clemente disrupts the discourse on another level as well. It is a reminder of his self-described "second-class U.S. citizenship" as a Puerto Rican from la Isla, who is black and speaks Spanish: a disruption to both baseball and his nation of citizenship.[40]

Following the Flag? Contested Contradictions

Theologians are insiders, and my perspective arises from within the church of béisbol—I was raised a Yankee fan, and chose to be ecumenical by supporting the Mets as well. Interreligious by diaspora—I root for the Washington Nationals and on occasion Chicago teams claim my temporary loyalty. In 2004, I was "traded to Chicago," as I understand and articulate my move to the faculty of a graduate theological school located in the "Windy City." It coincided with the trade of then Yankee pitcher José Contreras to the White Sox. My first homesick act was to attend his first game in his new stadium—an act of solidarity among urban exiles.

In 2001, as All Hallows' Eve crossed into the feast of All Saints, Derek Jeter became Mr. November with a walk-off homerun, securing a Yankee come-from-behind World Series game four win in the Bronx. The Yankees went on to win three games in the 2001 World Series—all in dramatic fashion and all at home in the Bronx. For a diasporic New Yorker, watching in Washington D.C., those three wins in New York were a lifeline, a sign of stability but sadly not of recovery. In Washington, on the same day baseball resumed, anthrax entered our daily experience claiming the lives of two of our neighborhood postal workers, closing our post offices, radiating our mail. After three weeks of silence, planes returned to our D.C. airspace but in front of my apartment window sat a Patriot missile battery aimed towards the airport—a sign of the new normal. The terror continued, and less than a year later, we were hiding from a sniper.

---

[40] For more on the memorialization of Roberto Clemente, see Carmen Nanko-Fernández, *¡El Santo! Baseball and the Canonization of Roberto Clemente* (Macon, Ga.: Mercer University Press, forthcoming).

From this perspective, and with eyes wide open, baseball is not a means of escape from quotidian misery but rather an active manifestation of resistance to suffering within the context of a complicated daily experience. Drawing on the scholarship of theologian Roberto Goizueta on the role of fiestas in Latin@´ life, I would propose that in some ways, baseball post-9/11 has the potential to function in a manner that celebrates life in defiance of all that seeks to demean and bring harm.[41] At the intersection of faith and popular culture there exists the possibility of affirming the graciousness of life and relationships, and of celebrating the present as intrinsically linked to both an honestly remembered and interrogated past and a hoped-for and just future, a future of convivencia.

Intricately woven into the fabric of a real and/or imagined national identity, baseball is a factor in shaping collective understandings and responses to matters political. In 2012 as part of Memorial Day celebrations, the U.S. military was honored at ballparks across the country, and the logos on team caps sported camouflage in place of their usual colors. The U.S. Navy's Blue Angels flew over Citi Field, now home of the New York Mets, and the site of one of the more enduringly poignant, haunting and subtle 9/11 memorials—the cityscape logo with the Twin Towers darkened and covered in a ribbon. *God Bless America* graced the seventh-inning stretch of most if not all MLB ballparks (except those in Canada). I grew up in the "church of baseball"; however, I must confess to feeling like an alien in a foreign land in the seventh inning when the public address announcer requests that "we all rise...and join in the singing of *God Bless America*." I cannot say "Amen" to that in the "church of baseball" because there is more at stake. For me, this legacy of September 11, 2001, is an act of outing and othering that seeks to maintain the level of discourse in a clear-cut binary fashion that visually and aurally establishes who is patriotic and who is not. Competing visions of what it means to belong are squelched, critical questions are discouraged by patriotic peer pressure, and a national normative practice is rendered into a tradition as fans are evangelized by baseball, in Spalding's now haunting words, to "follow the flag."[42]

Resistance to this patriotic peer pressure came briefly from Puerto Rican ballplayer Carlos Delgado. In 2004, he protested the U.S. engagement in the war in Iraq by refusing to stand during seventh-inning renditions of *God Bless America*; he typically remained in the dugout. He

---

[41] Roberto S. Goizueta, "Fiesta: Life in the Subjunctive," in *From the Heart of Our People: Latino/a Explorations in Catholic Systematic Theology*, edited by Orlando O. Espín and Miguel H. Díaz, (Maryknoll, N.Y.: Orbis Books, 1999), pp. 84-99.

[42] Spalding, *op. cit.*, p. 14.

was protected in one way because he played with the Canadian-based Toronto Blue Jays, though this did not prevent particularly vocal fan responses in away games in stadiums like New York, let alone on the blogosphere. While Delgado had participated in the seventh-inning ritual in the 2003 season, the wars, coupled with his involvement in the resistance to the U.S. military use of Vieques, Puerto Rico, for weapons testing, struck a chord that triggered his personal expression of protest. Delgado, who self-identified as pro-peace, remarked, "[I]t takes a man to stand up for what he believes…Especially in a society where everything is supposed to be politically correct."[43] In the popular imagination, "Delgado's antiwar protest was also an attack against the victims of September 11. To protest 'God Bless America' during a baseball game was not antiwar, but anti-American."[44] In 2005, as a free agent he modified his position, such that if the teams courting him have a policy that he must participate in the seventh-inning tribute, then he would comply.

This issue was of significance to the Mets' ownership who signed him for the 2006 season once he allayed their fears in his remarks at the press conference announcing the trade to New York: "The Mets have a policy that everybody should stand for 'God Bless America' and I will be there. I will not cause any distractions to the ballclub…Just call me Employee Number 21."[45] There is a contradiction embedded in Delgado's politically correct remarks. He references himself in terms of his new uniform, "Employee Number 21," the number he had been longing to wear for years: the iconic number of his hero Roberto Clemente, often a thorn in the side of MLB because of his social justice stands. Ironically, in 2006 Delgado received MLB's Roberto Clemente Award, given annually to a player for "outstanding play on the field with devoted work in the community." In the award citations and press releases, his many charitable

---

[43] William Rhoden, "Delgado Makes a Stand by Taking a Seat," *New York* Times, July 21, 2004. Accessed July 30, 2013.
http://www.nytimes.com/2004/07/21/sports/baseball/21rhoden.html. See also Ron Borges, "Don't Boo Delgado for Iraq Protest," *NBC Sports*, July 22, 2004. Accessed July 30, 2013. http://nbcsports.msnbc.com/id/5482059/.
[44] Ángel G Flores-Rodríguez, "Baseball, 9/11, and Dissent: The Carlos Delgado Controversy," *OAH Magazine of History* 25 n. 3 (2011): 55.
[45] Dave Zirin, "The Silencing of Carlos Delgado," *The Nation*, December 7, 2005. Accessed July 30, 2013. http://www.thenation.com/article/silencing-carlos-delgado#. See also Adam Rubin, "Delgado Meets the Mets in PR," *New York Daily News*, January 14, 2005. Accessed July 30, 2013.
http://articles.nydailynews.com/2005-01-14/sports/18292674_1_agent-david-sloane-jeff-wilpon-mets-gm.

and community-oriented works are recognized, yet no mention is made of his political activism or pacifism with regards to Vieques or the wars in Iraq and Afghanistan.[46]

On Sunday, May 2, 2011, only one MLB game was still in progress: the New York Mets vs. the Phillies in Citizens Bank Park in Philadelphia. As fans' cell phones received the news, chants of "USA" spread across the ballpark, confusing many of the players on the field in the ninth inning of what would be a fourteen-inning game.[47] The news spread virally across the ballpark: Osama bin Laden had been killed by U.S. Navy Seals. In the words of Mets manager Terry Collins, "You almost want to just stop the game and have that girl come and sing another beautiful rendition of 'God Bless America.'"[48]

Sport is intricately woven through the fabric of nuestra vida cotidiana, our daily living, as the initial responses to and the ongoing memorialization of the events of 9/11 demonstrate. From my perspective as an Hurban@ theologian (Hispanic and urban), privileging daily lived experience as a source for our theologizing requires that critical attention be paid to the role and legacy of the ordinary. In the aftermath of this tragedy, approaches that read and interpret our quotidian texts and contexts without shying away from the complications, contestations, and contradictions are not only appropriate but necessary. New York baseball is not a metaphor for matters theological. Rather, it stands as a complex slice of our living

---

[46] "2006 Winner: Carlos Delgado, New York Mets," *Roberto Clemente Award*. Accessed July 30, 2013. http://mlb.mlb.com/mlb/official_info/community/clemente_history.jsp. This site also contains a link to the official MLB press release. For a transcript of the award ceremony see "MLB WORLD SERIES: CARDINALS v TIGERS," *ASAP Sports*, October 24, 2006. Accessed July 30, 2013. http://www.asapsports.com/show_interview.php?id=39774.

[47] "Mets/Phillies Fans Learn of Osama Bin Laden's Death, Erupt in 'USA' Chants," *CBS New York,* May 2, 2011. Accessed July 30, 2013. http://newyork.cbslocal.com/2011/05/02/fans-erupt-in-usa-chants-during-metsphillies-game-after-learning-of-osama-bin-laden-killing/. In an historical precedent in July 1943, the announcement of the resignation of Benito Mussolini at a Yankees v. White Sox game also resulted in spontaneous jubilation from a crowd that "began dancing in the aisles." Elias, *op. cit.*, Kindle edition, p. 135.

[48] Terry Collins cited in Todd Zolecki, "Philadelphia Freedom: Game Takes Backseat," May 2, 2011. Accessed July 30, 2013. http://mlb.mlb.com/news/article.jsp?ymd=20110501&content_id=18479234&vkey=news_nym&c_id=nym.

through and beyond extraordinary circumstances that continue to exert a profound hold on our memories.[49]

[49] This essay developed out of a paper presented in September 2011 at a conference in New York sponsored by St. John's University entitled *Making Meaning of 9/11 Ten Years After: Local Impacts, Global Implications*. The piece was further refined at the 2012 Colloquium of the Academy of Catholic Hispanic Theologians of the United States (ACHTUS). Thanks to my colleague, Professor Jean-Pierre Ruiz from St. John's University, and ACHTUS for their helpful insights.

PART II

MEMORIALIZING 9/11

CHAPTER FIVE

TALES OF THE FORGOTTEN: RECLAIMING THE RESTAURANT AT THE END OF THE WORLD

KENNETH WOMACK

While the trauma and tragedy surrounding the events of September 11th, 2001 have been memorialized in numerous works of nonfiction and fiction alike, the celebrated Windows on the World restaurant has enjoyed surprisingly little attention in spite of its distinguished place in the life of New York City's illustrious culinary culture. This is especially true of the restaurant's cooks and wait staff, several of whom were undocumented workers. Not surprisingly, nonfiction accounts almost universally concentrate on Assistant General Manager Christine Olender's desperate telephone calls for help as the North Tower teetered towards destruction. In contrast with Martín Espada's evocative poem "Alabanza: In Praise of Local 100," fictive works such as Frédéric Beigbeder's *Windows on the World* (2005) and Andrea White's young-adult, sci-fi novel *Windows on the World: The UpCity Chronicles* (2011) render the restaurateurs as faceless, secondary participants in the drama of 9/11.[1] Yet their story in general—and the story of Windows on the World in particular—have an extensive and distinguished plotline of their own. [2]

---

[1] Martín Espada, "Alabanza: In Praise of Local 100," in *Alabanza: New and Selected Poems, 1982-2002* (New York: Norton, 2003), pp. 231-32; Frédéric Beigbeder, *Windows on the World*, translated by Frank Wynne. (New York: Miramax, 2005); and Andrea White, *Windows on the World: The UpCity Chronicles* (South Hampton, N.H.: Namelos, 2011). I am indebted to Dr. Carmen Nanko-Fernández, who shared Espada's evocative poem with me during the *Making Meaning of 9/11 Ten Years After: Local Impacts, Global Implications* conference in September 2011 at St. John's University's Manhattan Campus.

[2] In addition to the works by Espada, Beigbeder, and White, the literary response to the events of 9/11 include, among a host of others, William Gibson, *Pattern Recognition* (New York: Putnam, 2003); Jonathan Safran Foer, *Extremely Loud*

In the food and drink trade, rooftop restaurants have long been notorious for being kitschy affairs designed, more often than not, to fleece giddy, unsuspecting tourists with the highest possible markup. There is even an old axiom suggesting that the food quality decreases in proportion with every additional foot of altitude. When Joe Baum began imagining the food services offerings for the World Trade Center complex in 1970, he had much larger plans on his mind. As one of New York City's great food-service entrepreneurs, Baum was confronted with the Herculean task of providing a self-contained system of restaurants and eateries for an expected employee mass of some 40,000 people, along with 150,000 commuters who would pass through the complex on any given workday.[3] With such prodigious numbers of people, the World Trade Center would be the equivalent of a moderately-sized city all by itself.

During six years of development, Baum and his team created a complex of food-service venues that eventually included twenty-two different offerings, many of which enjoyed such pedestrian names as "Eat & Drink," "The Big Kitchen," "The Market Bar and Dining Room," and, in those pre-Starbuck's days, the "Coffee Express." But the crown jewel for the visionary behind such New York landmarks as the Four Seasons, La Fonda del Sol, and the Forum of the Twelve Caesars was always Windows on the World, the restaurant with the majestic views that would adorn the 107th floor of the North Tower.[4]

Ironically, the initial design of the World Trade Center did not include space for a sky-top restaurant. In fact, Minoru Yamasaki's blueprints for all of the floors were uniformly designed above the ground-floor lobby with the same narrow windowscapes that allowed natural light to enter the building without exposing employees to the soaring heights of the towers. As it turns out, this aspect of the architecture was par for the course for Yamasaki's creations; although famous for designing breathtaking skyscrapers, the architect was notoriously afraid of heights. Recognizing the need for public viewing spaces, members of the design team convinced

---

and Incredibly Close (New York: Houghton Mifflin, 2005); Jay McInerney, *The Good Life* (New York: Knopf, 2006); Don Delillo, *Falling Man* (New York: Scribner, 2007); and Colum McCann, *Let the Great World Spin* (New York: Random House, 2009); as well as such graphic novels as Art Spiegelman, *In the Shadow of No Towers* (New York: Viking Adult, 2008) and Alissa Torres, *American Widow*, illustrated by Sungyoon Cho, (New York: Villard, 2008).

[3] Kevin Zraly. "The Story of Windows on the World," in *idem.*, *Windows on the World Complete Wine Course: 2003 Edition—A Lively Guide* (New York: Sterling, 2003), pp. ix-xxiv, p. ix.

[4] *Ibid.*, pp. x-xi.

a reluctant Yamasaki to alter his literally narrow vision for the buildings'
exterior during the latter stages of the design phase. In so doing, he
begrudgingly agreed to widen and elongate the windows on the 107th
floors of each tower to accommodate eventual restaurant and observation
spaces.[5]

Armed with a $17 million budget, Baum divided the 107th floor
Windows on the World complex of the North Tower into five sub-venues,
including "The Restaurant" (which seated 300 guests); "The City Lights
Bar"; the "Hors D'Oeuvrerie"; "The Cellar in the Sky" (which afforded
thirty-six guests with the opportunity to enjoy a seven-course, five-wine
meal in a working wine cellar); and a series of private banquet rooms.[6]
Understanding intuitively that rooftop restaurants were seen as second-tier
food establishments, Baum hired the best talent available, including the
renowned James Beard and Jacques Pépin to develop the menus. In so
doing, Baum had taken every precaution to avoid branding Windows on
the World as yet another New York City tourist trap.

When Windows on the World opened its doors in April 1976, Baum's
vision was rewarded amply, with *New York Magazine* hailing his creation
as "The Most Spectacular Restaurant in the World." The cover article,
written by the vaunted Gael Greene, described Windows on the World as a
veritable "miracle," given that prior to the opening of the World Trade
Center few people ventured downtown for anything other than working
among the bulls and the bears—much less sticking around to eat dinner
after dark. Writing in the pages of the *New York Times*, celebrated chef
and food critic Mimi Sheraton greeted the new restaurant with a rave
review, observing that "few additions to the local scene have been so
outright an affirmation of confidence in New York City's future as
Windows on the World, the stunning and lavish restaurant atop the North
Tower."[7]

For most of its twenty-five year history, the glittering success of
Windows on the World continued unabated, save for the truck-bomb
terrorist attack in February 1993. The explosion would claim the life of
Wilfredo Mercado, a receiving clerk who was on basement level B-1,

---

[5] James Glantz and Eric Lipton, *City in the Sky: The Rise and Fall of the World
Trade Center* (New York: Times, 2003), pp. 114-5.
[6] Zraly, *op. cit.*, p. ix.
[7] Quoted in Glanz and Lipton, *op. cit.*, p. 221. The culinary glitz that the restaurant
enjoyed during its heyday is mirrored by an ongoing public fascination with the
fabled rooftop eatery. Retail sites such as eBay frequently offer auctions for such
memorabilia as Windows on the World menus, matchboxes, and advertising
paraphernalia.

surveying the latest deliveries for the restaurant.[8] Windows on the World shuttered its spectacular views for more than three years due to the ensuing smoke damage and concerns over the building's structural integrity. The bombing also left some 300 restaurateurs suddenly out of work, with the exception of Kevin Zraly, the complex's celebrated cellarmaster, who continued to conduct wine-tasting classes at various locations around the Trade Center.

After a $25 million facelift, the restaurant reopened in 1996, and everything had changed considerably—even the food, which went from Beard's *haute cuisine* to the "New American" tastes of Philippe Feret, and later, in its final heyday, Michael Lomonaco. The sleekness of the Greatest Bar on Earth replaced the intimacy of the City Lights Bar and the Hors d'Oeuvrerie. The Cellar in the Sky was dismantled, and a new eatery, Wild Blue, opened up in its cozy cocoon above the Statue of Liberty. Additional banquet and meeting spaces were added on the 106th floor, providing Windows with two full acres of space. Even the main dining room on the 107th floor was reconceived, affording visitors with more expansive views of the city's northeastern quadrants.[9] It was a long time in coming, of course. Lower Manhattan had changed many times over, while Windows had grown rather long in the tooth, hanging onto its brassy 1970s style long past its expiration date.

With Lomonaco at the helm, Windows on the World enjoyed its most impressive reviews yet, scoring impressive results with Zagat and the *New York Times* alike. Indeed, during its final three years in operation, Windows on the World was the highest-grossing restaurant in the United States, earning $37 million in 2000, including $5 million in wine sales alone.[10]

Windows on the World's great fortune came to a sudden close, of course, with the events of September 11th, 2001, when American Airlines Flight 11 crashed into the northern façade between the 93rd and 99th floors of 1 World Trade Center. For the staff and guests in Windows on the World, it proved to be a death-blow. The damage rendered all of the stairwells and elevators, which were clustered around the building's core, impassable above the 91st floor. Some 1,300 people were trapped within

---

[8] Jim Dwyer, David Kocieniewski, Deidre Murphy, and Peg Tyre, *Two Seconds under the World: Terror Comes to America—The Conspiracy behind the World Trade Center Bombing* (New York: Crown, 1994), pp. 18-20, 29-30.

[9] Zraly, *op. cit.*, pp. x, xiii.

[10] Howard G. Goldberg, "Windows on the World: The Wine Community's True North," *The Wine News* (October-November, 2001). Accessed July 30, 2013. www.thewinenews.com/oct-nov01/comment.html and *ibid*, xxiv.

or above the impact zone, including the doomed souls on the 106th and 107th floors in the restaurant complex. Their number consisted of seventy-nine employees, ninety-two visitors and guests, including the Bronx Builders crew revamping the wine cellar and the contingent from the Risk Waters Financial Technology Conference, and perhaps as many as two additional people whose whereabouts were unaccounted for in the official record.[11]

After the towers had crumbled to the ground, the real misery began for the survivors, who were forced to scour the city in desperate, mostly futile quests to locate their loved ones. In the case of the missing staffers from Windows on the World, Chef Michael Lomonaco and head waiter Fekkak Mamdouh hastily assembled teams to search for survivors in the hospitals and the city morgue. As the restaurant's shop steward with the Hotel and Restaurant Employees Union Local 100, Mamdouh engaged in a heartbreaking search for his missing colleagues. In the end, all he was left with was the realization of the terrible and ineffable loss of life in the complex.[12]

But for the living, the suffering would swell beyond the attacks themselves. The aftermath of September 11th left more than 300 Windows employees suddenly unemployed. Eventually, the owners of Windows opened a restaurant in Times Square, rehiring a number of staffers from their former restaurant in the sky yet rejecting applications from a host of immigrant workers, including Mamdouh. In order to protest what he perceived to be a grave injustice, Mamdouh, along with organizer Saru Jayaraman, founded the Restaurant Opportunities Center. Through their activism, the Restaurant Opportunities Center succeeded in winning sixteen additional positions at the new restaurant in Times Square. They also fought unfair hiring practices and discrimination in New York City's restaurant culture.[13]

---

[11] See Zraly, *op. cit.*, pp. iv-v, for a listing of the seventy-three employees working in Windows on the World on the morning of September 11, 2001, along with the seven additional victims associated with the renovation of the complex's wine cellar.

[12] Rinku Sen and Fekkak Mamdouh, *The Accidental American: Immigration and Citizenship in the Age of Globalization* (San Francisco, Cal.: Berrett-Koehle, 2008).

[13] Steven Greenhouse, "Windows on the World Workers Say Their Boss Didn't Do Enough," *New York Times*, June 4, 2002. Accessed July 30, 2013. www.nytimes.com/2002/06/04/-nyregion/windows-on-the-world-workers-say-their-boss-didn-t-do-enough.html?src=pm.

To commemorate the lives of his lost colleagues, Mamdouh spearheaded the establishment of Colors, a cooperatively-owned Manhattan restaurant whose staff-owners hailed from more than a dozen nations. Meanwhile, Mamdouh continued to work on behalf of the Restaurant Opportunities Center—protecting the rights and interests of immigrants and non-immigrants alike. As for Windows' vaunted chef, Lomonaco co-founded the Windows of Hope Family Relief Fund in an effort to generate support for the families of the restaurant and food service workers lost in the attacks.[14]

The literary world's attempts to respond to the new realities associated with post-9/11 culture have been, for the most part, uneven and predictably variable. In many ways, Beigbeder's novel concerns itself with fiction's larger inabilities to account for victims of mass traumas such as 9/11. For much of *Windows on the World*, Beigbeder interrogates his authorial capacity for capturing the victims' lives in a truly meaningful, much less accurate fashion. As the novelist admits at the outset, "You know how it ends: everybody dies."[15] Recognizing the manner in which the specter of 9/11 implicates and involves nearly everyone and everything in its orbit, Beigbeder deliberately structures his novel in a bipartite design. In so doing, he recounts the tragedy minute-by-minute from two discrete vantage points: the first being the table of a divorced father and his two, pre-teen sons enjoying breakfast at Windows on the World on the morning of September 11, 2001; the second being Beigbeder's own authorial perspective while eating breakfast one year later at the famed Le Ciel de Paris, located on the 56th floor of the Tour Montparnasse, the tallest building in Paris. Ensconced in Le Ciel de Paris, Beigbeder laments that "writing this hyperrealist novel is made more difficult by reality itself. Since September 11, 2001, reality has not only outstripped fiction, it's destroying it. It's impossible to write about this subject, and yet it is impossible to write about anything else. Nothing else touches us."[16] Overwhelmed by the earth-shattering events in Lower Manhattan, Beigbeder-as-author simply cannot steal himself away from what he sees as a writerly obligation to narrate the unknowable tragedy unfolding inside the North Tower on that fateful morning.

---

[14] Having met its original goals on behalf of the victims' families, the Windows of Hope Family Relief Fund intends to continue its fundraising efforts through 2022, when the youngest surviving family members will have reached their twenty-first birthdays. See www.windowsofhope2001.com for additional information about the charity's mission and practices.

[15] Beigbeder, *op. cit.*, p. 1.

[16] *Ibid.*, p. 8.

To this end, Beigbeder deploys forty-three year-old Carthew Yorston, the divorced Texas real estate agent breakfasting with his sons at Windows on the World, as his eyewitness to the tragedy unfolding in the restaurant complex in the sky. Yet in reflecting upon his sons' untimely loss and the terrible demise of the Twin Towers, he also ponders the numbing disarray of his own soulless life in our postmodern world of flash over substance: "In two hours I'll be dead," he tells us. "In a way, I am dead already."[17] Mirroring Yorston's inner spiritual struggle, Beigbeder himself, alighting from Le Ciel de Paris one year hence, comes to grips with his own squandered, misspent existence: "From the top of the Tour Montparnasse I can, if I try, make out the School of my Wasted Youth."[18]Beigbeder's self-implicating—and, in many instances, self-indulgent—revelations about his personal predilections and failures seem, at times, positively vulgar in light of the larger tragedy unfolding at the World Trade Center. In the novel's most boorish (and unlikely) moment, Beigbeder depicts a pair of stock traders—a Ralph Lauren-clad blonde and a Kenneth Cole-wearing master-of-the-universe—having sex on a conference table fewer than fifteen minutes before the North Tower is finally laid to its doom. "Death is better than Viagra," the man mutters as their "passions blaze" along with the rapidly encroaching inferno.[19]

Windows on the World succeeds, if only occasionally, thanks to Beigbeder's well-timed instances of ironic caprice. For example, when Yorston summons the maître d' after a Brazilian businessman lights up a cigar in the restaurant's cozy confines, the novelist shrewdly narrates the absurd whimsy that straddles the line between life and death. With a scant ten minutes remaining before American Airlines Flight 11 deals its death-blow to the North Tower, the businessman beats a hasty exit for the express elevator in order to finish his cigar on the street, ironically sparing him from the coming onslaught and "thereby proves that a cigar can save your life."[20] If for nothing else, Beigbeder's novel triumphs in its knowing reflection of the absurdity of trying to capture the intensity and enormity of the disaster unfolding inside the towers. Yet at the same time, Beigbeder's writerly self cannot eschew the necessity of making the attempt: "I truly don't know why I wrote this book," Beigbeder admits, "Perhaps because I couldn't see the point of speaking of anything else. What is there to write? The only interesting subjects are those that are taboo. We must write what is forbidden," he adds. "Show the invisible,

---

[17] *Ibid.*, p. 5.
[18] *Ibid.*, p. 43.
[19] *Ibid.*, p. 281.
[20] *Ibid.*, p. 26.

speak the unspeakable."[21] It is in such moments—and in spite of its brazenness—that Beigbeder's novel bears consideration among the annals of 9/11 literature. As Alain-Philippe Durand argues, "The problem and difficulty of narrating representations of extreme violence in the context and aftermath of a contemporary tragic event are at the center of Beigbeder's *Windows on the World*." Perhaps even more significantly, Durand continues, "It is through fiction that one can get an understanding of what happened throughout the hours of the ineffable."[22]

In contrast with Beigbeder's novel, Espada's poem "Alabanza: In Praise of Local 100" reveals the manner in which verse counterpoises fiction's shortcomings in narrating the tragedy of 9/11 through poetry's more allusive powers. Dedicated to "the 43 members of Hotel Employees and Restaurant Employees Local 100, working at the Windows on the World restaurant, who lost their lives in the attack on the World Trade Center," Espada's poem creates a memorial not only to the 9/11 victims, but also to the community-making power of unions as part of the essential fabric of American culture.[23] In so doing, Espada establishes a veritable prayer *in memoriam* for the multinational victims, including several undocumented workers, who perished that morning:

> Praise Manhattan from a hundred and seven flights up,
> like Atlantis glimpsed through the windows of an ancient aquarium.
> Praise the great windows where immigrants from the kitchen
> could squint and almost see their world, hear the chant of nations:
> *Ecuador, México, Republica Dominicana,*
> *Haiti, Yemen, Ghana, Bangladesh.*[24]

As the Spanish word for praise, *alabanza* signifies, through Espada's deliberate repetition of the phrase throughout the poem, as a unifying structure for the poet's homily to the workers' lost humanity and individual uniquenesses:

> *Alabanza.* Praise the cook with the shaven head
> and a tattoo on his shoulder that said *Oye,*
> a blue-eyed Puerto Rican with people from Fajardo,
> the harbor of pirates centuries ago.

---

[21] *Ibid.*, p. 295.

[22] Alain-Philippe Durand, "Beyond the Extreme: Frédéric Beigbeder's *Windows on the World*," in *Novels of the Contemporary Extreme*, edited by Alain-Philippe Durand and Naomi Mandel, (New York: Continuum, 2006), pp. 109-20, 118.

[23] Espada, *op. cit.*, p. 231.

[24] *Ibid.*

> Praise the lighthouse in Fajardo, candle
> glimmering white to worship the dark saint of the sea.
> *Alabanza.* Praise the cook's yellow Pirates cap
> worn in the name of Roberto Clemente, his plane
> that flamed into the ocean loaded with cans for Nicaragua,
> for all the mouths chewing the ash of earthquakes."[25]

Beguilingly nameless in their loss, the victims in Espada's poem have their uniqueness recaptured through the undeniability of their individual essences, made manifest in the poet's rendering of the tattooed cook and the "blue-eyed Puerto Rican."

But even more significantly than their shared status as unionized workers, the victims depicted in Espada's verse find their unification through the moving, aesthetic power of music as it mingles with the culture-bridging mechanism of the culinary arts: "*Alabanza,*" Espada writes. "Praise the kitchen radio, dial clicked / even before the dial on the oven, so that music and Spanish / rose before bread. Praise the bread. *Alabanza.*" As if to underscore further the poem's essential merging of music and food, Espada goes on to "praise the busboy's music, the *chime-chime* / of his dishes and silverware in the tub."[26] Espada's poem finds its final, unifying power in its narration much later, when it depicts the eventual military conflicts that arose from the vestiges of 9/11 and our desperate need, so often blurred by the auspices of religion and nationalism, to engender intercultural understanding:

> *Alabanza.* When the war began, from Manhattan to Kabul
> two constellations of smoke rose and drifted to each other,
> mingling in icy air, and one said with an Afghan tongue:
> *Teach me to dance. We have no music here.*
> and the other said with a Spanish tongue:
> *I will teach you. Music is all we have.*[27]

As Espada's poem so eloquently demonstrates, in the end we are left to grapple with the same inalienable problem that defies history: our abiding need to enjoy genuine interconnection in disparate worlds riven by the community-destroying politics of religion and otherness. As *The Progressive*'s "Spoken Word" editor Josh Healey astutely writes, "If the earth of Lower Manhattan where the Twin Towers stood before 9/11 is sacred ground, then all the people who died that day in those towers are

---

[25] *Ibid.*

[26] *Ibid.*

[27] *Ibid.*, p. 232.

sacred too. All the people—including the immigrant workers who kept all 100+ floors clean, safe, and operable. Should there be a mosque near Ground Zero? Sure, why not. But if we want to honor all those who made the towers what they were, there should also be a union hall."[28]

In the end, the non-fictive story of Windows on the World, as with so many of the narratives from that horrible day, has much to do with the whimsy of chance and happenstance. For Neil Levin, the Port Authority's newly minted Executive Director, breakfast in Wild Blue turned out to be a fatal moment of chance.[29] Yet for the banker friend who intended to join him that morning, having to take a return elevator to the North Tower's lobby turned out to be the difference between life and death. For the Lower Manhattan Cultural Council's Liz Thompson and her breakfast party, survival was made possible by a well-timed decision to board the restaurant's last departing elevator.[30] And then there is the awful precision associated with restaurateurs like waiter Jan Maciejewski who opted to work as substitutes for one another on that fateful day.[31] As with so many tragedies of an epochal nature, a dramatically different sort of honor would be accrued to the dead. Not surprisingly, Olender distinguished herself during the final hour of Windows' existence, repeatedly summoning emergency personnel on her cell phone and leading her stricken coworkers to congregate around the office complex on the western side of the 106th floor, where the smoke was less concentrated.[32]

The destruction of the restaurant would also produce the so-called "Falling Man," the mysterious jumper tumbling through the sky in Richard Drew's Associated Press photograph and later investigated in Henry Singer's documentary *9/11: The Falling Man* (2006). Was it pastry sous-chef Norberto Hernandez—or, more likely, audio-visual specialist Jonathan Briley—who would emerge as the iconic symbol for the September 11th attacks? As with so many of the tragic narratives emanating from that particular day, we may never truly know.

---

28 Josh Healy, "Martín Espada—'Alabanza: In Praise of Local 100,'" *The Progressive*, September 2010. Accessed July 30, 2013.
http://progressive.org/video092010.html.
29 *The New York Times'* "Portraits of Grief" series, as collected in *Portraits: 9/11/01*, 2nd ed., edited by Janny Scott and Howell Raines, (New York: Times, 2003), #338.
30 Jim Dwyer and Kevin Flynn, *102 Minutes: The Untold Story of the Fight to Survive inside the Twin Towers* (New York: Times, 2005), p. 12.
31 *Portraits: 9/11/01, #* 357.
32 Dwyer and Flynn, *op. cit.*, pp. 39, 52.

And then there are the stories of Juan Lafuente and Dr. Sneha Anne Philip, missing persons whose fates have never been definitively ascertained—only that their lives seemed to have simultaneously ended with the devastation at the World Trade Center. Lafuente seemingly vanished into thin air on September 11th, having commuted from his home in Poughkeepsie to New York, where the Cuban immigrant worked at Citibank some eight blocks from the World Trade Center. Lafuente's last recorded act was swiping his MetroCard at the subway turnstile in Grand Central Terminal at 8:06 a.m. He typically exited the subway at Wall Street, two blocks south of the World Trade Center. While his daughters liked to speculate that their father entered the towers in order to assist emergency personnel—after all, he was a fire marshal at Citibank—the only evidence that points to his sudden demise in the North Tower were his plans, shared with a Poughkeepsie deli owner, to have breakfast at the Risk Waters Technology Conference. "It was a free breakfast," his wife Colette, the Mayor of Poughkeepsie, later recalled. "And Juan, you know, if there was an opportunity for a good breakfast at a great place and the price was right, he would go."[33]

If anything, Philip's disappearance is even more vexing and mysterious. An Indian-American physician and Battery Park City resident, Philip's last recorded act was purchasing household goods at Century 21 on September 10th. Her image is captured on the store's surveillance cameras. That evening, Philip's husband Ron Lieberman returned home to an empty apartment, assuming that his wife was out late or perhaps spending the night with a friend. As fate would have it, neither possibility would ever be confirmed. Mounting personal problems—including an incident at work that briefly landed Philip in jail—prompted a private investigator to conclude that she may have exploited the tragedy to disappear and establish a new identity elsewhere. Yet as with Lafuente, family members felt that Philip rushed into the burning towers in order to provide emergency assistance. In truth, her mother may have learned the actual nature of her daughter's fate. During an online chat the day before the attacks, Philip remarked that she intended to visit the Windows on the World complex, where a friend planned to be married the following spring.[34]

---

[33] Anemona Hartocollis, "9/11, a Man Went to Work: His Fate Is a Mystery," *New York Times,* May 9, 2002. Accessed July 30, 2013.
www.nytimes.com/2002/05/09/nyregion/9-11-a-man-went-to-work-his-fate-is-a-mystery.html.
[34] Mark Fass, "Last Seen on September 10th," *New York Magazine,* June 18, 2006. Accessed July 30, 2013. http://nymag.com/news/features/17336/.

Both Lafuente and Philip were eventually added to the victims list and their names inscribed in bronze on the National September 11 Memorial. Unfortunately, the same cannot be said for a trio of restaurant employees whose identities, given their undocumented immigrant status, have never officially been ascertained. They include Nana Akwasi Minkah, a banquet server; Arturo Alva Moreno; and Victor A. Martinez Pastrana, a dishwasher. Of the three, Moreno's case is particularly troubling, given that his family back in Mexico allegedly continues to seek answers regarding his sudden disappearance, which was coincident with 9/11. When questioned about Minkah, Moreno, and Pastrana's omission from the bronze plaques, an official from the National 9/11 Memorial and Museum at the World Trade Center Foundation noted that "the memorial will include the names of the 2,982 victims of the 9/11 attacks and the February 26, 1993, bombing, as confirmed by the victims' next-of-kin or other official agencies. However, although the heart of our mission is the commemoration of the lives that were lost, the 9/11 Memorial does not make individual determinations as to who is considered to be a 9/11 victim. The New York City Office of Chief Medical Examiner is the determining authority on 9/11 deaths from the World Trade Center and vicinity."[35]

This turn of events is hardly surprising, given the ongoing state of affairs involving the remaining DNA evidence, which is stored in a makeshift repository on FDR Drive. Walk-in storage units contain nearly 14,000 air-dried and vacuum-sealed human remains from the ruins of the World Trade Center. Remarkably, DNA tests have failed to identify some 9,000 remains, adding yet more layers of mystery to the fateful events of September 2001.[36] Eventually, the remains are scheduled to be relocated from their temporary location on the city's east side to a storage repository in the National September 11 Memorial and Museum. The medical examiner's office will continue to maintain custody of the remains, affording it the opportunity to conduct additional testing as future scientific

---

[35] From the author's May 2011 correspondence with Kai Twanmoh of the National September 11 Memorial and Museum. In addition, the victims' names featured on the memorial can be accessed through the museum's online searchable database located and accessed on July 30, 2013 at http://names.911memorial.org/#lang=en_US&page=search.

[36] For additional discussion regarding the complexities associated with the attack's resultant DNA evidence, see Robert C. Shaler, *Who They Were: Inside the World Trade Center DNA Story: The Unprecedented Effort to Identify the Missing* (New York: Free Press, 2005).

advances allow.[37] But for now, it is one more piece of the puzzle—however tangentially—involving the last hours of Windows on the World.

As with the vicissitudes of real life, the restaurant's coterie of waiters and staff continue to exist at the margins of narrative—nonfictive, fictive, poetic, or otherwise. Indeed, as Beigbeder himself remarks, "The only way to know what took place in the restaurant on the 107th Floor of the North Tower, World Trade Center on September 11th, 2001 is to invent it."[38] Besides Olender's recorded emergency telephone calls, the single surviving shred of evidence from the restaurant complex is a photograph of conference attendees and Bloomberg L.P. employees Peter Alderman and William Kelly. It is an oddly-placed revenant, to be sure, emerging, as it does, from a chance photograph at one of the kiosks at the Risk Waters Technology Conference on the 106th floor.[39] The photographer exited the building before the first plane struck, thus enshrining the photograph, along with a few pictures of firemen traversing the stairwells, as one of the scant few glimpses inside the towers that morning.[40] But even still, the most mind-numbing aspect of that terrible day squarely belongs to the survivors, who lost their loved ones due to the simple fact that they woke up that morning, rolled out of bed, and trundled off to work.

---

[37] Dan Barry, "A Repository for Remains of the Dead," *New York Times*, September 4, 2011. Accessed July 30, 2013.
www.nytimes.com/2011/09/04/us/sept-11-reckoning/dna.html?_r=1&hp.

[38] Beigbeder, *op. cit.*, p. 306.

[39] Dwyer and Flynn, *op. cit.*, p. 12.

[40] In addition to the surviving photograph of the Bloomberg L.P. employees, scant few pictures exist from inside the Twin Towers on the morning of September 11th. The remaining photographic evidence exists in Jules and Gédéon Naudet's documentary *9/11*, which features images from inside the lobby of the North Tower during the fire-rescue operation, and the work of amateur photographer John Labriola, whose work was later collected in John Labriola, *Walking Forward, Looking Back: Lessons from the World Trade Center—A Survivor's Story* (Irvington, N.Y.: Hylas, 2003).

CHAPTER SIX

"REFLECTING ABSENCE": THE MEMORIALIZATION OF 9/11

INGA MEIER

According to a recent *NJ.com* article, "The [World Trade Center] site now draws about 10,000 visitors a day, which would put it on pace to match or exceed the 3.5 million who visit the Statue of Liberty and Empire State Building annually."[1] In a city that hosted 50 million tourists in 2011[2], the National 9/11 Memorial and Museum represents its most visited tourist attraction, included as a prime destination on numerous 9/11 tours now offered throughout New York.

Like so many sites of memorialization, "Ground Zero"[3] is faced with the challenge of representing the unrepresentable while attempting to

---

[1] The Associated Press, "NYC 9/11 Memorial Popular Among Tourists," *NJ.com*, December 29, 2011. Accessed March March 22, 2012. http://www.nj.com/news/index.ssf/2011/12/nyc_911_memorial_popular_among.html.

[2] Thomson Reuters, "New York Set for Record 50 Million Tourists," December 20, 2011. March 22, 2012. http://www.reuters.com/article/2011/12/20/us-travel-newyork-idUSTRE7BJ1WQ20111220.

[3] The term "Ground Zero" is itself a contested one. According to the OED, "Ground Zero" refers to "that part of the ground situated immediately under an exploding bomb, especially an atomic one." First used in the context of the Manhattan Project and the subsequent bombings of Hiroshima and Nagasaki in 1945, the term has since been used in the context of other disasters and, more recently, the attacks on the World Trade Center on September 11, 2001. The first known use of the term in the context of 9/11 was by Mark Walsh, a Fox News Freelancer, who, in an interview with Rick Leventhal, stated, "Those guys [from the 7th Precinct of the FDNY] were all right there at Ground Zero when those things went down." Leventhal picked up the term less than two minutes later, setting up an interview with another eyewitness, stating, "[S]ome of those people—they haven't recovered them yet and that's a big issue right now, trying to get the rescue workers and the emergency crews to the building. There were police

reconcile a multitude of divergent perspectives—torn between its function(s) as memorial architecture on the one hand and the interests of developers, the business community, victims' families, survivors, artists, news media, and politicians on the other. This essay will examine to what extent the memorial and museum at the former site of the World Trade Center have or have not succeeded in negotiating these competing interests as construction has progressed over the last decade. To what degree does "Ground Zero" elucidate the events it seeks to memorialize and represent? How is absence represented? How does the site negotiate its efforts to revitalize Lower Manhattan while simultaneously marking a violent act?

In my effort to formulate a framework for addressing these questions within a historiographical context of memorialization, I am informed by geographer Kenneth E. Foote's *Shadowed Ground: America's Landscapes of Violence and Tragedy*, in which he posits four distinct categories of memorialization: sanctification, obliteration, designation, and rectification:

> Sanctification occurs when events are seen to hold some lasting positive meaning that people wish to remember—a lesson in heroism or perhaps a sacrifice for community. A memorial or monument is the result. Obliteration results from particularly shameful events people would prefer to forget—for example a mass murder or gangster killing. As a consequence, all evidence is destroyed or effaced. Designation and rectification fall between these extremes. Designation, or the marking of a site, simply denotes that something 'important' has happened there. Rectification involves removing the signs of violence and tragedy and returning a site to use, implying no positive or lasting meaning.[4]

---

officers there and rescue crew there, when this was all happening, and they were all at Ground Zero when it all went down." Peter Jennings on ABC, Jim Axelrod on CBS, and Rehema Ellis on NBC all used the term later that day. Since then, the term "Ground Zero" has increasingly come to refer to the site itself. Needless to say, the re-appropriation of a term originally used to describe an act of violence committed by the United States in 1945 to describe an act of violence committed against the United States in 2001 is highly problematic, particularly when applied by a news corporation as ideologically biased as Fox News. While I prefer to describe the sixteen acres of the former World Trade Center using the more neutral term "the site," to avoid repetition and to acknowledge that the site is more commonly referred to as "Ground Zero," I will sometimes use the latter term. However, because the term is itself a constructed one, when using it, I will frame it in quotation marks.

[4] Kenneth E. Foote, *Shadowed Ground: America's Landscapes of Violence and Tragedy* (Austin: University of Texas Press, 2003), p. 9.

Borrowing from Foote's categories, I will argue that the sixteen-acre site of the former World Trade Center constitutes a tenuous union between sanctification and rectification.

In this regard then, the site is unique. In Shanksville, Pennsylvania, the crash site of United Airlines 93, the land where the memorial is located is largely rural, much of it located at a former stone quarry. While the land had to be acquired by the federal government before construction of the memorial could begin, no previously existing structures needed to be rebuilt. No "rectification" in Foote's sense was therefore necessary. The Flight 93 Memorial may thus be understood as a purely "sanctified" site. By contrast, American Airlines Flight 177 caused damage to a significant portion of the Pentagon on 9/11. Because the Pentagon was already undergoing renovations at the time of the crash, the task of rebuilding fell on contractors already working on the building, allowing the process to be completed within a year. Though a small memorial and chapel are located within the Pentagon at the site of impact and are accessible to the public during guided tours, the primary public memorial is located adjacent to the building, where much of the wreckage was located and where the victims were brought in the immediate aftermath. The memorial is thus separate from the building itself. While the Pentagon itself may therefore be understood as "rectified," the memorial, located on former parking and lawn space, is "sanctified."

By contrast, the sixteen-acre site of the former World Trade Center must function in both regards simultaneously, attempting to commemorate the lives lost through a memorial and museum while seeking to reclaim the site's functionality and usability through numerous office towers, a cultural center, and a transportation hub. As Daniel Libeskind, the site's master planner, states, "It's the balance between the memory of what happened and also using the opportunity to create a twenty-first century New York."[5] The site must then, by necessity, straddle the line between "sanctification" and "rectification."

---

[5] "Reclaiming the Skyline: Part 1," *Rising: Rebuilding Ground Zero*, written by Jessica Lyne de Ve and Kate Cohen, directed by David Nutter, Discovery Channel. August 25, 2011.

Fig. 6.1: "Ground Zero", 2007

Fig. 6.2 "Ground Zero", 2011

Boundaries and Markers

According to Foote, sanctified sites generally feature five characteristics. The first of these is that "they are often clearly bounded from the surrounding environment and marked with great specificity as to what happened where."[6] Following the attacks on the Twin Towers and their subsequent collapse, the site, along with much of Lower Manhattan, was closed off to pedestrians not involved with the rescue efforts. In fact, most of Lower Manhattan below Canal Street was closed off and evacuated, with some residents not able to return to their homes for a year.[7] Further, all bridges and tunnels into or out of Manhattan were closed off to non-emergency vehicular traffic into the following day.[8] Virtually all of these closures were due to security and safety concerns.

Since then, access to the site has remained heavily restricted. In the fall of 2011, two viewing platforms were erected—one, for victims' relatives, at "Ground Zero" itself and another, nearby, for additional visitors. These platforms soon became living memorials in their own right, with visitors frequently leaving mementos at the site. One organization, ArtAID, lined the platforms with a "wall of remembrance" listing the victims' names.[9] Following the recovery effort, this wall was dismantled and moved to the Union Square subway station, where it was dedicated on Memorial Day 2005.

As of August 2013, the former site of "Ground Zero" remains surrounded by a twelve-foot construction fence, which is further enhanced by barbed wire. The site's interior is only visible from above—either from a footbridge crossing the adjacent West Street or from surrounding buildings. Access to the memorial requires a visitor's pass, which must be reserved in advance. Upon arrival, visitors gain access via a clearly marked entrance. After entering, visitors must further pass through a separate building, where they pass through metal detectors and have their bags scanned. Before finally gaining access to the site, visitors must then

---

[6] Foote, *op. cit.*, p. 9.
[7] Alison Blais and Lynn Rasic, *A Place of Remembrance: Official Book of the National September 11 Memorial* (Washington, D.C.: National Geographic Society, 2011), p. 79.
[8] Closures of this magnitude in response to violent events are rare. The closest historical corollary in the United States likely occurred at the assassination of President Abraham Lincoln on Good Friday, April 14, 1865. Following the assassination, Secretary of War Edward Stanton ordered numerous bridges and roads in and around Washington, D.C., closed.
[9] Blais and Rasic, *op. cit.*, p. 97.

walk roughly half the site's sixteen-acre perimeter and show their pass at numerous checkpoints. It remains unclear to what degree these various measures might be altered once, in addition to other structures being built on the site, the museum and One World Trade Center are completed. However, even after construction upon the site is completed, it will likely take some time before the sutures connecting these sixteen acres to the surrounding cityscape are no longer visible.

Longevity

The second characteristic noted by Foote is that "sanctified sites are usually carefully maintained for long periods of time—decades, generations, and centuries"—a notion mirrored in the rhetoric regarding the memorial and museum.[10] The mission statement for the 9/11 Memorial thus reads in part, "May the lives remembered, the deeds recognized, and the spirit reawakened be eternal beacons, which reaffirm respect for life, strengthen our resolve to preserve freedom, and inspire an end to hatred, ignorance and intolerance."[11] The museum, similarly, seeks to "educate for a better future."[12] Consequently, efforts are underway to ensure the sustainability of the site on two levels.

Firstly, the heightened security measures both around the site (as partially described above) and in the engineering of One World Trade Center are designed to prevent and minimize the impact of potential future terrorist attacks. Due to the "target attractiveness" of the site, One World Trade Center is raised on a 200-ft. protective pedestal and its core surrounded by blast walls made of steel and concrete. Designed by architect David Childs, the building is both the "tallest and strongest" in the history of the United States.[13]

Secondly, both the memorial and the museum pursue aggressive fundraising efforts to ensure not only the structures' construction but also the memorial's sustainability. While visitor passes are free, for example, the site currently features two gift shops—one at the 9/11 Memorial Preview site on Vesey Street and another on West Street at the 9/11 Memorial Visitor Center. The 9/11 Memorial website also offers numerous possibilities for donations: charter memberships and the

---

[10] Foote, *op. cit.*, p. 9.
[11] 9/11 Memorial, "The Memorial Mission," *9/11memorial.org*. Accessed May 31, 2012. http://www.911memorial.org/
[12] 9/11 Memorial, "The Memorial Museum Mission," *9/11memorial.org*. Accessed May 31, 2012. http://www.911memorial.org/message-museum-director.
[13] "Reclaiming the Skyline: Part 1."

sponsorship of cobblestones, glades, and pavers adorning the memorial plaza. Even coins tossed at the roots of the survivor tree are collected as donations to the site.[14] On a larger scale, Signs of Support, a business support initiative, seeks financial aid from local and national businesses. These private fundraising efforts are heavily bolstered by a $250 million contribution from the Lower Manhattan Development Corp (LMDC) for the National 9/11 Memorial and Museum, $80 million from the State of New York for the National 9/11 Museum pavilion, and additional funds from the Port Authority of New York and New Jersey.[15]

The Private and the Public

The third characteristic mentioned by Foote is "a change of ownership, often a transfer from private to public stewardship."[16] In this regard, S. 1537, a bill introduced by Senator Daniel K. Inouye (Hawaii–D) on September 9, 2011, proposed transferring the title of the National 9/11 Memorial and Museum to the National Park Service and providing $20 million of the estimated $60 million dollars required annually to maintain the memorial and run the museum.[17] In September 2002, the Flight 93 National Memorial Act (Public Law 107-226, 116 Stat. 1345) officially transferred ownership of the Flight 93 crash site and designated the memorial to be administered by the National Park Service. Though this process was not without complications in Shanksville, the fact that an analogous bill was not proposed for the former World Trade Center until recently is likely due to the additional complexities at the site of the latter.[18]

---

[14] "Survivor Tree" refers to a pear tree located at the site of the former Twin Towers, which survived the buildings' collapse. The tree, now four times taller than at the time of the attacks, and thereby significantly taller than the newly planted trees in the memorial plaza, has grown to over thirty feet and continues to thrive. The term is possibly borrowed from the Oklahoma City National Memorial, which similarly holds a "survivor tree", an American elm.

[15] 9/11 Memorial, "Public-Private Partnership," *9/11memorial.org*. Accessed May 31, 2012. http://www.911memorial.org/public-private-partnership.

[16] Foote, *op. cit.*, p. 9.

[17] Patrick McGeehan, "Bill Would Provide Federal Funds for 9/11 Memorial," *New York Times on the Web*, September 13, 2011. Accessed May 20, 2012. http://cityroom.blogs.nytimes.com/2011/09/13/bill-would-provide-federal-funds-for-911-memorial/.

[18] Of the 2,977 reported fatalities on 9/11, all but 224 died at the sixteen-acre World Trade Center site—in the planes, on the ground, or in the towers. Consequently, the cleanup and recovery effort alone lasted until May 2002.

Ritual Commemoration

"Fourth," Foote states, "sanctified sites frequently attract continued ritual commemoration, such as annual memorial services or pilgrimage."[19] The first memorial event held at the site occurred on October 28, 2001, shortly after the structurally-compromised slurry wall had been fortified. While individual services had been held as victims' bodies were recovered, this marked the first instance of a large-scale, public memorial service at the site. At the time, the cleanup and recovery efforts were still underway and were temporarily halted for the service. 4,167 people were still considered "missing," with 506 bodies recovered and 454 identified.[20] Family members, many of whom attended the site for the first time following the attacks, received urns containing ashes from the rubble. Both Mayor Rudy Giuliani and Governor George Pataki were in attendance, with speeches by religious leaders from various faiths: Catholic, Jewish, Protestant, and Muslim.[21]

The six-month anniversary of the attacks was marked by "Tribute in Light," an art installation designed by architects John Bennett and Gustavo Bonevardi of PROUN Space Studio, artists Julian LaVerdiere and Paul Myoda, architect Richard Nash Gould, and lighting designer Paul Marantz. Composed of eighty-eight light fixtures, forming two shafts of light in the approximate location where the towers once stood, "Tribute in Light" could be seen from up to sixty miles away on clear nights. Despite funding challenges, the art installation has shone on every annual anniversary since the attacks.

Annual memorial services have been held at the site since 2001. The names of the victims are read aloud, with both politicians and family members in attendance. According to Public Law 107-89, the day has been designated "Patriot Day." Additionally, on May 5, 2011, three days after the shooting and death of Osama Bin Laden, President Obama laid a

---

Litigation between Larry Silverstein, the leaseholder of buildings 1, 2, 4, and 5, the Port Authority of New York and New Jersey (arguably the "owner" of the sixteen acres) and various insurance companies further delayed progress for a number of years.

[19] Foote, *op. cit.*, p. 9.

[20] CNN, "Memorial service set for Ground Zero," *CNN.com/U.S,* October 28, 2001. Accessed May 20, 2012.
http://edition.cnn.com/2001/US/10/28/rec.giuliani.memorial/index.html.

[21] Jim Zarroli, "Memorial Service at Ground Zero," *npr.org,* October 28, 2001. Accessed May 20, 2012.
http://www.npr.org/templates/story/story.php?storyId=1132260.

wreath at the foot of the survivor tree after meeting with firefighters, police, and family members. The visit marked the president's first visit since assuming office.

Fig. 6.3 Tribute in Light, 2009

Additional Memorials

The fifth characteristic outlined by Foote is that "sanctified sites often attract additional and sometimes even unrelated monuments and memorials through a process of accretion. That is, once sanctified, these sites seem to act as foci for other commemorative efforts."[22] In the days and weeks that followed 9/11, a number of makeshift memorials sprang up across New York. Most immediately, candles appeared on doorsteps. Similarly, American flags were mounted on houses, storefronts, and car antennae as an expression of solidarity.

Ironically, one of the more lasting and iconic acts of memorialization was never intended as such, but rather served a more practical function. Though now regarded as a footnote in the attacks, the destruction of the 360 foot-high antenna on the roof of the North Tower was one of the

---

[22] Foote, *op. cit.*, p. 9.

significant consequences of the collapse of the towers, affecting television coverage in the area. Further, cell phone networks became overloaded because of calls between those immediately affected and their loved ones.

Unable to obtain information from other resources, people started crafting handmade "missing" signs, searching for their loved ones. In the days immediately after the attacks, the term "missing" was the one most commonly applied to those lost. With reports of cell phone signals coming from under the wreckage,[23] hospitals calling for blood donations in expectation of the wounded (who, a few exceptions notwithstanding, never materialized), and occasional reports in the following days of people being recovered (twenty in all),[24] the use of the term "missing" did not indicate a state of denial as much as it did a well-founded sense of hope.

But gradually that hope faded, as did the "missing" signs. However, the signs have acquired a new meaning as memorials over time, standing in for the deceased themselves. The Museum of the City of New York has taken great pains to preserve a temporary construction fence at Bellevue Hospital, which "became an icon of the city's response to the tragedy. Covered with posters of the missing, it also included statements of support from New Yorkers and people around the country."[25] Originally presented as part of a one-week exhibition from September 1, 2006 to September 7,

---

[23] To date, none of these rumors are known to have been verified.

[24] Two Port Authority officers, John McLoughlin and William Jimeno, were rescued from rubble surrounding a freight elevator. Their story is told by Oliver Stone in his 2006 *World Trade Center*, a film which contains numerous factual errors. Pasquale Buzzelli, a structural engineer for the Port Authority, and Genelle Guzman, a secretary, were rescued from the remains of the B-Stairwell of the North Tower. Other members of their group, further behind, did not survive. Most survivors were rescued from a different section of the same stairwell, sometimes referred to as the "miracle" stairwell: Firefighters Billy Butler, Tommy Falco, Jay Jonas, Michael Meldrum, Sal D'Agastino, and Matt Komorowski of Ladder Company 6; Firefighter Mickey Kross of Engine Company 16, Firefighters Jim McGlynn, Rob Bacon, Jeff Coniglio, and Jim Efthimiaddes of Engine Company 39; Port Authority Police Officer Dave Lim; Battalion Chief Rich Picciotto of the 11th Battalion; and civilian Josephine Harris. Additionally, Tom Canavan, an employee of First Union Bank, managed to free himself. A further, unidentified man, ahead of Canavan on the stairwell they were descending crawled out as well. The number of survivors is sometimes listed as eighteen or nineteen, depending on the inclusion or not of the unidentified man.

[25] Museum of the City of New York, "Past Exhibitions: September 11, 2001: The Bellevue Wall of Prayer," *mcny.org* 2012. Accessed May 20, 2012. http://www.mcny.org/exhibitions/past/453.html.

2006, an eighty-foot section of the wall has now become part of the museum's permanent archive and is lent out to various institutions.

Fig. 6.4 "Missing" signs at the 9/11 Tribute Center, 2007

Fig. 6.5 "Missing" Sign at the 9/11 Tribute Center, 2007

Fig. 6.6 St. Paul's Chapel, 2011

Fig. 6.7 St. Paul's Chapel, 2011

The signs were also featured prominently at the Tribute WTC 9/11 Visitor Center, a 6,000 ft. exhibit presented by the September 11th Families Association, which was meant to function as a temporary museum until the opening of the official memorial in 2009.[26] Here, the signs served simultaneously as a culmination of the artifacts, images, and recordings of events immediately following 9/11 and as artistic objects of juxtaposition. The center consists of two levels. The upper, street level is divided into a series of four small galleries, labeled in order "World Trade Center: Community Remembered", "Passage Through Time: September 11th", "Aftermath: Rescue and Recovery", and "Tribute." A fifth gallery, "Voices of Hope" is located on the lower level. In sequence, the galleries create a narrative of loss and hope, guiding visitors through the history of the World Trade Center from its inception through the 1993 and 2001 attacks, and finally to a possibility of hope.

St. Paul's Chapel, located on Trinity Place adjacent to the World Trade Center, likewise houses a museum. Often referred to as the "little chapel that stood," St. Paul's was undamaged by the towers' collapse and housed rescue and recovery workers in the attacks' aftermath until May 2002. There, workers could find food and shelter while podiatrists, massage therapists, chiropractors, and musicians offered their services. The chapel features an exhibit chronicling this period as well as a display of postcards, photos, drawings and numerous other items sent to the workers and the chapel.

Memorials can also be found throughout the United States on a local level, honoring victims who were born or lived in these locales. To aid this effort, roughly 2,000 pieces of World Trade Center steel were made available by the City of New York and the Port Authority of New York and New Jersey.[27] Often, these memorials integrate steel from the towers and/or from the sites in Shanksville and Washington D.C. The Maryland 9/11 Memorial in front of the Baltimore Trade Center serves as a typical example. Dedicated by Governor Martin O'Malley on Sept. 11, 2011, the memorial "honors the people of Maryland who were lost" and consists of steel from the New York World Trade Center and limestone from the Pentagon. Further, black granite reflects the heroism of the passengers and crew of United Flight 93.

---

[26] David W. Dunlap, "Tribute center, an 'Interim Destination' Memorial, Gets Set to Open," *New York Times on the Web*, September 6, 2006. Accessed May 20, 2012. http://query.nytimes.com/gst/fullpage.html?res=9F05EFD91631F935A3575AC0A9609C8B63.

[27] Blais and Rasic, *op. cit.*, p. 113.

Fig. 6.8 Maryland 9/11 Memorial, 2011: L-R: Limestone from the Pentagon with black granite and white marble with dedication.

Fig. 6.9 Maryland 9/11 Memorial, 2011: Steel from the World Trade

In addition to these types of memorials, seven and a half tons of steel from the World Trade Center were also repurposed to form the bow of the aircraft carrier U.S.S. New York. According to Cmdr. Quentin King, the on-site Navy program manager representative,

> The significance of where the WTC steel is located on the 684-foot-long ship symbolizes the strength and resiliency of the citizens of New York as it sails forward around the world. It sends a message of America becoming stronger as a result, coming together as a country and ready to move forward as we make our way through the world.[28]

The ship was christened on March 1, 2008 in Avondale, Louisiana, and commissioned on November 7, 2009 at the Intrepid Air Museum in Manhattan. At the christening, Deputy Secretary of Defense Gordon England stated,

> On the day the towers fell...all Americans were New Yorkers. Some people still question why terrorists killed 3,000 people of 60 nationalities that day. I've concluded that they killed 3,000 because they did not know how to kill 30,000, 300,000 or 3 million, but they would have if they could have...and they are still trying. This is not a war of our choosing. This is not a war we can ignore. This is not a war that will end if we walk away from the battlefield. This fight, brought to our shores that day, is a struggle that will require strong, steady and sustained leadership with the enduring need for a strong military...and ships like NEW YORK.[29]

Finally, numerous museums in New York and Washington, D.C., hold archives related to 9/11, displaying them in permanent and temporary exhibits. The New York City Fire Museum has dedicated a significant portion of its space to two adjoining 9/11 memorial rooms. According to the museum's publicity, these rooms feature "cases displaying tools used and items recovered from the Ground Zero recovery effort; a video and interactive computer station where visitors can digitally browse profiles and photographs of the fallen, newspaper coverage of the attacks, and images of nationwide tributes to the FDNY; and a wall-size timeline chronicling that day's tragic events."[30] One of the rooms also houses the

---

[28] USS New York LPD-21, "Construction," *ussnewyork.com*, 2011. Accessed May 20, 2012. www.ussnewyork.com/ussny_construction.html.

[29] USS New York LPD-21. "Christening," *ussnewyork.com*, 2011. Accessed May 20. 2013. http://www.ussnewyork.com/ussny_christening.html.

[30] New York City Fire Museum. 2012. "9/11 Memorial Room," *nycfiremuseum.org* 2012. Accessed May 20, 2012. http://www.nycfiremuseum.org/gallery_page.cfm?alias=permanent-ex-911.

coat and helmet of Father Mychal Judge, the chaplain of the FDNY, and
the first certified casualty of the attacks.[31]

Fig. 6.10 NYC Fire Museum: The Coat and Helmet of Father Judge, 2011

The New-York Historical Society displays some of its 9/11 artifacts in
the Henry Luce III Center for the Study of American Culture. The
collection houses thousands of objects, many of which are also displayed
during special exhibitions, such as "Remembering 9/11" which ran from
September 8, 2011 to February 4, 2012 in commemoration of the tenth
anniversary of the attacks. The New York State Museum in Albany also
houses its own collection, entitled "Rescue, Recovery, Response."
"Rescue" addresses the first twenty-four hours following the attacks;
"Recovery" contains objects collected in the hours and days following the
attacks; and "Response" contains numerous memorials and memorial
objects. Items in the collection include a piece of fuselage, a steel beam

---

[31] Though other victims died prior to Judge, his was the first body recovered and
catalogued by the coroner as "victim 0001." Numerous memorials have been
erected to Judge specifically and calls have been made to canonize him.

with an embedded airplane piece, a fire truck and a section of fence from Liberty Street and Broadway covered with memorial objects.

Fig. 6.11 NYC Fire Museum: 9/11 Memorial, 2011

Lastly, the National Museum of American History in Washington, D.C., holds a vast collection of materials related to 9/11. A small portion of these items is displayed in the museum's ongoing "The Price of Freedom: Americans at War" exhibit. Like the New-York Historical Society, the Smithsonian features additional objects in special exhibitions, the most recent being "September 11: Remembrance and Reflection" from September 3, 2011 to September 11, 2011. Similarly to the New York State Museum in Albany, the holdings are categorized as rescue, recovery, and response. According to the Smithsonian, the collection is "a work in progress. It embodies the best efforts of staff across the National Museum of American History to document and preserve a wide range of stories about September 11. Each object, as material evidence of the attacks and their immediate aftermath, is a piece of a large and complex story. The collections will grow as we gain historical perspective and a greater understanding of the events of September 11."[32]

[32] Smithsonian Institute, "September 11: Bearing Witness to History: The Collection," *americanhistory.si.edu*, September 29, 2011. Accessed May 20, 2012. http://americanhistory.si.edu/september11/collection/about.asp.

Absence

In addition to Foote's description of "sanctification," I would like to add two additional characteristics more broadly consistent with commemorative efforts, not just with "sanctification." The first of these is that memorials generally tend to wrestle with and engage in some notion of absence. While One World Trade Center,[33] the WTC Transportation Hub, and the Performing Arts Center[34] are all designed to look towards the future, the National 9/11 Museum and Memorial are deeply rooted in the site's violent past. The most prominent features of the latter are undoubtedly the footprints of the former Twin Towers, which constitute the heart of the Memorial. Like all sites of 9/11 memorialization, "Ground Zero" faces with the challenge of representing what cannot be represented, namely, a loss of life framed as an absence. At all three 9/11 sites—the Pentagon, the World Trade Center and Shanksville—the majority of human remains are so small or damaged that they can only be identified through the latest DNA technology, or in some cases cannot be identified at all. The term "vaporized", which would sound more familiar in a science fiction context, has been applied repeatedly to the damage inflicted by the intensity of the fires and explosions. Thus, the challenge in memorializing the lives lost is a difficult one.

To assist in determining the design of the memorial, members of the Lower Manhattan Development Corporation (LMDC) and its advisory councils visited a number of prominent memorials in the fall of 2012: the Oklahoma City National Memorial, memorials in New York, the National Law Enforcement Officers Memorial, and the National Mall in Washington D.C.[35] While a number of lessons were learned in this process, the most important of these was the opportunities for creating dialogue about the design process that include as many voices as possible. In formulating guidelines to settle upon a design, the LMDC drew in particular on similar guidelines formulated by Jan Scruggs, a Vietnam

---

[33] While One World Trade Center will ultimately reach 1776 feet, 3 World Trade Center, part of Daniel Libeskind's envisioned "spiral" of buildings on the site, has been capped at seven stories, seventy-three less than planned due to a shortage of tenants.

[34] The future of the Performing Arts Center is highly questionable. As of 2012, roughly only $155 million had been secured of a needed $450 million to build the 1,000-seat theatre designed by Frank Gehry. Its only remaining prospective tenant, the Joyce Theater, a modern dance company, is rumored to be seeking an alternative space.

[35] Blais and Rasic, *op. cit.*, p. 188.

veteran and the president and founder of the Vietnam Veterans Memorial Fund. In 1979, Scruggs had developed the idea "to create a memorial to the three million men and women, who [had] served in the nation's longest and most controversial war to date."[36] Scrugg's arguably greatest innovation in the development of the memorial was to solicit designs through an anonymous, international competition, open to both professionals and amateurs. More than 1,400 proposals were submitted, making the competition to design the Vietnam Veterans Memorial the largest architectural design competition to date. Scruggs formulated three requirements: 1) The memorial had to contain all of the names of the dead or missing; 2) The memorial had to be harmonious with the site; and 3) The memorial had to be free of political statements.[37] The selected proposal, designed by architecture student Maya Lin, not only addressed all of these requirements but also stood out for its simplicity.

After September 11, 2001, the LMDC administered a similar competition to find the most suitable memorial, issuing the following guidelines:

> Remember and honor the thousands of innocent men, women, and children murdered by terrorists in the horrific attacks of February 26, 1993 and September 11, 2001.
>
> Respect this place made sacred through tragic loss.
>
> Recognize the endurance of those who survived, the courage of those who risked their lives to save others, and the compassion of all who supported us in our darkest hours.
>
> May the lives remembered, the deeds recognized, and the spirit reawakened be eternal beacons, which reaffirm respect for life, strengthen our resolve to preserve freedom, and inspire an end to hatred, ignorance and intolerance.[38]

The LMDC selected a design by Michael Arad (later enhanced by landscape architect Peter Walker) from over 5,000 submissions that incorporated all of these elements. Central to Arad's design were the "footprints" of the two towers in the form of "two large voids containing

---

[36]*Remembering Vietnam: The Wall at 25*, produced and written by Lynn Kessler, A Smithsonian Channel Production, 2007.

[37] *Ibid.*

[38] LMDC, *World Trade Center Site Memorial Competition Guidelines* (New York: 2003), p. 18.

recessed pools."[39] As evidenced in series of public forums regarding the site, a large number of victims' family members had felt it inappropriate to rebuild on "sacred ground." In addition to building around the footprints, the design also eventually included a repository below ground to house unidentified remains. However, the details of this repository have evolved over time. Originally conceived as a symbolic vessel—a tomb for the unknown—the repository has become far more complex:

> The underground vault…will house unidentified remains and be accessible only to staff of New York City's chief medical examiner's office, which will continue to attempt to identify the remains as technology improves.
>
> The space will be adjoined by a small private room for the exclusive use of victims' families, who will be able to see into the repository—a working laboratory as much as it is a tomb—through a window.
>
> The area will be sealed off from the memorial museum that will fill the rest of the mostly subterranean structure. Visitors will see only a wall bearing a quotation from Virgil's epic poem "Aeneid" wrought in steel salvaged from the fallen towers: "No day shall erase you from the memory of time."[40]

This area remains a contested space among victims' families, with its final reception, once it is built, still to be determined.

Naming the Dead

The second characteristic I would like to introduce is that memorials tend to engage in efforts to name the dead. Historically speaking, the practice of naming the dead constitutes a relatively recent phenomenon. As architecture and art historian Kirk Savage writes:

> After the U.S. Civil War, the practice of naming the dead on public monuments became commonplace, even as those monuments moved out of the cemetery and into the street and town square. […While] the soldier statues that often accompanied these monuments were generic. The names

---

[39] Michael Arad and Peter Walker, "World Trade Center Site Memorial Competition: Reflecting Absence," *wtcsitememorial.org,* 2002-2007. Accessed May 20, 2012. http://wtcsitememorial.org/fin7.html.
[40] Thomson Reuters, "Plan for 9/11 remains disturbs relatives of the dead," *msnbc.com*, March 9, 2012. Accessed May 20, 2012.
http://today.msnbc.msn.com/id/41741280/ns/today-entertainment/t/plan-remains-disturbs-relatives-dead/#.T9jUFu1-S20.

by contrast represented specific individuals and were supposed to keep their memory and their example alive long after all who knew them had passed away.[41]

The inscription of individual names became even more systematic after World War I and reached an artistic high point in Maya Lin's celebrated Vietnam Veterans Memorial in Washington, D.C., which remains the only comprehensive list in stone or metal of national war dead in the U.S.[42] Built in 1982 amidst significant controversy, the memorial's wall has since become a site of pilgrimage for veterans of the war in Vietnam, who come to pay their respects. At the wall, visitors touch the names of fallen comrades or family members, and create rubbings of the names, which are arrayed on a series of seventy black, granite panels. Together, these panels arranged along two sides that converge at an angle of 125°, pointing to the northeast corners of the Washington Monument and the Lincoln Memorial. The largest of these panels, reaching over ten feet, bears 137 lines of names, the smallest only one. The names are categorized only by year and whether the individual is confirmed either dead or missing.

The Oklahoma City National Memorial, commemorating the victims of the April 19, 1995 bombing of the Alfred P. Murrah Federal Building, is composed of 168 empty chairs that bear the names of the dead on a site located where the building once stood. Each chair is located in one of nine rows, symbolizing the floor on which the victim worked at the time of the bombing and further arranged according to the blast pattern. Smaller chairs represent children, while three unborn children killed that day are listed on the chairs of their mothers.

The names at the Pentagon memorial are arranged in a similar manner. Here, the names are engraved on wing-shaped benches, which are grouped in two ways. First, the benches are arranged by the birth year of the victim. Second, the direction of the bench indicates the location of the victim at the time of the impact of American Airlines Flight 77. The benches facing the building represent victims who died on the flight. Benches facing away from the building represent those who were inside the Pentagon at the time of impact. The name of the individual killed in the attack is located at the top of the bench. Below each bench, there is a small reflecting pool. If family members of the victim died in the attack as well, their names are engraved below in the pool itself.

---

[41] Kirk Savage, "Faces of the dead," *kirksavage.pitt.edu*, August 6, 2011. Accessed May 20, 2012. http://www.kirksavage.pitt.edu/?p=209.
[42] *Ibid.*

At the Flight 93 National Memorial in Shanksville, the names of those who died were initially found in two locations. The first was on a series of memorial benches facing the crash site. The second was a series of forty slate angels, referred to as the "Angels of Freedom," located between the benches and the crash site. While the National Park Service erected the benches in advance of the memorial's construction, the angels were crafted and erected by the public. However, both of these temporary memorials became replaced with a permanent memorial, the newly erected "Wall of Names," which consists of forty white marble panels along a black granite walkway that marks Flight 93's flight path.

At the World Trade Center, the names are located on bronze parapets surrounding the footprints of the fallen towers. These names include not only those of individuals who died there on September 11, 2001, but also those of the victims of the attack on February 6, 1993 and all those who died on all four planes and at the crash sites in New York, at the Pentagon, and in Shanksville. First responders are listed as their own group. Within these groupings, names are listed according to affiliations, referred to as "adjacencies," in close proximity to loved ones, relatives, friends, and colleagues.

Fig. 6.12 The National 9/11 Pentagon Memorial, 2012

Fig. 6.13 Bench at the National 9/11 Pentagon Memorial for Dana Falkenberg, 2012

Fig. 6.14 Benches at the Flight 93 National Memorial in Shanksville, 2009

Fig. 6.15 "Angels of Freedom" at the Flight 93 National Memorial, 2009

In all of these instances—whether in Oklahoma City, Washington, D.C., Shanksville, or Manhattan—the naming of the dead is of utmost importance. Often, these efforts are enhanced by the fact that, as Kirk Savage points out, "[…] faces—or, more precisely, photographs of faces —have become ever more prominent in commemorative practice."[43] In New York, these faces are made visible not only through the previously discussed "missing" signs, but will also be visible as photographs displayed in the museum.

Rectification

As I have previously stated, the former site of the Twin Towers is not only "sanctified" but also "rectified." Foote specifically defines rectification as "the process through which a tragedy site is put right and used again." He further explains that rectification is generally the most common response to sites affected by violence.[44] Generally, rectified sites are those associated with accidental violence and are therefore "likely to disappear from the

---

[43] *Ibid.*
[44] Foote, *op. cit.*, p. 23.

landscape."[45] Sanctification constitutes an active response of memorialization, but rectification is usually limited to those actions allowing the site to be returned to use. However, the site continues to attract attention when the event "claims many victims from a single group and induces a sense of community loss", both also features of sanctified sites.[46]

By any measure, the cleanup and recovery efforts at "Ground Zero" were massive: "2,700 vertical feet of structural materials had been compressed into a mountainous, smoldering pile of scraps of steel, splinters of concrete, tangled rebar, and unrecognizable material."[47] The fires, which reached 2000°F and continued to burn for months, were not fully extinguished until December 19, 2001. At the height of the recovery, 5,000 individuals worked on the pile, including firefighters, police officers, engineers, construction workers, ironworkers, the American Red Cross, the Salvation Army, medical personnel, massage therapists, and podiatrists. Since then, more than a decade has passed and construction at the site remains ongoing. While it will be some time before construction at the site is completed, Libeskind's plans seek to replace not only the destroyed buildings, but also to expand upon them.[48]

Conclusion

While the public's responses to planned construction at the World Trade Center site following 9/11 ranged from wanting to leave the site of the former Twin Towers as an empty void to wanting to rebuild the Twin Towers exactly as they were, neither of these extremes served as a tenable solution. The site could be neither purely "sanctified" nor "rectified." The lives lost had to be memorialized correctly, but the harsh reality that sixteen acres of prime real estate in Lower Manhattan could not remain

---

[45] *Ibid.*

[46] *Ibid.*

[47] Blais and Rasic, *op. cit.*, p. 70.

[48] While that plan has undergone numerous alterations—some of which have been the cause of significant discord—Libeskind stands by his vision, stating, "As a master planner, I understood that what is important is the interpretation. I didn't want to create a shackle for the designers. I wanted to give a creative space for people to work creatively with their own interpretation. ...I don't want to minimize—there were challenges with Larry (Silverstein). I think that's the nature of creating a work of this scale." Blair Kamin, "Discord aside, architect embraces memorial," *Chicago Tribune*, August 15, 2011. Accessed August 10, 2013. http://articles.chicagotribune.com/2011-08-15/entertainment/ct-ent-0815-memorial-libeskind-20110815_1_master-plan-ground-zero-architect.

undeveloped also had to be faced. The attempts to address both of these concerns simultaneously have led to numerous controversies surrounding "Ground Zero," but they also mark the former site of the Twin Towers as one that is unique within the landscape of memorial architecture.

CHAPTER SEVEN

REMEMBERING THOSE WHO DID NOT COME HOME: CHALLENGES OF DESIGNING SEPTEMBER 11TH MEMORIALS IN NEW JERSEY

KAREN FRANCK AND PHILIP SPERANZA

The national September 11 memorials at the World Trade Center in New York, at the Pentagon in Washington D.C., and in Shanksville, Pennsylvania, are large and well known but there are at least 700 additional, often much smaller memorials to September 11th throughout the United States. Some were completed as early as 2002, others only in 2011. Most are in New York, New Jersey, Connecticut, and Massachusetts, the home states of most of the victims, but they also appear throughout the nation and in other countries as well. In New Jersey, which lost 691 residents in the attack, counties, municipalities, fire stations, country clubs, private firms as well as educational, religious and other institutions have commemorated the lives that were lost. More than 200 public, visual memorials can be found that not only recognize the lost lives of state residents but that also commemorate the lives of all those who died: firefighters and policemen, graduates of New Jersey high schools and universities, employees of New Jersey-based firms and institutions, and the efforts of rescue and recovery workers. The locations often reflect who is being remembered: in or near the train station from which the honored resident or residents commuted to New York; on the campus of a school or university; next to a fire station; at a country club or church; and also in large county parks, smaller town squares and local parks.

While many forms of September 11th commemoration in New Jersey are small and may be easily passed by or recognized only by local residents, these memorials are surprisingly widespread, with some towns having more than one. Moreover, the forms of commemoration are nearly as varied. A review reveals three general types: dedications, objects, and landscaped settings. Dedications consist of the naming of existing structures. In some towns a street, an existing bridge, a building or a sports facility may have been named, or re-named, after a local resident. In Edison, a street retains its name, Annette Drive, but now an additional sign reads "Dedicated to Scott Scherzer" and in smaller letters on the same sign "Edison remembers 9-11-2001." In Leonia, tennis courts in the county park are named after Leonia resident and tennis player Andy Kim. In Cranbury, the post office was dedicated to Todd Beamer, a Cranbury resident on United Flight 93 who helped foil the hijackers' attempt to fly the plane to Washington D.C. In New Vernon, the gymnasium at The Harding School has been named after graduate Matthew Sellitto. Commemoration of this kind follows an earlier tradition in the U.S. of "living memorials" in which new civic buildings, such as armories or auditoria, were built as World War II war memorials, the idea being at that time that memorials with a practical use were preferable to monuments.[1] The dedications in New Jersey are of existing structures, while the term "living memorial" is now applied more generally to memorials comprised of trees and gardens or to interactive memorial websites.

Memorials consisting of a single, freestanding object placed in an existing setting take a variety of forms. The most frequent is a boulder or stone marker with a metal plaque that lists the names of residents in that town or county who perished in the attacks. This has long been a way to remember soldiers. Many towns in New Jersey and other states list the names of local residents who died in military service to their country during a war, and sometimes those who served and survived, on similar boulders in memorial parks and squares. The discrete memorial object may also serve a purpose as a kind of public furniture: a flagpole; a bench, as in Dunnellen and Hawthorne; a clock tower, as in Rozelle Park; or a gazebo, as in Jackson and Monroe. Again one can recognize earlier memorial traditions: clock towers were frequently installed as memorials to World War I throughout the U.K. In a time with fewer watches, they were deemed to be practical memorials, in comparison to mere monuments.[2] In Australia, larger versions of gazebos—band shells—were a popular way to honor those who served in World War II.

A few of the object memorials in New Jersey consist of a sculpture along the lines of what traditionally have been considered 'monuments.'

---

[1] Andrew M. Shanker, "Planning Memory: Living Memorials in the United States during World War II," *The Art Bulletin* 84 n. 1 (2002): 130-147.
[2] Ken S. Inglis, "The Homecoming: The War Memorial Movement in Cambridge, England," *Journal of Contemporary History* 27 n. 4 (1992): 583-605.

Among these are figures cast in metal, such as the silhouette of an ironworker standing on rubble to honor the work of rescue and recovery workers at the Dauntless Efforts 9/11 Memorial in Jersey City; the bronze figure of a kneeling firefighter stands in front of the Wyckoff Volunteer Department. The sculpture may also be abstract but clearly represent the Twin Towers. One example is the Catholic Cemeteries 9/11 Memorial in Newark—a metal structure suggesting the towers connected by a cross. Structural steel fragments from the towers also serve as object memorials, standing alone, as on the Hudson River waterfront in Jersey City, or incorporated into a larger sculpture, as in Chatham. Such fragments are available from the Port Authority at no cost (except that of transport) and now appear as or in September 11th memorials throughout the U.S. and in other countries. Two thousand pieces have been distributed worldwide, with 124 towns in New Jersey receiving at least one.

A very common type of September 11th memorial in New Jersey is an outdoor space that one can enter with the feeling of being 'inside' the space, an experience more full engaging than simply viewing a plaque. In a few cases, the space is a grove of trees, such as at Pier A Park in Hoboken or in Liberty State Park in Jersey City. These were funded by the USDA Forest Service under the Living Memorials Project for communities in the metropolitan areas of New York and Washington, D.C., and in southwest Pennsylvania. It is much more common for the memorial space to be a landscaped setting that creates a sense of enclosure through some combination of hedges, other plants, stone markers, boulders with plaques, benches, paths and possibly a sculpture or steel fragment from the towers, a flagpole and a paved ground surface. They offer a place for people to spend time alone or with others and for communities to hold ritual events on Memorial Day, Veterans Day and anniversaries of September 11th. These memorials vary in size from larger county memorials such as the Essex County September 11th Memorial in Eagle Rock Reservation to smaller, more intimate spaces that are described below.

Compared to memorials that are single discrete objects, spatial memorials are historically more recent. Emerging in the U.S. towards the end of the nineteenth century, they offer visitors a "space of engagement" rather than just an object to view.[3] The first examples of what Kirk Savage has called "spatial monuments" in the U.S. consisted of a stone statue

---

[3] Please see forthcoming book Quentin Stevens and Karen A. Franck, *Memorials as Spaces of Engagement: Memorial Design, Use and Meaning* (London: Routledge, 2014).

placed upon a stone platform that visitors reached by climbing steps.[4] The formality of the earlier type of statue monument was maintained but now the visitor also entered a memorial space. A very grand example of this kind of spatial monument is the Lincoln Memorial in Washington, D.C., completed in 1922. Today the overwhelming majority of spatial memorials are not raised platforms but on the ground plane and are not nearly as grand or as formal as they were previously (with one exception being the World War II Memorial in Washington, D.C.). In all cases, however, one enters a space made physically and visually distinct from the surrounding environment, although often closely connected to it.

Given our shared interest in architecture, landscape architecture and urban design, we visited a dozen September 11th spatial memorials in New Jersey in the winter of 2011, selecting a number from Sheena Chi's online photographs that showed variations in design, orientation and content.[5] In this essay, we focus on seven of them. All are distinct settings within an existing context, and through design employ various means to engage with that context and to recognize the identities of those being commemorated.

Site Design and Spatial Organization

The seven relatively small spatial memorials we visited in New Jersey towns and suburbs are all located in existing parks or open spaces, often close to streets and sometimes near municipal buildings or houses. The memorials in Rutherford, Westwood Closter, Hazlet, and Monroe are set in existing parks of different sizes, while in Old Bridge the memorial is an open area next to the town library. In Westfield and Westwood, towns with train stations, the memorials are located close to the stations. The design of each memorial responds to the particular conditions of these contexts. Often the memorial straddles two worlds of engagement—of pedestrians and people in vehicles—and is visually accessible to people in both worlds. The design of these memorials accommodates the experience the memorials in two different scales, producing two similar but also different stories.

---

[4] Kirk Savage, *Monument Wars: Washington D.C., the National Mall and the Transformation of the Memorial Landscape* (Berkeley: University of California Press, 2009).

[5] Sheena Chi's 2500 photos of 9/11 Memorials at http://911memorials.org/?p=39. Additional listings and photographs of September 11th memorials can be found at the following websites, which were additional sources for this essay. Accessed July 21, 2013. http://voicesofseptember11.org/dev/content.php?idtocitems=1,6 and http://www.livingmemorialsproject.net/.

The September 11th memorial in Remembrance Park in Closter is located along a seam running between a deep forest and a neighborhood of single-family houses. From the park's parking area, one reaches the circular space of the memorial via a meandering path, which is part of a network of paths into the park. The names of the two Closter victims appear on the opposite, inside walls of a stone archway. A tall black granite slab is displaced from the center of the circle. Below it, embedded in the paved ground surface, is a steel fragment of the World Trade Center. A path leading from the arch to the adjacent street and suburban neighborhood follows the orientation of the archway and the slab, both of which can be clearly seen by those passing in cars. The memorial, set in an open green space against a background of tall trees, changes the normal driving experience of the surrounding area: the memorial in its park setting is experienced as a visual opening into an urban room.

From a passing vehicle, the memorial is experienced only visually, as the archway and the black slab in the forest. The names on the archway and the steel fragment embedded in the ground are not visible from such a distance or speed; nor can they be touched. The tall stone slab has an ample presence against the background of taller trees that loom over it. The circular clearing, the archway and the slab provide a glimpse of a focused moment of human intervention in the natural setting of the park. When approached by the pedestrian, the memorial is experienced at a finer scale of understanding, revealing its smaller, textual details. Once within the setting of the memorial circle, a view of the suburban context is framed both through the archway and in the reflections on the dark granite slab. One can see the central hole in the slab and read the time, 8:46 a.m., embedded below the warped steel section embedded in the ground. One can touch the steel or the names in the archway. And one may continue on into the rest of the park. The visual accessibility of the memorial operates at two scales—of the car and the pedestrian. The opening of the urban wall extending to the backdrop of the forest acknowledges the speed of passing vehicles, while the carefully detailed node within the park, inviting close inspection by those on foot, communicates the more detailed story of the consequences of September 11th for the town of Closter.

As in Closter, the Old Bridge 9/11 Memorial is located in an open space between a busy county road, Cottrell Avenue, and an amenity for residents—the Old Bridge Public Library. Again the memorial space takes the form of a circular precinct visible to drivers passing in vehicles and to people approaching the memorial on foot. However, drivers this time see

Fig. 7.1 9/11 Memorial with Closter's Remembrance Park in the background

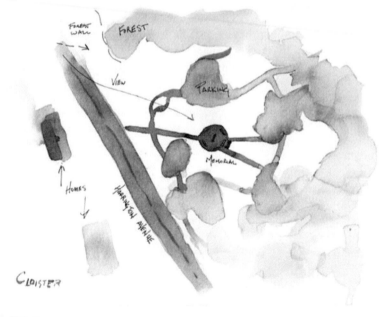

Fig. 7.2 Site plan of 9/11 Memorial in Closter: A Room Opening into a Forest

Fig. 7.3 View of 9/11 Memorial in Old Bridge approaching on foot, Cottrell Road beyond

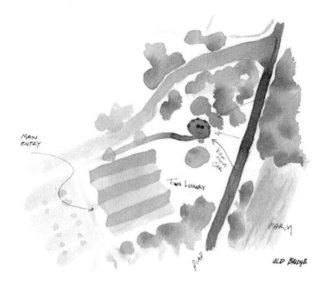

Fig. 7.4 9/11 Memorial in Old Bridge: Site plan shows path to the memorial, stelae, and Cottrell Road

only two tall slabs with the proportion of the World Trade Center towers and a flagpole emerging from a low hedge. The hedge creates an enclosed space and protects that enclosure from the speed and noise of passing vehicles while also obscuring the view of the memorial from Cottrell Avenue. As in Closter, the Old Bridge 9/11 Memorial reveals a different story when approached by pedestrians, since the low hedge hides smaller elements of the memorial. Since the memorial is not on a pedestrian route to the library or to anywhere else, it is a destination site: one makes a conscious decision to approach and enter it.

The 9/11 Memorial in Hazlet possesses similar qualities: a circular setting placed in an open space between a busy street, Union Avenue, and a community building, the Hazlet Municipal Center. As in Old Bridge, the parking area and main entrance to the Center are located away from the street, leaving the memorial separated from the main pedestrian route to the building. Neither memorial is sited along a path leading to the entrance of a community building, rendering each a destination. The memorials and the paths leading to them have been added to these sites without acknowledging the existing conditions or the existing patterns of movement. Unlike in Old Bridge, drivers viewing the Hazlet memorial from the road, which is about twenty-five feet from the memorial, have a clear view of both the benches enclosing the memorial space and the central stone. One variation on the circular spatial organization seen in many of these memorials is apparent. Like other memorials, the circular geometry defines an occupiable space that often includes a taller central element. At Hazlet, this is a single stele, inscribed and enclosed by a circle of eight benches. In Hazlet, however, the benches do not completely enclose the space but instead leave it open at places on the perimeter to give access to the inner precinct of the circle.

In all three cases, the memorial is located between the street and a community amenity. What is different, and important, are the real world distances in the three contexts and the paths that shape how one experiences the architecture of these memorials. In Closter, the memorial addresses both the vehicle and the pedestrian equally effectively, being directly on the pathway of each and serving both as a pedestrian destination in itself and as a site one might see or visit on the way to the rest of the park. In Old Bridge and Hazlet, the location of the memorial and its relationship with the surrounding context constrains the drivers' view in the case of Old Bridge and pedestrians' access in both Hazlet and Old Bridge.

The September 11th memorial in Rutherford can be found in a downtown park with streets and houses bordering its three sides. The park includes other memorials, benches, a band shell, and a playground. Unlike the memorials in more suburban locations, this one has no vertical element that would make it easily visible from passing vehicles. On-street parking further obscures the memorial, despite the slower speed required of cars on these more urban streets. Indeed, it was difficult to see the memorial when driving to the park; it was only when we walked along the adjacent sidewalk that we glimpsed it.

The Rutherford memorial, again a circular precinct, is within ten to fifteen feet of the closest street and sidewalk. This memorial, not easily visible from cars and within a park one might pass through or visit for other reasons, is directed more toward the pedestrian than people in cars. The material characteristics of the memorial further enhance the intimate experience of a visitor on foot. A steel beam recovered from the World Trade Center has been placed close to the paved ground surface of the memorial space with the names of Rutherford's victims appearing next to it (fig. 7.6).

As in Closter, the material characteristics of this fragment invite an up-close, tactile engagement; this fragment, larger and rusting, recalls the large scale of the building and the destructiveness of the event. The approach to the Closter memorial is open with the memorial in a broad opening of the forest wall. It stands out. In Rutherford, the memorial can only be experienced up close and relies on existing activities of the more densely populated city, favoring the pedestrian experience over the vehicular experience. The memorial in Rutherford may be a destination, but it is also part of an existing pattern of everyday urban movement and park activity.

The Westfield memorial, "A Walk for Dads", further extends this idea of engaging with the daily life of the city: it takes the form of a pathway leading from New Jersey Transit (NJT) train station to the west and south sides of the town. Commuters on their way home from the station pause at the end of the pathway, waiting for the light to change to cross Route 28. And those cars passing on North Avenue West, Plaza Avenue and Route 28, or also waiting for the light to change, have a clear view of the entire memorial. Like Closter, but in a very different way, the memorial addresses the experience of those walking and those driving. The memorial 'attaches' itself to its site,[6] participating in the everyday flow of people and vehicles through a vibrant junction in the stop and go

---

[6] Bruno Latour and Albena Yaneva, "Give Me a Gun and I Will Make All Buildings Move: An Ant's View of Architecture," in *Explorations in Architecture: Teaching, Design, Research*, edited by R. Geiser, (Basel: Birkhäuser, 2008).

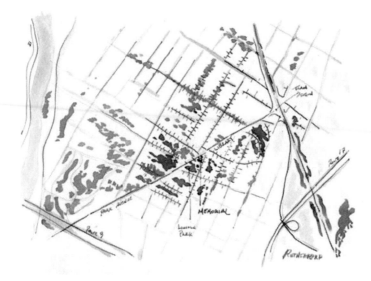

Fig. 7.5 9/11 Memorial in Lincoln Park, Rutherford: Site plan shows dense urban context and proximity to Park Avenue

Fig. 7.6 9/11 Memorial in Rutherford: Close-up view of a rusted fragment from the World Trade Center

Fig. 7.7 Memorial in Westfield. Site plan shows pedestrian, vehicular, and NJT movement

movement. It is not only a destination. Its spatial organization is unusual: it reinforces an existing path rather than creating an enclosed precinct like Closter, Old Bridge, Rutherford, and Hazlet.

The design of this memorial as a pathway in front of the rhythmic passing of NJT trains to New York City reinforces the relationship of the town to the city. Its linear site design becomes its principal spatial organization; twelve stelae and one large obelisk are situated along the line leading to and from the station. At the obelisk at the center of the line, a circle is inscribed to one side. During two visits, we observed people moving along the path without stopping at the obelisk. They were on their way somewhere else, activating the line of the path, not the circle of the obelisk. Rather than creating a new pattern of movement, one to and within a circular precinct, the memorial in Closter recognizes and celebrates an existing pattern of movement. This is very unusual for the New Jersey memorials we visited and for spatial memorials generally. They are nearly always precincts separated in some way from existing, everyday patterns of movement.

In Westfield, the memorial's spatial organization comes from within the site, tracing the walking path and the larger network of multimodal transit that connects the people of Westfield to New York City. The organization is not foreign or autonomous but locks the memorial into a place and speaks to the social behavior of a culture of commuting shared by all those being remembered. Writer Anna Klingmann points out that place making from the 'inside-out' is successful when "architects, urban planners, and politicians recognize architecture as an engine to reveal and accelerate a city's inherent (conditions)."[7] As the memorial acknowledges the specific flow of participation at the site it acts as a framework that adapts to variations in that flow. The participation and the framework together are attuned to the existing culture of commuting and the moments of quiet when the community is not moving back and forth to New York City.

Time and Light

During weekday rush hours in Westfield, the memorial path and the adjacent streets are busy with movement. Both the placement and the design of the memorial acknowledge the spatial seam of the commute to and from New York and also the seam of time of the commuter's schedule. One is reminded that many of those who died on September 11th, including those from Westfield, were commuters to the city. To engage aspects of time and light is another challenge in the design of memorials. Doing so successfully enhances people's experience of the memorial and acknowledges the culture of that place, as the memorial in Westfield does.

Every year on September 11th at 8:46 a.m., a beam of light passes through a small hole in the tall, dark slab at the Closter memorial, illuminating the polished, warped piece of steel embedded in the ground below the silhouette of the slab. The capture of this light generates a sense of place and time and triggers a memory across time. The publicized annual anniversary ceremony at the Closter memorial invites the public to participate in that periodic event. Throughout the year, the people of Closter may well anticipate the moment when light will connect time with the place of the memorial. If scientists are correct, perhaps this is similar to the way people anticipated the solstice and equinox celebrations at Stonehenge. Japanese architect Tadao Ando speaks to the use of light as a means to connect architecture to site when he writes: "The architectural pursuit implies a responsibility to find and draw out a site's formal

---

[7] Anna Klingmann, *Brandscapes: Architecture in the Experience Economy* (Cambridge, Mass.: MIT Press, 2007), p. 253.

characteristics, along with its cultural traditions, climate, and natural environmental features, the city structure that forms its backdrop, and the living patterns and age-old customs that people will carry into the future."[8]

The reflective surfaces of the polished granite monument in Hazlet reflect the figure of the visitor, the surrounding trees and, depending on the weather, the clouds above, collapsing the surrounding setting into the memorial. The similarly reflective surface of the wall at the Vietnam Veterans Memorial set a precedent for may subsequent memorials. Polished stone surfaces provide an opportunity to focus not the object of the memorial but on the setting and the people present at the exact time of viewing. Such a surface provides a spiritual lens into the world of the stone, as if one had transcended time to enter the commemorated event.

The warped steel at Closter and the rusting steel fragment at Rutherford provide tactile experiences that move one to understand the event the memorial commemorates in a visceral way. The material qualities of these fragments—the initial shaping of the first and continuing rusting of the second—instantly communicate the force and significance of the remembered event in a way that is not simply symbolic or purely visual. People can understand that at a precise time, a force of heat and pressure so strong caused the strange shape of the steel, while the decay of other fragment is inexorable. The shape of the bent piece is fixed in time and each year the moment of its transformation from straight to curved is marked with light.

In Westfield, it is artificial light that enhances experiences of the memorial, as seen in fig. 7.8. A light below each small stele illuminates the pathway, guiding commuters to and from work before dawn and after dusk. Light within the large glass obelisk illuminates the memorial to people passing by in vehicles. Depending upon the time of sunrise and sunset, commuters pass through what becomes a more special place because of the lights. As in Closter, this synchronicity of the light with the passage of commuters is a periodic occurrence, giving further significance to the day that commuters left for work but did not return.

In this respect, the New Jersey monuments have something in common with the National 9/11 Pentagon Memorial in Washington D.C. The spatial organization of that memorial is also connected to the time of the event being commemorated. Its design recognizes a pattern of movement that occurred at the precise moment when Flight 77 hit the building. To achieve this, the memorial benches, one for each victim, are arranged

---

[8] Tadao Ando, "Toward New Horizons in Architecture," in *Theorizing a New Agenda for Architecture: An Anthology of Architectural Theory 1965-1995*, edited by Kate Nesbitt, (New York: Princeton Architectural Press, 1996), p. 460.

either facing the Pentagon, to represent victims who were on the plane, or facing away from the building, to represent victims who were in the building. Time is also recognized through the ordering of the benches by the year of the victim's birth—from youngest to oldest. This spatial organization provides a framework for more specific stories of families to emerge, as demonstrated, for example, when five blue roses of a family connect five otherwise dispersed benches.

Fig. 7.8 Memorial in Westfield: View at dusk along "A Walk for Dads"

In the Pentagon memorial, like the ones we visited in New Jersey, the spatial organization of the site connects the memorial to a place and to the specifics of an event. In addition, they all present an open-ended condition that allows the memorial to evolve with real time human participation. The changing values of each community are allowed to play out over time.

Naming Individuals

A prominent and widely shared feature of memorials to the victims of terrorism is the listing of their names. This way of publicly recognizing the loss of life of ordinary individuals has its roots in the tradition of honoring the lives of common soldiers by listing their names on war memorials, a practice adopted in the U.S. after the Civil War. The Allied forces' decision to do so in Europe after World War I marked a significant change in the design of large-scale war memorials, so well-illustrated in Edwin Lutyens's design of the arches at Thiepval, France, on which the names of the 73,367 soldiers who died in 1916 in the Battle of the Somme are incised.[9] According to Maya Lin, it was partly Lutyens's design that inspired her winning submission for the design of the Vietnam Veterans Memorial in Washington, D.C., which makes the names of those who died or are missing in action such a prominent and moving element of the memorial.

Whose names to list, and where and how to do so are challenges faced by designers of all September 11th memorials. This challenge is met with great design ingenuity at the National 9/11 Pentagon Memorial and at the National September 11 Memorial in New York City only after intense and painful discussions with, and conflicts between, relatives of local victims throughout the design phase. In New Jersey, September 11th memorials nearly always give the name or names of residents or past residents killed in the attacks. Sometimes the names of all the victims are also listed, as in Westfield. The memorial in Monroe is unusual in giving the names not just of residents who died on individual markers but also on a plaque in the adjacent gazebo. The names of relatives of Monroe residents who died are paired with the names of their families.

Many memorials also display the names of people or organizations that donated funds for the building of the memorial; these names most commonly appear on brick pavers on the ground surface, as in Bayonne and Hazlet. In Hazlet, the names of those people or organizations that donated additional funds for the eight granite benches are incised on them. Brass plaques may also list the names of town or county elected officials who were serving when the memorial was built or those who served on committees responsible for creating them.

---

[9] Peter S. Hawkins, "Naming Names: The Art of Memory and the NAMES Project AIDS Quilt," *Critical Inquiry* 19 n. 4 (1993):752-779.

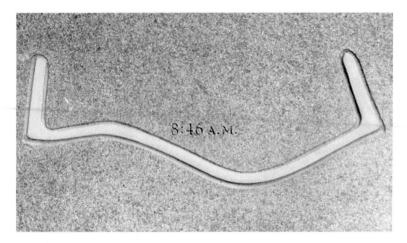

Fig. 7.9 9/11 Memorial in Closter. Warped steel from the World Trade Center embedded in the ground surface, showing the time of Flight 11's impact

Fig. 7.10 9/11 Memorial in Hazlet Veterans Park: Benches encircle central monument

Fig. 7.11 9/11 Memorial in Veterans Park, Westwood: One of four markers honoring residents who died on September 11th.

In the memorials we visited in New Jersey, the names of victims are shown on the surface or surfaces of a single form, possibly a wall, a plaque, or a freestanding monument. Often the list is alphabetical or grouped in some other way. A very different approach is to give each victim's name a freestanding stone marker symbolically reminiscent of a tombstone through the association of one person with one object in the landscape. Just the person's name may be given, as in Westfield and Closter. Additional information may include the dates of birth and death and, less frequently, a photograph sandblasted onto the surface of the memorial. A person's role as firefighter or police officer may be portrayed; sometimes, familial relationships are suggested as well. In Westfield, the name of the memorial, "A Walk for Dads", poignantly reveals a particular familial relationship. On the memorial in Hazlet, the pairing of the images of a man and a woman with the same last name along with the image of an angel placed below them makes painfully clear who was lost and their relationship to each other, as seen in figure 7.10.

In the memorials we visited in New Jersey, the lists of names have a uniform pattern within any given memorial, giving exactly the same kind of information in the same format for each individual, with the exceptions being indications of who is a firefighter, police officer, or emergency rescue worker. The September 11th memorial in Westwood is very unusual in this respect: precisely the opposite is true. The lengthy texts appearing beneath the names and photographs of each person killed vary dramatically in content and tone, suggesting that each family contributed the text they wished to appear, as seen in fig. 7.11.

The Individual and the Collective

Many memorials to victims of terrorism, both large and small, are likely to incorporate a freestanding physical object in honor of each individual killed. In the National 9/11 Pentagon Memorial, a bench honors each person; in the Oklahoma City National Memorial, it is a chair, though despite the architects' intentions, the chairs are roped off from the adjacent pathway. And in the London 7 July Memorial to the 2005 bombings, fifty-two stainless steel stelae honor the fifty-two victims purely symbolically: they do not bear the victims' names. These are listed collectively on an adjacent plaque. As we observed in New Jersey, they create individual memorials within the larger, collective one when the individual markers are associated with particular individuals through the name placed upon each one. In this way, they give friends and family a place to leave small tokens, photographs, potted plants, flowers or, in the Jewish tradition, small stones. Such practices recognize and reinforce the role of the marker as a kind of tombstone.

In Westfield, the individual markers are small stone stelae that line the edge of the pathway. Each one is lit at night while a central glass obelisk, lit from within, displays the name of every victim. In Monroe, vertical granite slabs, also in a semi-circle, have varying elevations, suggesting the New York skyline that appears in the distance. In Old Bridge, each individual marker is a granite box; together, they form a semicircle around a central stone stele, and each is also lit from below. Their flat tops are particularly accommodating for placing small objects and photographs (fig. 7.12).

The creation of individual memorials within a larger whole, however, does not require freestanding objects. At the Staten Island September 11th Memorial, small niches in rows on the inside walls of the two large cement 'wings' of the memorial are marked with the name and stone silhouette of each victim. These provide small, protected spaces for leaving notes,

Fig. 7.12 Memorial in Old Bridge: One of twelve small granite blocks honoring residents who died on September 11th

photographs, mementoes, and other items. As the Vietnam Veterans Memorial demonstrates, it is also possible for names incised on a flat surface to serve as individual memorials; when people can reach a name, they can touch it, photograph it, or make a rubbing. The possibility that individual names might become memorials in themselves is further enhanced by the design and placement of these names on the bronze parapet surrounding the two reflecting pools at the National September 11 Memorial at the World Trade Center. The letters of the names are cut widely and deeply enough to enable visitors to insert flowers, small flags, or other items into the letters. There is also sufficient space around each name for it to stand on its own and for visitors to tape a note or a photograph adjacent to it. At night, light from below illuminates each name.

More Questions

The large number of memorials to September 11th in New Jersey illustrates the general, widely observed increase in public memorials in the U.S., particularly since the 1980s.[10] The reasons for this increase are not clear. However, it is certainly understandable that local governments, other organizations, and individuals responded to the intentional and brutal deaths of so many civilian men and women as well as children and unborn babies on September 11, 2001 with permanent, public forms of commemoration in the landscape. This response is particularly likely if some of those who perished were residents of one's own town. In this essay, we have described and reflected upon memorials built in New Jersey, looking at the similarities they share with earlier traditions and with other larger memorials. We have given close attention to spatial memorials—outdoor spaces one enters—focusing on their location, their relationship to the surrounding context, how they incorporate light and address time, and how they represent the identities of the victims being honored.

We know that these memorials are sites for collective commemorative activities, particularly on the anniversary of September 11th. Detailed documentation of those ritual events and an assessment of how design supports or hinders them would be useful. It is evident from the flowers, plants, photographs, and mementoes placed at the memorials that friends and relatives visit them as one might visit a cemetery. It is very possible that individuals or groups visit on occasions significant to the individual victim, such as birthdays or wedding anniversaries. We do not know, however, whether families feel that the memorials meet their needs for a place to remember and to grieve or how the larger community perceives the memorial. Perhaps some family members feel that the Westfield memorial, as a frequently traveled pathway close to highly trafficked roads, does not give them sufficient privacy or solitude when they visit. In this case, the needs of families may well differ from those of the community members generally, who may appreciate the public quality of this memorial and its integration into the daily life of the town.

Given that our research focuses on the completed design, we did not learn much about the process by which these memorials were created: how the sites were chosen, how funds were raised, how the spaces and the elements within them were designed, and who participated in all these

---

[10] Erika Doss, *Memorial Mania: Public Feeling in America* (Chicago, Ill.: University of Chicago Press, 2010).

decisions. We do know that architect Steven Arcella designed the memorial in Closter and that the committee responsible for the Westfield memorial included architect Mark Fischbach and landscape architect Craig Stock. Sculptor Blaise Batko designed the memorials in Old Bridge and Monroe, while the design for Hazlet's memorial came from a committee of residents with guidance from Joseph Uras Monuments. It is clear that families made specific contributions to the memorial in Westwood and we know that Batko met with family members to hear their stories and to present his design. Funding frequently came from contributions by residents and local organizations. But this gives only a very small glimpse into the process and reveals nothing of the challenges or conflicts that were faced along the way, the rationale behind the decisions that were made, or the alternatives that were rejected.

Designing national public memorials is often a highly contentious process as evident in the modifications made to the original design of the Vietnam Veterans Memorial and, more recently, to the designs of both the National September 11 Memorial in New York and the Dwight D. Eisenhower Memorial in Washington, D.C.[11] Smaller scale, local memorials are also likely to generate conflict. For example, in Rutherford some residents expressed outrage in an online blog that a memorial to September 11th victims would be placed in Veterans Park, which until then contained only war memorials honoring soldiers. As public memorials continue to be a frequent means of commemorating events and lives and so continue to raise many of the design challenges we have described here, it is important to understand more about the process of their creation.

---

[11] Allison Blais and Lynn Rasic describe some of the conflicts that occurred during the design of the National September 11 Memorial in their book *A Place of Remembrance: Official Book of the National September 11 Memorial* (Washington, D.C.: National Geographic, 2011).

CHAPTER EIGHT

FROM GROUND ZERO TO PARK 51: COSMOPOLITANISM IN THE WAKE OF 9/11

JOSEPH L. V. DONICA

Today, our fellow citizens, our way of life, our very freedom came under attack in a series of deliberate and deadly terrorist acts.
—George W. Bush, September 11, 2001

Compassion begins with the local. But if our moral natures and our emotional natures are to live in any sort of harmony, we must find devices through which to extend our strong emotions and our ability to imagine the situation of others to the world of human life as a whole. Since compassion contains thought, it can be educated. We can take this disaster as an occasion for narrowing our focus, distrusting the rest of the world, and feeling solidarity with America alone.
—Martha Nussbaum, *For Love of Country?* (2002)

The widespread animosity toward Muslim-Americans since 9/11 and the lengths to which the Muslim-American community was forced to defend its own rights to citizenship were vividly illustrated when Representative Keith Ellison (D-MN), the first Muslim elected to Congress, defended Muslim-Americans at a March 2011 Congressional hearing on radical Islam. He closed his remarks by recounting the story of Mohammed Salman Hamdani, a twenty-three-year-old paramedic, New York City police cadet, Muslim-American, and one of the first responders at the World Trade Center on 9/11 to die at the site. Through tears, Ellison recounted the *New York Times*'s eulogy for Hamdani, concluding:

He wanted to be seen as an all-American kid. He wore No. 79 on the high school football team in Bayside, Queens, where he lived, and he was called Sal by his friends...He became a research assistant at Rockefeller University and drove an ambulance part-time. One Christmas, he sang in Handel's Messiah in Queens. He saw all the Star Wars movies, and it was well known that his new Honda was the one with the 'Young Jedi' license plates...His life should not be defined as a member of an ethnic group or a member of a religion, but as an American who gave everything for his fellow citizens. Mohamed Salman Hamdani is us. He is every American. He is our neighbor.[1]

Since 9/11, members of the Muslim-American community have had to convince the nation of their patriotism in order to be 'tolerated' in the public sphere or given a stake in the commons. Jeffrey Melnick draws from John Updike's 2006 "wretched snatched-from-the-headlines novel *Terrorist*", whose cast of characters are "cardboard cutouts of a tortured half-Arab, an oversexed African-American teenager, and an embittered but noble Jew" to conclude sadly that this is "the new math of race relations in the United States after 9/11." If Melnick is right, then Representative Ellison's apology for Muslim-Americans is the new math's differential equation.[2] By ascribing an almost hyper-patriotism to Hamdani to convince Congress that not all Muslims are radicals, he creates two categories of Muslims: radicals and patriots. The structure of thought that produces this dichotomy precludes a Muslim-American critique of U.S. policies since 9/11, however.

With Muslim-Americans so frequently forced to defend their faith and cultural practices, 9/11 has reintroduced a need across many academic disciplines to reevaluate the basis for cosmopolitan norms in American culture. Such a call comes as a reaction to the overt imperial response of the Us-versus-Them mentality that has made the object of American resentment both elusive and yet specifically Middle Eastern. Did the U.S. feel animosity towards all radical terrorists or all people claiming Islam as their religion? Muslims were racialized and radicalized so as to simplify and concentrate American animosity against what is a very diverse group of people. Despite such animosity, a radically reconfigured politics of Otherness has also emerged as a counterforce to 9/11's culture of perpetual disaster. This new politics engages the imagination of persons who seek to understand 9/11 not only in an anti-imperial frame, but also in one attuned to the radical alterity of the Other as a subject. Doing so may hold out an opportunity to renew cosmopolitanism. Though many observers see a return to an imperialist foreign policy in the post-9/11

---

[1] Keith Ellison, "Keith Ellison's Testimony at the Muslim Radicalization Hearing," *The Atlantic*, March 10, 2011. Accessed September 22, 2011. http://www.theatlantic.com/politics/archive/2011/03/keith-ellisons-testimony-at-the-muslim-radicalization-hearing/72294/.

[2] Jeffrey Melnick, *9/11 Culture: America Under Construction* (West Sussex: Wiley, 2009), pp. 120-1.

United States, even a potential new American Century, others take a contrary view of these same events, one that makes possible a form of cosmopolitanism defined by how we conceptualize our responsibility to the cultural and personal Other and the recognition of ourselves as Other. In the best case scenario, this resistance to American imperialism can foster a sense of progressive subjectivity that serves not only as a model for political representations of Otherness, but also as a site for the kind of democratic practice where cosmopolitanism must thrive for social change to occur.

This essay addresses the ways 9/11 compromised the project of cosmopolitanism many people think reached its peak in the 1990s, along with the way the cosmopolitanism project has, in turn, affected how we interpret the complex events now simply known as "9/11." I turn to recent literature that has advocated a cosmopolitan alternative to the pervasive nationalism that arose after 9/11 not merely to question it but also to consider a cosmopolitan challenge to it. For how "actually existing" cosmopolitanism works in our post-9/11 world, I look to the cases of the "World Trade Center Cross," Fritz Koeing's "The Sphere," and the controversy surrounding the plans for an Islamic community center in Lower Manhattan. These cases reveal a shift from the cosmopolitan hopes that Minoru Yamasaki had for his World Trade Center to this more recent retrenched nationalist posture. Despite cosmopolitanism's setbacks over the past decade, there remains hope that local grassroots projects may be able to challenge nationalistic projects now synonymous with the crippling effects that global capitalism has long visited upon the world's most vulnerable citizens.

Coming to Terms with Cosmopolitanism

Speaking of the compromised cosmopolitan political projects of the past decade, David Harvey draws out the contrast in both President George W. Bush's and Prime Minister Tony Blair's 9/11 speeches between the "high moral tone" of their rhetoric and the "ugly facts on the ground":

> The documented murder through torture of prisoners under U.S. care in Bagram in Afghanistan; the degrading photographs from Abu Ghraib; the denial of Geneva Convention rights to anyone deemed by the Bush administration to be unlawful or enemy combatants; the painful pictures of shuffling prisoners held without trial for years in Guantanamo Bay; the U.S. Army refusal to keep records of 'collateral deaths' thought to number more than 100,000 in Iraq in the first year of occupation; the 'rendition' for

interrogation to countries that practice torture of suspects arbitrarily (and, it turns out, often mistakenly) picked up anywhere in the world.[3]

This contrast between language and actions reflects the inability of cosmopolitanism to reach beyond at best a superficial justification of imperial projects. It thus makes clear that cosmopolitanism must find a new social basis to keep it from devolving into mere rhetoric. Bush's and Blair's language is performative in the way the term "crimes against humanity" was at the Nuremberg Trials. Both Bush and Blair had first to construe 9/11 as a category of event without precedent, not unlike arguments that characterize the Holocaust as historically unique. In describing the use of this new term at Nuremberg, Derrida states that "[T]his sort of transformation structured the theatrical space in which the grand forgiveness, the grand scene of repentance…is played, sincerely or not."[4]

The unfortunate aspect of this collision between language and facts is that 9/11 was a moment that highlighted so many long-unanswered questions about cosmopolitanism. These questions might have been answered differently had there been a focus on cultural difference and participatory democratic practice based on diversity, rather than trumpeting vague notions of freedom and justice. The malleable nature of the language of cosmopolitanism has caused Paul Gilroy, a noted theorist on the subject at King's College London, to abandon the concept as helpful when dealing with the deeply entrenched racism found around the globe. It should be noted, however, that Gilroy's sense of cosmopolitanism consists of a vaguely defined attitude toward the Other that falls short of radical ethics.[5] By contrast, Bruce Robbins, a professor of humanities at Columbia University, searches for an "actually existing cosmopolitanism" that gives it the real teeth it needs to fight bias. As Robbins sees it, "Actually existing cosmopolitanism is a reality of (re)attachment, multiple attachments, or attachment at a distance."[6] With this in mind, it becomes possible to nurture such authentic attachments rather than simply create synthetic ones propped up by the vacuous language which Bush and Blair use.

---

[3] David Harvey, *Cosmopolitanism and the Geographies of Freedom* (New York: Columbia University Press, 2009), p. 3.
[4] Jacques Derrida, *On Cosmopolitanism and Forgiveness*, translated by Michael Hughes, (London: Routledge, 2010), p. 29.
[5] Paul Gilroy, *Postcolonial Melancholia* (New York: Columbia University Press, 2005).
[6] Bruce W. Robbins, *Cosmopolitanism from the Viewpoint of Violence* (Durham, N.C.: Duke University Press, 2012), p. 3.

Gilroy goes on further to argue that in cosmopolitanism's bid to make us all citizens of the world, "racial difference obstructs empathy and makes ethnocentrism inescapable. [Thus] it becomes impossible even to imagine what it is like to be somebody else."[7] Gilroy points out cosmopolitanism's failure to bring about the "socialist and Feminist movements that were committed to the observance of what might be termed an open, nonnational solidarity."[8] He laments the inability of cosmopolitanism, which lacks any real ethical force when reduced to rhetoric, to bring about "oppositional utopias."[9] His perspective resembles Harvey's in that each sees Blair's approach to the Iraq War as the cosmopolitan alternative to Bush's approach, though both are still different forms of imperialism in the end.

While cosmopolitanism offers a substantive alternative to multiculturalism's emphasis on tolerance as the proper ethic in a globalized world, it is not without its discontents. Those commentators who reduce a cosmopolitan ethic to something ornamental rather than a quality vital to a democratic public sphere should think again. Especially after 9/11, proponents of cosmopolitanism have envisioned U.S. society in terms of broadening equality across lines of race, class, gender, ethnicity, and, increasingly, sexuality. However, the confusion of cosmopolitan culture with multiculturalism, which replaces a transformed interpersonal ethic with mere tolerance, has created multiple social barriers to inter-cultural dialogue and cooperation in the past decade—the recent animosity toward Muslim-Americans being one such example.

Rooting democratic practice in cosmopolitan ethics encounters problems because a country's laws only operate within its existing geographical and cultural boundaries. When a democracy equates justice with fairness, as John Rawls does when he connects "the theory of justice with the theory of rational choice," it is difficult to conceptualize what cosmopolitan relations would look like "outside of legal systems."[10] Since the Enlightenment, an ethics of universalism has sought to dissolve the distinction between citizen and foreigner, and instead promote a view where everyone everywhere is equal to all others and each has an ethical responsibility to another as a fellow human. Immanuel Kant, for example, conceived a cosmopolitanism that transcended geographical boundaries, yet came into conflict with the legal systems defined by such boundaries.

---

[7] Gilroy, *op. cit.*, p. 63.

[8] *Ibid.*, p. 25.

[9] *Ibid.*, p. 26.

[10] John Rawls, *A Theory of Justice* (Cambridge, Mass..: Belknap-Harvard, 1971), p. 113.

Seyla Benhabib's recent critique of Kant's position argues that, "[P]olitical actors need bounded communities—whether they be cities, regions, states, or transnational institutions—within which they can establish mechanisms of representation, accountability, participation, and deliberation."[11] In short, Benhabib contends that our ethics do not match our politics. She concludes that cosmopolitanism can take us no further than the law of a bounded community, "because cosmopolitanism must inevitably collide with the boundaries required by democratic authority."[12] This leads her to seek an alternative in the obligation of hospitality that citizens of particular states have toward Others from beyond their borders. Benhabib thus does not settle for a thin or weak version of cosmopolitanism. A citizen's ethical obligations toward these Others may, in fact, require opposition to certain laws.

Does this conflict between law and ethical obligation require us to abandon cosmopolitanism as a mere attitude or even imaginary in favor of some alternative solution? Or must we work through the conflict between hospitality and state interests in order to realize a more dynamic cosmopolitanism that can operate in tandem with the legal system? Martha Nussbaum's solution to this problem is one of the more extreme. She advocates that we disavow loyalty to any nation or state and proposes instead that we think of ourselves as citizens of the whole world. Written a few years before 9/11, Nussbaum had naively assumed that the greater familiarity with other cultures fostered by multicultural education would ensure affection for those other cultures.[13] While certainly attractive from an ethical perspective, this position became untenable after 9/11 as many U.S. citizens felt hostility rather than empathy toward unfamiliar cultures during the "War on Terror."

Nussbaum first put forth her controversial plan for a cosmopolitan education in an essay in the *Boston Review* in 1996. It later appeared in an anthology that included essays critical of her view that cosmopolitanism is antipodal to patriotism because it connects human lines of sympathy across borders. Moreover, it sees identification with the familiar as the most dangerous political move in an age when people and production operate globally, not just locally. Criticism of Nussbaum centers on her belief that a cosmopolitan attitude necessarily entails a devaluation of one's civic commitment to the nation. She frames this as a tension within

[11] Seyla Benhabib, *Another Cosmopolitanism* (Oxford: Oxford University Press, 2006), p. 169.
[12] Robert Post, "Introduction," in *Another Cosmopolitanism*, edited by Seyla Benhabib, (Oxford: Oxford University Press, 2006), pp. 1-9, 9.
[13] Martha Nussbaum, *For Love of Country?* (Boston: Beacon, 1996).

our pedagogy over whether we educate students to be citizens of a specific country or, as she desires, to be "citizens of the world." The ancient Stoic philosopher Hierocles proposed a form of cosmopolitanism that balanced human lines of affiliation so that human relations—personal and political—met "somehow toward the center."[14] Nusshaum's concern comes down to an issue of Otherness, as she wonders, "[H]ow far the politics of nationalism really is from the politics of difference."[15] Nussbaum argues that the Stoics' version of cosmopolitanism radically claims that "we should give our first allegiance to no mere form of government, no temporal power, but to the moral community made up by the humanity of all human beings."[16] Nussbaum proposes a Kantian education that attempts to free citizens at an early age from the bonds of national identity. In doing so, "the life of the cosmopolitan, who puts right before country and universal reason before the symbols of national belonging, need not be boring, flat, or lacking in love."[17]

Any solution to conflicts over cultural Otherness may lie somewhere between Benhabib's desire to work within the boundaries of nation-states and Nussbaum's desire to ignore all national boundaries. For this task, we would do well to consider how we conceptualize the self and its now compromised relationship with the Other since 9/11. Judith Butler's work on the "grievable life" and the fragility of all life offers an opportunity to explore anew the rift between the self and the Other.[18] Butler explodes cosmopolitanism's traditional conception of the Other with a radical ethics that orients the problem of the self and its existence within circles or flows of relationality. While Benhabib's view seems cynical and Nussbaum's utopian, Butler sees a practical yet critical politics emerging at the site where a culture begins to recognize Otherness. She proposes a more open relationship and breaks down socially-constituted categories that create subjects instead of citizens. In *Giving Account of Oneself*, Butler turns to the problem that Nussbaum raises: how do we account for our own anti-cosmopolitan actions—or any others for that matter—that fail to take up the ethical obligation to care and protect the Other? Butler simplifies the question by asking how one gives account of oneself when called upon by another to do so.

Butler counters the common accusation that cosmopolitanism's privileging of global ties over local ones prevents it from doing the hard,

---

[14] *Ibid.*, p. 9.
[15] *Ibid.*, p. 5.
[16] *Ibid.*, p. 7.
[17] *Ibid.*, p. 17.
[18] Judith Butler, *Frames of War: When is Life Grievable?* (London: Verso, 2009).

ethically-driven work of responding to Otherness. Butler's analysis of the self's own journey into subjectivity rescues cosmopolitanism from the charge it responds to globalization by rejecting the Other. Nussbaum only re-formulates Kant's original Enlightenment cosmopolitan project. In contrast, Butler breaks new theoretical ground by considering Adorno's concept of ethical violence as it bears on the role of relationality in discussions of cosmopolitanism. Ethical violence occurs, Adorno says, when moral questions arise after a collective ethos ceases to hold sway. Adorno sees a tension between ethos and morality "such that a waning of the former is the condition for the waxing of the latter."[19] In short, the ethos of a defunct collective must use violence to create the illusion it still exists. As this process unfolds, Butler reminds us that "no 'I' can stand apart from the social conditions of its emergence."[20] But how does one give a moral account of the "I" without resorting to the ethical violence inherent in the social context out of which it arises? Butler solves this problem by arguing that the "I," while arising from the moral norms of the collective, "is not causally induced by those norms." Therefore, "when the 'I' seeks to give an account of itself, it can start with itself."[21] This is the case because any account that the "I" will give is one of relationality that enables the "I" to connect to any set of moral norms. Butler's ultimate interest lies in understanding how a "deliberating subject" becomes critically aware when the "I" finds itself out of sync with the moral norms of the collective. For her, this is how social theory and "even morality itself emerges."[22]

Adorno sees a negative dialectics arise "when claims of collectivity turn out *not* to be collective, when claims of abstract universality turn out *not* to be universal."[23] After 9/11, there were many claims to collectivity and universality, but Butler's insistence that the "I" give an account of itself forces us to ask basic questions about how relationality holds any collective body together and, even more, to question any claim to collectivity. Here Butler's cosmopolitanism emerges:

> It is one thing to say that a subject must be able to appropriate norms, but another to say that there must be norms that prepare a place within the ontological field for a subject. In the first instance, norms are there, at an

---

[19] *Ibid.*, p. 4.
[20] *Ibid.*, p. 7.
[21] *Ibid.*, pp. 7-8.
[22] *Ibid.*, p. 8.
[23] *Ibid.*

exterior distance, and the task is to find a way of appropriating them, taking them on, establishing a living relation to them.[24]

According to Butler, a "living relation" must include a critical stance toward ethical norms. Thus, for cosmopolitanism to overcome the superficial "tolerance" that multiculturalism lends to projects that claim universality, it must criticize the ethical norms on which it is based. Butler insists we reflect on the way that suffering forces a person to give an account of oneself. Personal suffering creates the condition under which a person can become self-conscious. Butler cites Nietzsche's claim that we give such an account because we are accountable to a system of justice and punishment. According to Nietzsche, fear motivates our urge to give an account of our actions. Butler, however, wants to know if conditions for the formation of subjectivity exist under which we give account to another that is not motivated by fear. It is always another person, she insists, who is the impetus for each of us to begin to tell our own story. One's story thus becomes both the answer to the questioning of the Other and the starting point for subjectivity.

Understanding how a subject takes form is important because, as Butler says, "[T]he very terms by which we give an account, by which we make ourselves intelligible to ourselves and to others...are social in character, and they establish social norms."[25] After 9/11, have the terms changed by which the Other asks us to give an account of not only the events of the day but also of how we relate ourselves to the Other? Key to Butler's argument is equating a critical politics with ethics, or at least making critical politics an outgrowth of ethics. And indeed, this critical politics "at times requires a first-person account of oneself."[26] Such self-exploration helps us determine how we might "continue in a dialogue where no common ground can be assumed, where one is, at [sic] it were, at the limits of what one knows yet still under the demand to offer and receive acknowledgment."[27] Here Butler brings the discussion of Otherness back to the heart of cosmopolitan culture. She presents moral norms created by the global flow of culture that transcend their origins. These norms suggest that a truly open mindset can be realized that makes the self vulnerable to the Other when the self gives its own account.

If Butler is correct that vulnerability is the only ethical response to suffering, then Slavoj Žižek's question about the state of happiness after

---

[24] *Ibid.*, p. 9.
[25] *Ibid.*, p. 21.
[26] *Ibid.*
[27] *Ibid.*

9/11 is the wrong one to ask. He wants to know the difference between "soft" racial harassment and a brutal neo-Nazi physical attack. Is this, he asks, "[A]ll that remains of the difference between civilization and barbarism?"[28] He admits that "soft" racial harassment is worse because it allows spectators to ignore it, pass by, and go on without examining their own racist behaviors. As citizens give account of themselves in the face of loss, they can begin to break down some of their more entrenched loyalties and un-cosmopolitan behaviors, such as the soft racism so prevalent after 9/11. Žižek rightly asks us to examine the fragility of the current state of global cosmopolitanism by imagining something far worse than 9/11. He asks us to imagine an asteroid on its way to the earth or a nuclear attack on a major city. In such an instance, "how insignificant and ridiculous our most passionate ideologico-political struggles would look all of a sudden." What would not seem ridiculous, however, "are 'impossible' ethical acts."[29] Real cosmopolitanism arises from these impossible ethical acts. And yet an examination of these acts shows that both the act and the world they gesture toward are not impossible but already in existence, not in any large systematic formation but in everyday encounters with the Other. With this sense of possibility, Žižek puts forward his case for an ethics that begins with the utter alterity of the Other.

The most important questions after 9/11 are not simply those about the cultural differences between the U.S. and the Middle East, but also those that interrogate the many local differences among U.S. citizens. These differences, be they economic, religious, racial, ethnic, gender, and sexual in nature, have become much more divisive in the past decade. A more meaningful conversation is the one that confronts Otherness in all its current manifestations. Long a mainstay in the academy, the notion of Otherness has steadily lost meaning as it has become more conceptually capacious since the days of "high" literary theory. However, as Derek Attridge has recently argued, "one of the most salient and vexing questions of our time" is determining "what is entailed in responding to otherness."[30] The disaster of 9/11 has renewed interest in the term by creating a sharper awareness of hitherto unnoticed aspects of our relationship with the Other. The deep pain felt across the nation for those who had lost so much after 9/11 reveals that "the 'experience' of alterity may challenge and refashion the concept of experience itself."[31]

---

[28] Slavoj Žižek, *Welcome to the Desert of the Real* (London: Verso, 2002), p. 113.
[29] *Ibid.*, p. 117.
[30] Derek Attridge, *The Singularity of Literature* (London: Routledge, 2004), p. 15.
[31] *Ibid.*, p. 19.

The Cross and the Globe

The experience of Otherness since 9/11 and the fragility of the Other's alterity became revealed in two physical reminders of cosmopolitan culture's dramatic shift since Yamasaki's original design of the World Trade Center. Two steel beams, now referred to as the "World Trade Center Cross", were found amidst the towers' rubble and soon became a sacred symbol where people left messages and even prayed at its base. Their sanctification became formalized when the beams were erected on a pedestal near the former WTC plaza and blessed with water by a Catholic priest. The inscription placed on the cross reads, "The Cross at Ground Zero—Founded September 13, 2001; Blessed October 4, 2001; Temporarily Relocated October 15, 2006. Will Return to WTC Museum, a sign of comfort for all." A lawsuit by an atheist group failed to stop the installation of the cross in the National September 11 Museum and Memorial in July 2011. The controversial WTC cross injected a dangerous sectarian element that reinforced the belief among many U.S. citizens that Western economic dominance was rooted in Christian tradition. For these people, the beams were "Miracle Debris" that provided comfort and protection at the site. By making these beams sacred, narrative commemoration took precedence over the contemplation of loss. The message communicated by the WTC Cross thus became more important than learning from the loss at the site.

What makes the cross's presence even more conspicuous is what they replace. Minoru Yamasaki had designed the original towers in the World Trade Center as symbols of how world trade can foster world peace. To epitomize this symbolism, he included a sculpture of a globe designed by Fritz Koenig in the middle of the plaza. James Glanz and Eric Lipton recount the role that Austin Tobin, director of the Port Authority, and Guy Tozzoli, the project manager, saw for this sculpture, entitled *The Sphere*:

> Tobin inaugurated an art program that put, most visibly, a twenty-five-foot-high bronze sphere by the German artist Fritz Koenig within a fountain at the center of the plaza. Tobin and Tozzoli decided that the sphere, a stylized map of the earth, symbolized world peace through trade, although Koenig wasn't so sure.[32]

The Sphere was heavily damaged when the buildings collapsed on top of it, but it was still recognizable as a globe. The damaged sculpture is now

---

[32] James Glantz and Eric Lipton, *City in the Sky: The Rise and Fall of the World Trade Center* (New York: Holt, 2003), p. 2.

permanently placed in Battery Park just south of the WTC, where it includes an inscription on a plaque that reads:

> For three decades, this sculpture stood in the plaza of the World Trade Center. Entitled "The Sphere", it was conceived by artist Fritz Koenig as a symbol of world peace. It was damaged during the tragic events of September 11, 2001, but endures as an icon of hope and the indestructible spirit of this country.

Yamasaki's vision for world peace was destroyed as the towers rose, and their destruction only serves as a sign that the U.S.'s national spirit is destructible. The inscription mars the hope that Yamasaki had originally instilled in his design. What hope *The Sphere* did communicate is now absent from the World Trade Center, where an explicitly sectarian religious symbol has replaced this earlier monument to cosmopolitanism to which the U.S. once aspired.

A single symbol such as a cross or a sphere representing the globe can have vastly different meanings, and it is important to parse these differences given the essential cultural importance of symbols in a secular society. Site-specific artwork usually has historical significance linked to that place. Hence a cross means something depending on its geographic location. Charles Taylor mentions that in modern societies, the rise of secularism helped to push a certain concept of God out of the public sphere. This concept of God is, in Taylor's words, the "[A]ction-transcendent grounding of society in higher time" that gives authority to the ruling government of a country.[33] With the rise of secularism, this concept of God became replaced in the public sphere by "the imaginaries that have emerged from the order of mutual benefit."[34] However, since 2001 we have seen a resurgence of the idea of God as the primary actor in the public sphere. Even in the 2012 Republican primary debates, the role of God in public life arguably assumed more importance than at any other time in our nation's history.

This concept of God as the primary actor in the public sphere animates the sentiment in favor of the "Ground Zero" Cross As of yet, no 9/11 memorial commemorates the disaster as a localized loss. Such a memorial does not exist because the meaning of 9/11 as a local disaster has been little explored in the broader culture. 9/11 was translated as a national disaster almost immediately. Examining symbols that challenge

---

[33] Charles Taylor, *Modern Social Imaginaries* (Durham, N.C.: Duke University Press, 2004), p. 186.
[34] *Ibid.*

cosmopolitan culture becomes important given the power of the visual in today's media. The visual effect of the WTC site on the millions of tourists is immense, and the ability of memorials and sites of loss to shape a nation's cosmopolitan sensibilities should not be overlooked.

From Ground Zero to Park 51

If memorials can prompt communities to question the role of citizens after a disaster, they can also introduce new ways of experiencing citizenship. David Simpson points out that in the history of American memorials, there is little precedent for memorializing ordinary citizens. He asks, for example, why we have not commemorated the loss of common soldiers and civilians in the Iraq War. He wants to work against using forms of commemoration that exploit sentimentality to tell a narrative of national destiny. This sense of destiny certainly informs much of the official memorialization of 9/11. Simpson argues that memorials not only bear witness and translate trauma; they can also teach, archive, and make space sacred. A frequently-voiced desire is for the new World Trade Center to serve as an "affirmation of global solidarity", one that allows us to see ourselves in the Other by standing for humanity rather than American power.[35] Someday the WTC site may have such a discursive function, but for now we must look elsewhere for signs of global solidarity.

These signs can perhaps be found in the plans to build an Islamic community center two blocks away from the World Trade Center. Called Park 51 for its address, or the Cordoba House, it will sponsor interfaith dialogue and introduce community programs to reinvigorate Lower Manhattan. Its design has not been as controversial as the World Trade Center's, but many people have questioned building the center, sparking a heated and ugly debate with implications that reach far beyond the memorial. The proposed thirteen-story community center will include a five-hundred-seat auditorium, theater, performing arts center, fitness center, swimming pool, basketball court, childcare area, bookstore, culinary school, art studio, food court, 9/11 memorial, and a prayer space that is not an official mosque. Its planners insist the center will be "a platform for multi-faith dialogue" that "will strive to promote inter-community peace, tolerance and understanding locally in New York City,

---

[35] Linda S. Kauffman, "World Trauma Center," *American Literary History* 21 (2009): 647-659, 657.

nationally in America, and globally."[36] Here the intersection of the local with the global offers to transform cosmopolitan culture; it also invites a long-overdue discussion in this country. At a time when Muslim-Americans are often vehemently disparaged in the U.S., Park 51 can function as a memorial by asking communities to contemplate the implications of loss rather than succumb to rage.

Park 51 has aroused opposition from conservative groups, such as the Tea Party, and also from some family members of the victims of 9/11. Even though these groups adamantly opposed the center, Manhattan Community Board 1 gave its approval, as did Mayor Michael Bloomberg and President Barack Obama. Announced in 2009 in the *New York Times*, the project did not receive much protest until Pamela Geller and Robert Spencer launched a campaign against the center with the conservative group they named "Stop Islamization of America."[37] This organization used bus ads to protest the project and was the first to call the project the "Ground Zero Mosque." The project's planners insisted that the center was based on medieval Córdoba in Spain, where Muslims, Christians, and Jews existed peacefully; the *New York Times*' report that the original World Trade Center had Muslim religious facilities has not calmed the protesters' anxieties, however.[38] Imam Rauf, the principal planner behind the project, insists that no money from the center will be taken from Hamas or Iran, yet the controversy has not abated. Support and opposition to the project have divided not only 9/11 family members, but also the Muslim-American community and politicians. The controversy has left many Muslims feeling as if much of the nation has no stake in the future of their communities. In August 2010, a CNN poll showed 68 percent of Americans opposed building the center and 29 percent supported it. These numbers show how little has happened since 9/11 to foster a cosmopolitan culture that appeals to reason rather than rage.

In an interview, Imam Feisal Abdul Rauf states his hopes for the center:

---

[36] *Cordoba Initiative: Improving Muslim-West Relations.* Cordoba Initiative, 2008. Accessed September 16, 2011. http://www.cordobainitiative.org/about/imam-feisal/.

[37] Justin Eliot, "How the 'Ground Zero Mosque' Fear Mongering Began," *Salon. Salon.com.*, August 16, 2010. Accessed September 16, 2011. http://www.salon.com/2010/08/16/ground_zero_mosque_origins/.

[38] Samuel G. Fredman, "Muslims and Islam were Part of Twin Towers' Life," *The New York Times*, September 10, 2010. Accessed September 16, 2011. http://www.nytimes.com/2010/09/11/nyregion/11religion.html?pagewanted=all&_r=0.

We wanted to establish a community centre that would focus on a number of things which I believe that we as Muslims need to achieve. Most importantly, to evolve a definition of what we mean by American Muslims...So we have a task to do [and that is to ask,] how do we express ourselves as British Muslims, French Muslims, German Muslims and American Muslims? This is...one of the key aspects of this Cordoba House project...Inter-faith dialogue has evolved beyond just dialogue with each other to understand each other's traditions, to building coalitions around issues of common cause. There are many things in which we are the same as other faith communities, because the real divide is not between Islam and the West or Muslims and Christians, or Muslims and Hindus, but between the moderates of all these faith traditions and the extremists.[39]

Here Rauf alludes to the center's potential to encourage grassroots projects that open physical and conceptual spaces shut down after 9/11, including a dialogue as to why Otherness must be vigilantly guarded not only through cultural memory but also by communities actively engaged in radical democratic practices that affect everyone's lives. Since 9/11, Lower Manhattan has struggled to keep businesses open and create a vibrant community for commerce, recreation, and the arts. Park 51 promises not only to give people a say in the future of their own communities, but also to provide programs to improve people's lives. However difficult it may be for physical symbols to inculcate cosmopolitan sensibilities, such a space in Lower Manhattan would help promote the kind of inter-cultural cooperation and dialogue necessary to transform American society into a more open and inclusive community.

While not a comprehensive solution to the problem of anti-cosmopolitan thinking after 9/11, five characteristics of what viable cosmopolitanism might look like after 9/11 emerge from the debate surrounding Park 51. First, cosmopolitanism must abandon the Enlightenment proposition that defines universal citizenship by reference to white European men. Second, real cosmopolitanism should not be synonymous with mere tolerance. Discussing her view that tolerance not be the primary value in modern society, Wendy Brown argues that the "culturalization" of political conflict fosters a dangerous us-versus-them mentality by insisting "'we' have culture while culture has 'them,' or we *have* culture while they *are* a culture."[40] This disparity makes liberal societies the supposedly neutral arbiters of "culture", while illiberal

---

[39] Feisal Abdul Rauf, "Interview by Narayan Lakshman", *The Hindu*, 2011.
[40] Wendy Brown, *Regulating Aversion: Tolerance in the Age of Identity and Empire* (Princeton, N.J.: Princeton University Press, 2006), p. 151.

societies have cultures "disposed toward barbarism."[41] Muslims must not simply be tolerated but also included in democratic practices predicated on their rights as citizens. Third, to counter nationalism, cosmopolitanism must not fetishize the cultural Other as some kind of extraordinary citizen. Fourth, cosmopolitanism should strive to develop a sense of self with Benhabib's emphasis on hospitality in mind that welcomes the Other when called upon to do so. Last, cosmopolitanism should encourage criticism alongside participation as the twin values of democratic practice as well as ensure safe spaces for all citizens to offer such criticism.

Conclusion

The debate over the building of Park 51 has obliterated what Emmanuel Levinas, in *Time and the Other,* calls the "mystery" of the other person. The entire project of ethics for Levinas moves toward alterity, not totality. How can we claim to know the motives, desires, and intentions of a person who is completely other than us?[42] Levinas challenges a paradigm that seeks full comprehension of the Other by offering one that delights in the mystery of that Other. That mystery fuels cosmopolitan progress and gives feet to democratic practice. In his insightful study of America's culture of commemoration after 9/11, David Simpson asks, "Has the world changed since 9/11?" If the world has not changed, he goes on, "Then who has an interest in claiming that it has?" He then turns to the more central question upon which the first two questions hinge: "Whose world are we talking about?"[43] If someone's perception of the world changed after 9/11, then we can say that the world has changed. If the collective perceptions of a culture have changed, we can begin to track and make sense of those changes. As ideas of cosmopolitanism, ethics, and Otherness keep arising in discussions of 9/11 and its visual culture, the question about how to live in the world necessarily changes.

We have seen shifts in how people live since 9/11 and how we have all adjusted to new norms of safety and paranoia. The Muslim-American community, though, had the most to lose after 9/11. A space was opened for the Bush Administration to declare war on an entire culture, but 9/11 also opened up new avenues for discovering our multiple selves. Post-9/11

---

[41] *Ibid.*

[42] Emmanuel Levinas, *Time and the Other*, translated by Richard A. Cohen, (Pittsburgh, Penn..: Dusquesne University Press, 1987).

[43] David Simpson, *9/11: The Culture of Commemoration* (Chicago, Ill.: University of Chicago Press, 2006), p. 1.

cosmopolitanism has become a way to realize our local, national, and global connections and responsibilities. Rather than serve as an instrument of state-sponsored dreams of empire, it offers a critical start to realize the potential transformation that ethics affords. 9/11 caused us to question our global aspirations and presumptuous imperialism by bringing our allegiances back to the local. At the same time, however, a cosmopolitan spirit arose globally to seek out connections that repair the historical rifts that divide cultures. In doing so, post-9/11 cosmopolitanism creates a way for citizens not simply to tolerate each other but also to assume responsibility for the well-being of each other as citizens, not of the U. S. but of the world.

PART THREE:

RESPONDING TO 9/11

CHAPTER NINE

LESSONS LEARNED AND LOST: ETHNOGRAPHIC INSIGHTS ON POST-9/11 CULTURES OF RESCUE AND RECOVERY

BARRETT P. BRENTON AND ANNE M. GALVIN

The heroic actions undertaken by first responders on 9/11 now stand as symbolic manifestations of self-sacrifice in times of crisis. As the extent of the tragedy unfolded, the institutional cultures of organizations prepared to respond to emergency situations were tested beyond their limits. Volunteer responders also defined the scope and direction of the actions that followed. What emerged were lessons learned and lost concerning best practices for planning proactive and reactive responses to mass disasters. This essay reviews and analyzes the significant role that a local New York City-based agency played in responding to 9/11. It also draws comparisons with the 2010 Haitian Earthquake and 2005's Hurricane Katrina with respect to disaster response and management in order to understand how changing disaster narratives shape the delivery of recovery resources.

The professional response of anthropologists to 9/11 was multifold. Some forensic anthropologists became first responders, going to the scene even before the first tower collapsed. Others continue the work of identifying individuals to this day. Biological anthropologists and archaeologists offered their services and equipment for the seemingly insurmountable recovery of victims at one of the world's largest crime scenes. Cultural anthropologists and linguists worked with the media to dispel misunderstandings about the Islamic world. Linguists helped to sort out other biases lost in translation. Medical anthropologists assisted in assessing the impact of 9/11 on both physical and mental public health. Post-9/11 has been a time for the anthropological profession to attempt to make sense not only of the disaster, but of the consequences of the disaster responses that followed.

As anthropologists, we strive to distance ourselves from our own perspectives. For example, this essay will reveal conflicting opinions held by different groups of people and the respective agencies which generated them. We thus attempt to make sense of a diversity of perspectives through a comparative and contextual framework of analysis for understanding phenomena—in this case, disaster response strategies and their related narratives.

Case Study: Safe Horizon and the Ethnography of Organizational Culture in Times of Crisis

Safe Horizon, a New York City based social service agency, played a leading role on September 12, 2001 with its immediate response to the tragedy and through its assistance to state and city officials in the aftermath. In addition to other larger national emergency response organizations, such as the American Red Cross, the Salvation Army, and Catholic Charities, Safe Horizon established a central position in Lower Manhattan, coordinating access to social services and financial assistance to victims and their families. As days and weeks passed, Safe Horizon's importance as an emergency responder became more defined and increasingly apparent. The organization's leadership and staff were lauded for the effective and efficient results of their work.

The following is a brief description and analysis of a case study on the ethnography of organizational culture in times of crisis that highlights "heroic" actions and intense commitment through the efforts of one agency in a post-9/11 world. There is no doubt that Safe Horizon's role greatly enhanced New York City's effectiveness in responding to this human tragedy. However, an analysis of post-disaster narratives from staff at all levels of the organization reveals structural strains and unanticipated divisions within the organization, providing lessons both learned and lost concerning emergency responses to crises.

The case study is based on qualitative ethnographic research that one of the co-authors (Brenton) conducted with a team that included Renée C. Fox, Helen E. Sheehan, Victor M. Lidz, and Heike Thiel de Bocanegra. We draw heavily from the 2004 report "Safe Horizon after September 11, 2001: A Study of Organizational Stress and Change" and subsequent 2009 publication "Heroic Action and Its Discontents; Safe Horizon's Response to 9/11." Both studies were prepared with support from The Andrew W. Mellon Foundation under the auspices of The Solomon Asch Center for

Study of Ethnopolitical Conflict, housed at the University of Pennsylvania during the research period and now at Bryn Mawr College.[1] Safe Horizon was founded in 1978 as Victim Services, Inc., to operate reception centers at law courts for victims of crimes and to serve as a communications system to inform witnesses when they would be needed in court. In addition to its presence in the courts, the staff worked in police precincts, district attorneys' offices, medical facilities, and some forty schools, serving victims of domestic violence, sexual assault, and other crimes. Before 9/11, it had community offices in all five boroughs of New York City, operated nearly 75 programs at some 100 locations, had 800 employees, and served some 250,000 clients annually.[2]

Since Safe Horizon was an established pre-9/11grantee of the New York State Crime Victim Board (CVB), it was able to compensate victims of crime and their families for out-of-pocket losses. By September 12, the agency's leadership had already begun developing a plan for distributing CVB funds to 9/11 victims. This was linked to Family Assistance Centers that coordinated a range of referral services to meet individual client needs in cooperation with the Federal Emergency Management Agency (FEMA) and other local, state, and national agencies. Safe Horizon was in a unique position to create Borough Assistance Centers in their already existing offices located throughout the outer boroughs of the city.

The primary Family Assistance Center was established by the Mayor's Office at Pier 94 on the Hudson River. This was the center of relief operations in the city. Work at Pier 94 was seen by Safe Horizon staff and others as "front-line" action. With already established hotlines for victims of domestic violence and other crimes, the organization also created a new hotline to field 9/11-related calls. They received hundreds of calls a day and thousands per week until the end of 2001. In addition, Safe Horizon was instrumental in "providing guidance and training to a sizeable number of professionals in social work, psychology, and related fields in how to provide services for the effects of trauma."[3]

As an organization deeply rooted in every New York City borough, Safe Horizon had the best first-hand local knowledge of the city's complex

---

[1] Renée C. Fox, Victor M. Lidz, Helen E. Sheehan, Barrett P. Brenton, and Heike Thiel de Bocanegra, "Safe Horizon after September 11, 2001: A Study of Organizational Stress and Change," Final report submitted to the Solomon Asch Center for Study of Ethnopolitical Conflict, and the Mellon Foundation, 2004, and *idem.*, "Heroic action and its discontents: Safe Horizon's response to 9/11," *Social Science and Modern Society* 46 n. 4 (2009): 308-318.

[2] Fox, *et. al.*, "Heroic Action," p. 309.

[3] *Ibid.*, p. 311.

infrastructure of political, social, financial, educational, and medical institutions. With this local knowledge of NYC institutional cultures, it was an agency poised to respond quickly to post-9/11 efforts. The organization "spoke with the voice of New York and of New Yorkers in ways and to a degree that were not matched by agencies with more geographically distant national structures of management and control. The local attributes of Safe Horizon also helped its staff to communicate effectively and reassuringly with 9/11 victims."[4]

The required interviews for CVB compensation were an incredibly emotional experience for all parties involved. Safe Horizon went to great lengths to provide a psychologically supportive interview system to cope with these feelings. "Some clients were so traumatized that they had difficulty in describing their situations, or even 'went blank' when asked why they had come to the pier. Others had difficulty in collecting required documents. Some were overcome by intense, labile emotions. Many clients had an acute need to tell detailed stories of their losses."[5] In addition, the largely middle to upper-middle class clientele could at time become impatient or agitated when they did not receive the kind of prompt service they generally expected from professionals. This contrasted with the reactions of the less-privileged individuals whom Safe Horizon staff generally served in their traditional non-9/11 capacity.

A real challenge for Safe Horizon was that the high client demand created a need to speed up the interview process. In response, some staff members worked around the clock in the first weeks following 9/11. These "front-line" activities took both an emotional and physical toll; however, for many of them, "...the gratification and sense of meaning that they felt in being able to bring hands-on solace and help to those who were suffering from the devastation of 9/11, outweighed the stresses that they experienced in their personal relationships..."[6] They also felt a sense of exhilaration in being recognized as "heroes" by management and the media. This created a professional divide at Pier 94 between veteran staff trained in psychological and social services for trauma victims who knew their limits and less experienced staff members and volunteers who pushed themselves beyond their capabilities in the rush of the moment. Veteran staff cautioned against what became termed "the madness of the Pier." Without "establishing boundaries" or "setting limits", they might be consumed by 9/11 work and "develop "compassion fatigue" or become

---

[4] *Ibid.*
[5] *Ibid.*, p. 312.
[6] *Ibid.*, p. 313.

"high" or "hooked" on trauma and "glory" and be labeled as "Trauma Junkies."[7]

This "heroization" added to what began to emerge as the "big divide" within Safe Harbor between the prioritization of 9/11 operations and the still highly demanding daily operations of the organization, which did not diminish because of the tragedy. Post-disaster responders consistently struggle with the need to balance within their own personal and professional identities the intensity of emergency response activities and the rhythm of their day-to-day lives. All staff respectfully recognized each other's professional and personal contributions and dedication to the organization's mission. However, intra-agency tensions became revealed when the phrase "going to the pier" came to be considered the most exemplary response to the 9/11 emergency, and the time that staff spent working at that site was called "hero hours."[8]

Safe Horizon's unyielding commitment to serving all victims equally, coupled with the enormous public response of compassion and funding for 9/11-related programs, resulted in a "two-tiered" situation. Priority seemed to be given to well-funded 9/11 programs over the always underfunded traditional victim services. This disparity was troubling to those throughout the organization. In short, "[T]hey saw an unjust distinction being drawn between the 'privileged trauma' of 9/11 victims and the suffering of traditional clients, whose predicaments were pushed outside the 'circle of concern.'" "The welfare mom...her loss, her trauma [is] as severe as anybody that lost a family member [in 9/11]," a staff member vehemently affirmed. For the staff of non-9/11 programs, salary and resource inequities constituted a "strange" and unfair "disconnect" from existing Safe Horizon programs that relied on minimal funding and low staff salaries under city or state contracts.[9]

This divide "challenged the universalistic and egalitarian principles and organizational culture on which Safe Horizon was founded—namely the beliefs that 'a victim is a victim is a victim'; that the suffering of all victims merits respectful compassion; that 'a staff person is a staff person is a staff person'; and that everyone engaged in serving victims should be treated equitably."[10] Realizing the discrepancy, Safe Horizon's leadership hoped that they would be able to leverage their 9/11 response to advocate effectively for more resources for *all* victims. This view is at the core of its mission statement: "[to] provide support, prevent violence, and promote

[7] *Ibid.*, p. 314.
[8] *Ibid.*
[9] *Ibid.*, p. 315.
[10] *Ibid.*, p. 316.

justice for victims of crime and abuse, their families and communities." It supports an organizational culture that promotes at its core an ethos of solidarity between staff members and victims. This culture of cohesion sustained the agency before, during, and after 9/11.[11]

A critical lesson to be learned from the response of Safe Horizon to the crises of 9/11 is that, unlike responses from larger more nationally-based organization, "Safe Horizon was better able to engage well-trained professionals with experience pertinent to the traumas of 9/11...Its management distinguished itself by its cooperation with other agencies and by sharing its expertise on local conditions—knowing with whom to speak in city and state government and knowing the racial, ethnic, and community diversity of New Yorkers."[12] As anthropologists, we well know the importance of local knowledge in both understanding and responding to any situation.

The lesson that we hope is not lost is this case is that phenomena associated with "heroism" were "often accompanied by a degree of *over-commitment* that entailed substantial, even perilous, physical, psychological, and interpersonal costs."[13] Organizations must be fully prepared to reduce the emotional and physical toll that the "heroic" acts of over-committed individuals can inflict upon themselves. Doing so can also lessen divisions in the institutional culture of an organization. In the end, Safe Horizon distributed over $250 million in assistance to some 26,000 victims and family members, and provided additional services to tens of thousands more. The organization continues to be proud of its role it in the post-9/11 recovery and remains strongly committed to its original mission to provide services to victims of crime and abuse, their families, and communities throughout the boroughs of New York City. True to their convictions and ethos of solidarity, the slogan on their webpage currently reads "Safe Horizon moves victims of violence from crisis to confidence."[14]

Time, Memory, and Disaster Narrative

The examination of Safe Horizon's ethos—"a victim is a victim is a victim"—in the context of its response to 9/11 provides valuable insight into how disaster narratives change over time, taking different forms

---

[11] *Ibid.*
[12] *Ibid.*, p. 317.
[13] *Ibid.*
[14] www.Safehorizon.org. Accessed July 1, 2012.

depending upon the population defined as "victims." These narratives and the identities that accompany them influence how disaster relief is administered. As seen in the case of the 9/11 service recipients, social position deeply influenced how they sought out services, while the nature of the tragedy they faced—one that was defined by nationalism, patriotism, and heroism on the part of victims and first responders—also helped to demarcate them as worthy recipients of aid. However, with the passage of time, the narratives surrounding their experience of terror changed, as did the identities of those affected.

Researchers studying the acquisition of social services have noted that certain identities are valued over others based upon the settings and narratives in which they are embedded. Narratives are created using cultural knowledge that helps guide understandings of what is likely to happen and who is likely to behave in particular ways within the narrative.[15] Narratives help to establish the cultural criteria by which eligibility for services is determined. For example, as time passed following 9/11 and it became clear that first responders fell sick with long-term illnesses caused by exposure to toxins at Ground Zero, a debate opened up about which illnesses would be "eligible" for first responder medical assistance programs and which may have developed because of lifestyle choices predating the terrorist attacks. Here there is a gap between the "epidemiological substantiation of plausible links between environmental exposure and illness onset" and the "social acceptance of illness."[16]

Debate was particularly fraught in relation to the spike in lung cancer rates amongst first responders. The question of personal responsibility versus exposure to toxins during an act of heroism entered into the public discourse around first responders only after a significant amount of time had passed and identities and narratives associated with the attack had begun to change. Eventually, the purposefully developed narrative of abandonment and ethical responsibility prompted renewed advocacy work on behalf of the "forgotten heroes."[17] Indeed, it can be argued that the hope and conflict felt throughout the 9/11 rescue, recovery, and rebuilding process can be better understood when we examine the cultural transformation of responders from hero to victim to patient. Time will also

---

[15] Lauren J. Silver, "Spaces of Encounter: Public Bureaucracy and the Making of Client Identities," *ETHOS* 38 n. 3 (2010): 275-296, p. 296.

[16] Lisa K. Vanderlinden, "Left in the Dust: Negotiating Environmental Illness in the Aftermath of 9/11," *Medical Anthropology: Cross-Cultural Studies in Health and Illness* 30 n. 1 (2011): 30-55.

[17] *Ibid.*

continue to shape these roles through narratives defined in part through the lens of medico-legal and 9/11 subcultural identities.

The role of narrative in constructions of "victim" identity and eligibility is equally clear in the disaster response following both the Haitian earthquake in 2010 and after Hurricane Katrina devastated New Orleans in 2005. In the Haitian case, the narrow identification of earthquake victim changed as services proved ineffective in providing long-term solutions to the problem of Internally Displaced Persons (IDP), housing, and the eruption of a cholera epidemic. Back in the United States, the victim identity in the wake of Hurricane Katrina was divided contentiously along racial lines, as it became clear that poor black populations were disproportionately disadvantaged in terms of their ability to evacuate, the amount of property damage, and the rate of mortality, as well as in terms of their ability to qualify for services and "recover." Many lessons were learned from 9/11, but what has time and memory lost in terms of how organizations are mobilized for disaster relief on an even more massive scale? The next case study highlights analogies that can be drawn from responses to the Haitian Earthquake of January 2010.

Case Study: Lessons on Perpetual Crises from the Haitian Earthquake of 2010

Though the circumstances of the 2010 Haitian earthquake disaster differ in significant ways from the tragedy of 9/11/2001, an examination of the post-earthquake response reveals similar discontinuities and contradictions in the nature of twenty-first century recovery effort models. Indeed, the Haitian earthquake and its aftermath highlight some issues that are consistent with the approach to disaster response after 9/11. In particular, we find that population vulnerability dramatically influences subjection to risk factors, levels of trauma, and response outcomes. Secondly, within predominant models of recovery, the label of "victim" changes over the duration of the response in relation to public discourses about the failure and success of the recovery efforts and conflicts over appropriate claims to aid.

Haiti's profound poverty, complex geo-political position, and notorious national politics clearly exacerbated the effects of the 7.0 Richter Scale earthquake that killed an estimated 300,000 people and reduced an additional 1. 5 million citizens to Internally Displaced Persons status, as the decaying dwellings and government buildings collapsed upon aid workers and residents. In addition, the lack of potable or even treatable water prior to the earthquake fostered a post-earthquake cholera epidemic that claimed even more victims. The international response to the earthquake was extraordinary, with over two billion private dollars donated within two months. A number of national governments made most of the aid commitments in response to news of the disaster and the ensuing flood of images depicting the pain and suffering of the Haitian people. The United States alone pledged 1.1 billion dollars in emergency aid.

The prevailing international disaster recovery model directs public funding through private entities like NGOs. One of the largest failures of the Haiti recovery response has been the delivery of aid to the Haitian people. The majority of the aid went to the Interim Haitian Recovery Commission established to oversee and coordinate the recovery process, not to the Haitian government itself. The condition of the IDP camps throughout Haiti calls into question the efficacy of this service delivery model. Reports from the camps reveal that nearly a year after the initial disaster, 40.5 percent still had no water and 30 percent lacked toilets; some others had only thirty toilets for more than 30,000 people. Only 10 percent of all IDP families even had a tent for shelter. The lack of coordination amongst hundreds of independently operating NGOs has resulted in patchy service provision and little structural accountability for those organizations that fail to fulfill their stated obligations.[18]

Within this systemic failure, the status of Haitian IDPs has also been redefined. In the early days after the earthquake, the survivors were perceived as poignant victims, worthy of aid. However, as the recovery efforts faltered, the victims became redefined in relation to their "failure" to depart from the camps. The IDPs reported efforts to oust them, accusing camp officials of shutting off water supplies and of rejecting food aid and other resources. Driving these actions was the rationale that if food, shelter, schooling, and health care was regularly made available in the camps, "people will never leave." Local authorities also regularly claimed that individuals faked IDP status and came into the camps during the day to take advantage of the resources and then returned to their homes at night. In this way, a population initially defined as "victims" was transformed into a resource drain because of the changing post-earthquake narrative and its perceived propensity for dependency. These character analyses tend to ignore the fact that most IDP camp residents no longer have homes and must rely on the camps for even the most minimal shelter. What is more, IDPs have genuine concerns about returning to existing

---

[18] Mark Schuller, *Mèt Kò Veye Kò: Foreign responsibility in the failure to protect against cholera and other man-made disasters*. January 22, 2011. Accessed July 15, 2013. http://ijdh.org/wordpress/wp-content/uploads/2011/01/Report-met-ko-veye-ko-final.pdf

sources of shelter because of uncertainties about structural damage possibly caused by the quake. Many also fear sleeping under concrete roofs after seeing family members buried by building rubble.[19]

Unfortunately, the depiction of the IDPs as living an improved lifestyle in the camps by collecting undeserved benefits has provided both national governments and NGOs with excuses to withhold most pledged government funds and private donations. In fact, members of the U.S. Congress referenced this narrative to justify deferring the 1.15 billion dollars that Congress had initially promised. According to Oxfam, only 5 percent of the rubble had been cleared, 15 percent of the temporary housing had been built, and less than 45 percent of the 2.5 billion dollars in aid had been disbursed a full year after the earthquake.[20]

Case Study: Lessons of Structural Inequality from New Orleans after Hurricane Katrina, 2005

The aftermath of Hurricane Katrina illustrates yet another example of how cultural narratives influence disaster response, "victim" identity, and assistance eligibility. Once again, there was a sense of shock that a tragedy of this magnitude could happen in a highly industrialized nation like the United States. The natural disaster brought racial and economic inequality within the country briefly to the center of national discourse. In August of 2005, 80 percent of the city of New Orleans was flooded when hurricane-induced storm surges broke through the levees. However, the effects of Katrina were not felt evenly across the population of New Orleans. African-American, poor, and elderly residents took the brunt of the harm due to longstanding economic and social problems in the city that became intensified by Katrina's uneven effects.[21]

The changing, culturally embedded disaster narratives that centered on the populations most deeply injured by the flooding influenced victim access to and eligibility for relief aid and provide particular insight into the social position of poorer New Orleaneans from the perspective of the American public at large. In what Nancy Scheper-Hughes has called a "slip of the tongue," local storm victims became widely mischaracterized

---

[19] Accessed July 15, 2013. http://sites.tufts.edu/jha/archives/869.

[20] Accessed July 1, 2012. http://www.cepr.net/index.php/blogs/relief-and-reconstruction-watch/relief-and-reconstruction-the-year-in-review-part-i.

[21] Marla Nelson, Marla, Renia Ehrenfeucht, and Shirley Laska, "Planning, Plans, and People: Professional Expertise, Local Knowledge, and Governmental Action in Post-Hurricane Katrina New Orleans," *Cityscape: A Journal of Policy Development and Research* 9 n. 3 (2007): 23-52.

as "refugees," a term that by definition refers to groups evicted from their home countries that then seek refuge in a receiving nation.[22] Adding an additional layer to this concept of disaster narrative, Scheper-Hughes, following Clifford Geertz, argues that, "At times of crisis and catastrophe, people seek explanation for what happened. Even a bad explanation can seem better than none at all."[23] In this case, the "bad explanation" included population stereotypes that ascribed to the victims laziness, stubbornness, and "refusal" or failure to act in time. Those killed, injured, or displaced because of Katrina were not delivered to the American public pre-packaged as patriotic heroes in the manner of 9/11 victims because of the markedly different causes of the trauma which each group suffered and because of differing social positions between northern and southern, white and black, high income and low income people. Yes, a diversity of people lost their lives on 9/11 but the overwhelming majority came from middle- to high-income households. Ironically, we may never know the number of unidentified individuals from the undocumented population who supported day-to-day business in the Twin Towers.

The Katrina victims, forced from their homes *and* their home state in many cases, were labeled "refugees," a title that failed to acknowledge their American-ness and the justice of their claims to the rights of citizenship. As the disaster unfolded, the effect became magnified when news outlets shifted coverage to report on outbreaks of "looting," sexual assault, and other forms of interpersonal violence rather than on the lack of disaster planning, poor population management, and increased militarism of state and local authorities. As the disaster narrative changed, images of helpless New Orleans' residents drowning, dying from dehydration, and waving items of clothing to alert slow-arriving rescue and recovery teams yielded to images of a criminal population running amok. Prisoners were shown escaping their cells and mixing in with the other hurricane victims, who were often depicted shattering store windows in search of food and other supplies.

Such narratives contributed to long-held stereotypes about African-Americans and African-American men, in particular. The stereotypes influenced local relief organizations, which located the threat with the external community and began withdrawing from the very populations they had been assembled to assist when confronted with internal reports of

---

[22] Nancy Scheper-Hughes, "Katrina: The Disaster and its Doubles," *Anthropology Today* 21 n. 6 (2005): 2-4.
[23] *Ibid.*, p. 2.

sexual assault against a largely Euro-American group of volunteers.[24] Long-time New Orleans residents who had experienced a history of neglect and indignity acutely perceived the denial of their citizenship claims, reinforcing their deep distrust of governmental bureaucracy.[25]

Once the displaced population became viewed as a burden on their receiving communities, their displacement became seen as an opportunity to rebuild New Orleans without all of the "social problems" created by vast economic and racial inequality. However, the national narrative and the local narrative were in many ways contradictory. According to the local narrative, these disadvantaged populations had become impediment to municipal, state, and federal redevelopment plans because of their *activism*. A strong sense of community and citizenship led them to form coalitions that advocated to redevelop their own neighborhoods in the face of development plans that often appeared to exclude them.[26]

Conclusions

The extremes of hope and conflict felt throughout the process of rescue, recovery, and rebuilding of communities can only be fully understood by analyzing the culturally-embedded identity transformations that take place over time. Changing cultural narratives redefined and transformed post-9/11 responders from hero to victim to patient. By comparing trajectories of disaster narrative in post-earthquake Haiti and post-Katrina New Orleans, better understanding can be gained about how stories of those affected by disaster shape claims to aid in the eyes of broader national and international audiences. These definitions dramatically influence service delivery by determining which recipients are "worthy" victims as opposed to those who allegedly enjoy an improved lifestyle by "taking advantage" of recovery related resources.

The regulated and unregulated responses reviewed in these comparisons reveal a number of challenges to achieving any type of sustainable long-term recovery model. In the post-9/11 recovery efforts, tensions between responders, survivors, and victim's families still spark highly emotional private and very public debates more than ten years after the tragedy. The role of both public and private institutions in effective disaster-related responses to 9/11, the Haitian Earthquake, and Hurricane Katrina can be

---

[24] Rachel E. Luft, "Looking for Common Ground: Relief Work in Post-Katrina New Orleans as an American Parable of Race and Gender Violence," *NWSA Journal* 20 n. 3 (2008): 5-31.

[25] Nelson, *op. cit.*

[26] *Ibid.*

further understood by drawing analogies with the 2004 Indian Ocean Tsunami, the 2011 Japanese Earthquake and Tsunami, and others. An analysis of disaster response to Hurricane Sandy in 2012 in New York City will provide a particularly poignant case for future comparisons.

The international humanitarian aid community constantly evaluates their emergency responses to acute crisis. The question of accountability, or lack thereof, to affected populations in both short- and long-term recovery efforts has emerged as a central area of concern. The 1994 genocide in Rwanda is often invoked as a worst case scenario of an international response that almost completely lacked any accountability. This wake-up call and the subsequent crises reviewed in this essay have led to a number of international quality and accountability initiatives, such as "The Sphere Project" and the "Humanitarian Accountability Partnership." In a major shift, victims of crises are now accorded a role in their own recovery efforts. A recent 2012 United Nations Food and Agricultural Organization (FAO) report[27] has supported a view that:

> ...promotes an underlying tenet that people affected by emergencies are end users and stakeholders rather than "beneficiaries" of humanitarian assistance, that they have a fundamental right to shape efforts to assist them, and that humanitarian actors have a duty to respond to people's expressions of their rights and needs. Accountability to affected populations (AAP) is a people-centered approach, sensitive to the dignity of all human beings...[28]

To address the issue of active participation and representation in the context of the disaster narratives summarized above, the following anthropologically-informed checklist of questions is useful for establishing a practical, program-focused starting point for integrating human agency into disaster response:[29]

Do all interest groups have a voice, including women, children, the aged, minority cultural groups and people living with disabilities?

Are community representatives truly representative of the communities? Does participation in relief programs occur independently of political, governmental or other power based representation structures?

---

[27] *FAO in Emergencies Guidance Note: Accountability to Affected Populations* (2012). United Nations Food and Agricultural Organization: Rome.
[28] *Ibid.*, p. 1.
[29] *Ibid.*, pp. 8-9.

Do communities or their representatives participate in developing criteria for targeting and selecting of those who receive assistance?

Disasters are often catalysts for profound social and cultural change of organizations and people. Again, we stress the overall importance of anthropologically and ethnographically informed analyses of post-disaster narratives and organizational cultures as a means for making future recommendations. They enhance our capacity to make meaning of disaster events while embracing the diverse contexts out of which actions become planned and realized, revealing the importance of accountability. This framework does present a number of challenges for achieving any type of sustainable long-term recovery since both regulated and unregulated responses are so often shaped through the memories and narratives constructed from past crises. With this in mind, we may better realize our roles as advocates when devising future policy based on lessons learned and lost. In the end, the best practices for planning proactive and reactive responses to mass disaster are those that are sensitive, responsible, and accountable to human dignity.

Chapter Ten

Teaching 9/11: The Memorial Quilt at Empire State College

Barbara Kantz and Amy Ruth Tobol

Ten years after the attacks on the World Trade Center, colleges and universities continue to look for ways to "teach" these events. As institutions of higher learning, colleges are devoted to collecting, reflecting, preserving, and creating new information. College communities provide venues for thinking about teachable issues as we explore ways to help students find intellectual and personal growth as well as meaning in disasters like 9/11, which so many of our student and we personally experienced.

We are intimately connected to the events and aftermath of 9/11 by our proximity to New York City. As educators at SUNY Empire State College, we work primarily with adult students in a non-traditional educational setting. Many of our students work in the city limits and belong to unions as police officers, firefighters, EMT's, electricians, plumbers, carpenters, and steel workers. Two of our police officer students died on the site, while a number of students employed in the towers also perished. In the days, months and years that followed, our students, especially those in the building trades, became involved in recovery and rebuilding operations. Some of our faculty members live within a few blocks of Ground Zero. So many of our students and staff were very directly affected by this tragedy.

In this essay, we will explore how college communities approached and offered teaching experiences for students and local residents. Then we will explore the unique experience of SUNY Empire State College, where our community undertook a memorial quilt project that we continue to use in our classes. Many colleges and universities commemorated the ten-year anniversary of 9/11 through a wide range of activities that provided teaching moments as well as occasions for healing and self-reflection. These anniversary events also provided an opportunity to collect new and historical artifacts that reveal the impact of 9/11 on the university, its members, and the broader culture. New "artifacts" were garnered through conducting interviews, reflections, speeches, oral histories, and the creation of works of art.

Purposeful activities on college campuses across the United States included candlelight vigils, remembrance ceremonies, concerts, read-ins, teach-ins, flag installations, expression boards, bell tolling, walks and runs, wreath laying, collaborations between town and gown, creation of memorial structures like fountains benches and plaques, T-shirt sales, panel discussions, unity walks, moments of silence, prayer services, messages sent to Ground Zero by emissaries, and a day of service. Panel discussions included topics on Osama Bin Laden, homeland security, civil liberties, interfaith relations, violence, memory, the so-called New World Order, and the Arab Spring. Panel discussants included Washington officials, CEO's, military professionals, media representatives, first responders, and family members of those lost. Frequently asked questions included ones about what we have learned and where we are going now ten years on, and how the U.S. and world have changed since 9/11. One college organized a panel discussion on the impact of the terrorist attacks on six academic disciplines. Colleges with religious missions offered church services with themes of unity, peace, forgiveness, interfaith worship, and even Buddhist reflections.[1] At Washington University in St. Louis, for example, students organized a "Ten Years Later" memorial event. In their minds "this event serves not only as a way to honor the memories of those lost in the attacks, but also as a way for us to reflect upon the way the attacks affect us as a community—locally, nationally, and internationally."[2] All of these teaching and learning activities help foster a strong sense of community found at a university.

Empire State College is a unique institution. Founded in 1971, the impetus for its establishment grew out of the challenges of the post-World War II era. The postwar university strove to meet two main demands. The first one was to educate employees for careers in industry, business, and government, while the second one was to train scientists and engineers to create new technologies to harness atomic energy and conquer outer space in the face of the real and perceived threats of the Cold War. The 1940's

---

[1] "Remembering 9/11: Ten Years Later." Accessed July 31, 2013. http://www.naicu.edu/special_initiatives/remembering-911-ten-years-later.
[2] "Ten Years Later, 9/11 remembered on WUSTL campus is a variety of ways." Accessed July 31, 2013. http://news.wustl.edu/news/Pages/22648.aspx.

and 1950's witnessed the founding of state university systems that fit this mold. In New York State, the state legislature, with the support of Governor Thomas E. Dewey, created the nation's largest and last state university in 1948—the State University of New York (SUNY)—in response to these new needs and the changing demographics of New York. New York experienced an influx of veterans after the war who, in addition to home buying, wanted to use the G.I. bill to obtain a college education. The various SUNY schools provided an affordable publicly-funded way for veterans to receive an education that made them marketable in this new postwar world. These older students, in turn, influenced the colleges they attended.[3]

In the 1960s, a markedly different set of circumstances influenced the goals, role, and curriculum of universities and colleges. Here institutions of higher learning had to respond to the issues raised by the civil rights, feminist and Vietnam anti-war movements, together with the sexual revolution, Kennedy assassination, and coming of age of iconoclastic war babies and baby boomers, all of whom demanded that the postwar research university be recast along more progressive lines. The ideal of a student-centered pedagogy became a central theme of the student and faculty activism of the 1960s, and non-traditional education became a goal of the progressive university. Access, relevance, and low-cost consumer delivery became the new modeling forces that shaped the university and its curriculum. Empire State College was founded during this tumultuous and exciting era.[4] SUNY Empire State College was the brainchild of then SUNY chancellor, Ernest Boyer, who envisioned a college that emphasized individual student-centered needs. He worked closely with James Hall, an assistant vice president of policy and planning at SUNY's central administration, who later became SUNY Empire State College's first president and led the institution for its first twenty-five years.[5]

The significance of SUNY Empire State College for this essay was, and still is, its emphasis on individualized degree programs that recognize

---

[3] James Hall with Barbara Kevles, ed., *In Opposition to Core Curriculum: Alternative Models for Undergraduate Education* (Westport, Conn: Greenwood Press, 1982) chapter two; and Lewis Mayhew, *Legacy of the Seventies* (San Francisco, Cal.: Jossey-Bass Publishers, 1977) chapter one.

[4] Hall, *op. cit*, p. 25; Mayhew, op. cit, p. 43. For a history of SUNY Empire State College, see Richard Bonnabeau, *The Promise Continues: Empire State College, the First 25 Years* (Albany, N.Y.: SUNY Empire State College, 1996). Also see Barbara Kantz, "Promises Kept: Empire State College on its 25th Anniversary," *Long Island Historical Journal* 10 n. 1 (1997): 56-70.

[5] *Empire State College News* 23 (Spring 1996): 3-5.

learning both inside and outside the classroom. The college is nontraditional in the students it serves, its model of pedagogy, and especially, its service delivery system. With its unique mentoring system, the college offers highly individualized and flexible programs of study with five admissions and enrollment periods. College credit can be offered by demonstrating prior learning gained in formal or informal settings. The college thus purposely allows a student to design his or her own degree plan.[6] A 2010 "Letter to the Editor" by Arthur Chickering, the founding academic vice president of SUNY Empire State College, referred to these founding principles when he wrote, "…we needed to help each person move as far as possible toward full maturity."[7]

Educational experiences at SUNY Empire State College are thus designed to integrate personal and professional accomplishments with what the adult student learns in the academy. Adult learning theorists argue that adults learn more quickly and fully when their learning has ready usefulness in their personal or work lives.[8] This explains why the response at SUNY Empire State College to a disaster like 9/11 immediately became, as a matter of course, part of the curriculum in the individualized degree programs of students. Ours is not an abstract education but rather one with a "whole person approach" that integrates personal life, work, and coursework into a useful whole. SUNY Empire State College has led the way, along with other progressive and innovative models of education, in promoting the notion that the personal can and should be integrated into academic learning.[9]

Nearly all our students have traditionally been working adults; many work off-hour shifts as law enforcement personnel, EMTs, and firefighters. Since our main mode of educational delivery is one-on-one, students meet with their faculty mentors face-to-face several times over a term to complete their course work. Each course is individually designed with their academic level and interests in mind. The faculty and staff know our students and the circumstances of their lives very well. It is not unusual for our students to share with us news about a birth, death, promotion, or job loss.

This deep personal, academic, and professional intimacy with our students means we wanted to create a safe environment for all of us to

---

[6] For more information on SUNY Empire State College, see www.esc.edu. Accessed July 31, 2013.
[7] "Letter to the Editor" in *All About Mentoring*, (Winter 2010): 38.
[8] M. S. Knowles, *Andragogy in Action: Applying Modern Principles of Adult Education* (San Francisco, Cal.: Jossey Bass, 1984).
[9] *Ibid.*

express the grief, outrage, and pain caused by 9/11. Preserving the memories of events and people formed an important part of our healing process. We therefore chose to create a community quilt called "United in Community and Memory" to memorialize those we lost as well as to make sense of the attacks. The project strove to highlight the college as a site for unity, collective work, and connection. The work of our community of faculty, students, professional employees, and alumni is now on permanent display at the college's Long Island Center in Hauppauge.

Fig. 10.1 Braglia Quilt Piece

We asked students, alumni, faculty, and friends to create individual blocks for our quilt. Rather than a conventional quilt, we strove for a quilt that could be displayed on walls and shared with others in public places. We eventually received enough blocks to create four hanging panels. These blocks reflect many of the techniques used in the past to create memorial quilts to tell very powerful, individual stories. Together, they form a collective, complex, and often paradoxical narrative of 9/11. Some of the blocks resemble those of the AIDS quilt that memorialize a particular person. Sylvia Carter, a student at the time, incorporated a piece of her mother's sweater in her block. Sylvia's mother had died in 2001, so 9/11 and her mother's death are forever intertwined in her memories, just as the sweater's crocheted red, white and blue rosettes connect to America.

Our office manager, Lisa Braglia, created her block in memory of a student who intended to enroll with us on September 13th. Lisa shared this about her block:

> Tommy's square is made out of denim, a fabric suited for hard work. I wanted it to represent him and all of the people at the World Trade Center who didn't sit in offices or behind desks. The shamrocks reflect his family heritage. His Mets are represented. The heart is made of electrical wire and the tools explain themselves. To make Tommy's square, I had to learn a skill that I've never tried: sewing. My beginner's effort shows. But as someone who repairs ripped hems with scotch tape, I hope I've imparted some of what Tommy was into his square. By honoring him, I've had to learn something new...his memory has given me that gift. For that, and of his wonderful but too short life, I will always remember him.

A number of people created squares as a way to remember our students, not as they died, but rather how they had lived. For example, co-author Barbara Kantz sewed her quilt square, "9/11 Evidence", to honor her student Tim Roy. A devoted New York City police sergeant who loved his work, Tim was cheerful, enthusiastic, and easy with conversation and learning. In our study together, he came to each meeting prepared to discuss with delight the books he was reading. He was also a good and clear writer. Tim's appointments were usually in mid-afternoon when I typically take lunch. Since I am hypoglycemic, I usually ate while we talked. The square in Tim's honor is therefore a dinner napkin from my home, a bright fabric with shard-shaped colors. The doily cut in the shape of a heart is stapled under a plastic bag called "evidence bag." The "evidence bag" is filled with a message: "Grief is a consequence of Love." Tim loved his work, his family, and his learning. I enjoyed our work together. I was deeply touched and delighted that one of Tim Roy's daughters spoke at the ten-year commemorative ceremony at Ground Zero. She said that she was glad that he had been her dad, observing "This would have pleased him immensely."

Other quilters used recognizable symbols of peace, patriotism, love, connection, and images of the World Trade Center buildings in their quilt blocks. An example of these motifs came in faculty member Silvia Chelala's block. She wrote this about the creation of her block:

Fig. 10.2 Kantz Quilt Piece

I tried to reproduce...the feeling of devastation and desolation I felt the first night I could go home. As I live nine blocks away from Ground Zero, I did not get back home until three days after. The first night I could go back, I took a subway to West Fourth which was the last station that the train would take me downtown.

When I got out, everything looked normal except that there were no cars. I walked, wearily, down La Guardia until I reached Houston. There I was stopped by a police block. I had to find identification that showed my address so that I could cross the barricade. I was so nervous. Someone had given me a mask which I found essential at that precise moment.

Once I showed my driver's license, I was allowed to continue walking south on West Broadway. There was complete silence. There was thick smoke that choked me. There were no people at a time in the early evening when most restaurants would have been filled with patrons. There were isolated store lights. What really frightened me was the quality of the air and the apparent stillness. The scene reminded me of a World War II movie, in black and white, with a lot of mist and smoke. The smoke was dense but it contained particles of something. I know that I had problems breathing. And the smell!!! It was horrible.

The square tries to capture the feelings of sadness, dismay, outrage, and fear. The two towers are really ghosts of the real fallen ones. The sparkles are the particles. The grey color is the smoke. On one side, I sewed a bookmark from the Borders bookstore originally located in one of the towers. I thought about the life, the music, the ideas, and the people that this little bookmark represented. I decided that the bookmark was a token of our memories, of how we will not forget. Images of the Twin Towers in this and other quilts have evolved into symbols that evoke contradictory feelings of power, pain, and pride. For many of us living in New York City, they had been a real touchstone and living part of our lives and our landscape. For others, the quilt was an opportunity to express conflicting feelings about the attacks. Faculty member Yvonne Murphy reflected on these emotions:

> When I decided to make a quilt block for this project my mind immediately went to the towers. They were always the compass by which I navigated north and south. For the...years I lived in Manhattan...they were my back yard. I have made the towers out of paper sewn with mending thread to cloth in order to illustrate how fragile and temporal even an omnipotent icon can be. The words, barely legible, are instructions about how to deal with the anniversary of a traumatic event. The instructions warn about dreams, memories, thoughts and feelings all of which haunt us now. I found the red, white and blue ribbon serendipitously in a dresser drawer; it stands for the hope that we will find meaning and healing in our grieving. At first, I wanted to fill the sky above the towers with stars...However, I couldn't help myself and I just kept embellishing and embellishing...I have had a lot of experience with grief. In the recent past, I have worked with dying children and their parents. My job as a poet was to guide them with writing about their hopes and fears as a way to manage and voice their experience. Whenever one of my students died, I would cope and grieve by constantly imaging the air and sky filled with the color and beauty of their lives. I borrow and imagine that now as I fill in what would be the air around the towers with the jeweled tones of the nearly 3,000 lives.

For her block, co-author Amy Ruth Tobol used abstract images to reflect her reactions to the attacks. The blue background represents the sky that day, while dots of red represent blood. I then printed peace signs and, finally, created a rubber block to stamp an abstract image representing the windows of the World Trade Center. The peace symbol is sometimes hidden, sometimes in full view. The beads used for the peace symbol in the upper-right hand corner are 1960s love beads. The embroidered word "imagine" evokes John Lennon's famous song about a peaceful world. I think the more abstract quality of my block reflects our distance from the event. The theme is more global and somehow less individual. Though I've always had a global perspective in my work as a lawyer, I was moving past some part of my personal pain in creating this block and thinking about how lucky I am. I am not faced with a 9/11 every day of my life as are people in the Middle East and elsewhere. And as idealistic as it may be, my block also represents my ongoing commitment to peaceful solutions.

Some blocks represent a wide variety of perspectives about the meaning of 9/11. Faculty member Nina Thorne's says of her block:

Fig. 10.3 Murphy Quilt Piece

A few weeks after 9/11, I found an article on the Tibetan-Buddhist practice of tonglen. In its essence, tonglen is a way to connect to others, to not feel alone. You sit down and think about all those who suffer a similar fate and instead of dwelling on your personal grief, you send out compassion.

Sunday mornings after reading the memorial section of the *New York Times* became my time for tonglen. In my mind, I reached out to the families who lost their children in the World Trade Center attack. This led me to think of the parents of Vietnam War casualties, the mothers and fathers of suicide bombers, the parents of all war casualties, and the parents who [had] lost their children to malnutrition, starvation, and violence. As my mind broadened its focus, I began to include any and all parents who lost their children throughout history and realized there was no end to this mediation. I also realized I was not alone.

When my son died, my daughter tattooed an eagle and a wolf on my lower back. To me, the tattoo symbolizes a permanent connection to my son. I have chosen to depict the tattoo as my contribution to the 9/11 memorial quilt. The text on the panel is part of a Native American poem. Underneath the eagle and the wolf hang six prayer ties...the ties are filled with tobacco. They are blessed with prayers and wishes and tied together with an unbroken cord...I have chosen the colors red, white and blue for my ties because my prayers are for the healing of America and for the victims of 9/11.

Once we gathered together the individual squares, a number of us brought in our sewing machines and sat together in one of the seminar rooms to sew the squares into four quilted panels that now hang on our office walls. Coming together and talking about the squares and what we saw in them provided us a venue to connect and actively feel a sense of community. We also realized a renewed appreciation of life and acknowledged the ways that the academy had entered the lives of students and our own. By narrating the story of grief through our quilting, grief was given a name, a home, and a place outside the self. Making the story of grief public was an important step in the healing process for some. In fact, research has indicated that quilting can provide an important vehicle for individual and collective healing[10] Our experience with the 9/11 quilt seems to have had that same effect.

For us, the memories and the impact of the World Trade Center attacks have been readily apparent over these past ten years because our quilt hangs in our Hauppauge office, a constant reminder of the complex narratives in our public memory that make meaning of the events of 9/11. The quilt we created in 2001 has been used regularly as a teaching device

---

[10] Carolyn H. Krone and Thomas M. Horner, "Quilting and Bereavement: Her Grief in the Quilt" *Uncoverings* 13 (1992): 109-126; Max Carocci, "Textiles of Healing: Native American AIDS Quilts" *Textile: The Journal of Cloth and Culture* 8 n. 1 (2010): 68-85; Cleve Jones and Jeff Dawson, *Stitching a Revolution: How the Quilt Put a Human Face on AIDS and Brought Healing to a Nation* (San Francisco, Cal.: Harper San Francisco, 2000).

every year in a small seminar we offer called "Arts and Healing." As part of the unit on fiber arts, we present our 9/11 quilt as an example of the historical dimensions of quilting as a medium of public memory.

Fig. 10.4 Tobol Quilt Piece

Our "United in Community and Memory" quilt forms part of a longer trajectory of quilt making to commemorate historical events or memorialize someone who has passed on. [11] In using the quilt to demonstrate to our students how quilts can both capture and illustrate memory and personal historical narratives through a variety of modes developed over the years. We discuss how slave quilts in the Antebellum

---

[11] On quilting and public memory, see Dee Briton, "Comfort in Cloth: The Syracuse University Remembrance Quilt," *Voices: The Journal of New York Folkore* 34 n. 3 (2008): 3-6.

South, for example, embedded symbols of the African cultures otherwise lost by enslaved people as they told their stories.[12] We demonstrate how communities in the 1800s and 1900s used memorial quilt as reminders of loved ones who passed on, often made from the deceased's clothes. Pioneer women often received signature or album quilts as gifts when they went west to forge new lives. These quilts kept them warm in the sewn embrace of friends and family.[13] Similarly, men and women today craft passage quilts as memorials to loved ones.[14] Finally, we examine quilts constructed to remember individuals and also serve as expressions of grief that bring public attention to social problems.[15] The NAMES Project to remember and bring attention to those who have died from the AIDS epidemic is one of the best known.[16]

By re-telling the story of how we created this quilt, we model how our students can capture the meaning they make of historical and personal events. In discussing the various squares and their historical context, students can discern that the narrative of 9/11 is not simple. Our memories, experiences and the meaning that has evolved for each of us depend on how we were physically, emotionally and socially situated at the time, and how our lives and historical events have evolved since. Such lessons not only offer students some insight into the way art can facilitate the process of making meaning and dealing with trauma, but illuminate how history is a complex and nuanced amalgam of varied narratives. We teach, then, how quilting offers a visual place to voice grief and make it public, to preserve memories, and to wrap oneself and loved ones in the warmth of these stitched emotions. Quilts, we contend, are not just utilitarian; they also function as windows into the social history of grief by preserving the past memories of our complex lives. The squares created for our 9/11 quilt function in the same way.

It is this story, then, that we tell to students who simply view the quilt or study it in our "Arts and Healing" seminar. They can reflect on these

---

[12] Gladys-Marie Fry. *Stitched from the Soul: Slave Quilts from the Ante-Bellum South* (New York: Penguin Books, 1990).

[13] Sue Prichard, *Quilts 1700-2010: Hidden Histories, Untold Stories* (London: V&A Publishing, 2010); Elise Schebler Roberts, *et. al.*, *The Quilt: History and Celebration of an Art Form* (Minneapolis, Minn..: Voyageur Press, 2007)

[14]Sabrina Gschwandtner, "Passage Quilts." *Fiberarts* (November/December 2008): 48-51.

[15] Ami Sims, *Alzheimer's: Forgetting Piece by Piece.* (Flint, Mich.: Mallory Press, 2007).

[16] Cindy Ruskin, *The Quilt: Stories from the NAMES Project* (New York: Pocket Books, 1988).

squares as they compare them to their own memories of that day and how their sense of history and their lives have evolved since. The quilt thus provides a venue to discuss the ever changing nature of "public memory" as a way to understand history. The quilt not only helped create a sense of community among those who made it, but also for subsequent generations of students at our college. As educators, it continues to remind us of our teaching obligations and our shared humanity, for the events of 9/11 are still with us in memory and as a lived aftermath. Slogans like "See Something, Say Something", checks at airports, the constancy of photo ID requests, returning veterans as new students under the G.I. Bill, are all parts of the legacy of 9/11.

The images and memories of 9/11 continue to inform us and challenge us as educators. In the words of Professor Robert Fanuzzi about the St. John's University Memorial Quilt exhibit:

> The historical dimensions of quilting as a medium of public memory show how our faculty and students were able to appropriate and find comfort and meaning. Though humans have faced unfathomable loss before and likely will again, we have the quilts to prove it.

We also have the quilts to remind us of the resiliency of our academic community and the possibilities of creating and teaching even in the wake of disaster.

CHAPTER ELEVEN

PEDAGOGICAL IMPLICATIONS OF SEPTEMBER 11TH: IS THERE ROOM FOR SAVING THE WORLD?

SEAN MURRAY

Like many educators, I have witnessed controversies and emotions sparked by the September 11th attacks enter the classroom on numerous occasions. Some of these moments were an intended part of the class session for the day; other instances happened spontaneously, erupting after a random student remark. The most recent instance occurred during spring 2011 in one of my English composition courses and falls into the latter category. I had just divided the class into small discussion groups, and as I circulated about the room, a student popped out of his chair, eager to chat with me. He blurted out something about a crowd-surfing experience, Lower Manhattan, and Ground Zero. I stared back at him, confused. The classroom was buzzing with student voices, and I was at a loss to process his comments. Eventually, he explained that he had traveled to Ground Zero in the middle of the night to celebrate Osama bin Laden's death, and had ended up surfing atop the throng of other revelers. I was speechless.

Up to this point in the term, I had enjoyed a positive rapport with this student, and did not want to ruin it by sharing my own unspoken disapproval. But he could sense my opinion by the expression on my face, so I eventually said quietly, "I'm not sure that's the best way to respond to what's happened..." But I was not quite enough. A nearby student, who was quite vocal in class and active in campus politics, had already overheard and jumped into the conversation: "Crowd surfing over somebody's death? What is wrong with people?!" As I recall, emotions spiked for a few seconds, then quickly subsided as students and I returned to the task at hand. But later that day, I could not put the episode out of my mind. How had I handled it? Did I have a right to put down one student's viewpoint? Had I unintentionally invited other students to gang up with me against one of their peers? What if the debate had really caught on, sweeping across the entire class? Would I have been able to channel the collective energy so that analysis and reflection subsumed the initial venting?

The question of how best to frame politically sensitive matters in the classroom—or whether even to broach such questions in the first place—is not new. While September 11th may have intensified such pedagogical and curricular questions, the means and ends of higher learning have certainly been contested ever since the early days of the university. In 2008, Stanley Fish entered this debate with his book, *Save the World on Your Own Time*. The argument posed in this work is important to consider for a number of reasons: 1) Fish, although having passed the age when many quietly retire, continues to write prolifically, and his voice resonates more strongly than ever beyond the walls of the academy; 2) he constructs a critique that is at odds with both conservative and liberal views on college teaching; and 3) given the topic of this volume, he examines several college controversies directly related to 9/11. Not surprisingly, more than a few scholars have challenged Fish's views. In this essay, after framing the particulars of Fish's position as well as those of his challengers, I suggest a compromise position that understands what he calls *academicization* as part of a process by which students are encouraged to think critically about their developing political convictions.

Stanley Fish, Academicization, and September 11th

Fish is no stranger to controversy. Over the course of his career, his pronouncements have acted as a lightning rod for members of the academic community and anyone else interested in university politics. His current blog for *The New York Times*, containing his weekly musings on issues both inside and outside the academy, is a good indicator of the strong reactions he tends to elicit from his audience. Perusing the hundreds of responses sparked by just a single entry can give one a sense of how Fish's convictions invariably fan the flames of heated debate. His book *Save the World on Your Own Time* is no exception, the title itself a direct provocation to those educators who see their teaching as linked to civic responsibility and political activism.

Essentially, Fish's prescription for teaching can be gleaned from three of the book's central chapters: "Do Your Job," "Don't Try to Do Someone Else's Job," and "Don't Let Anyone Else Do Your Job." What exactly is the job of a professor according to Fish? The key word here is "academicize," which involves taking a topic and "detach[ing] it from the context of its *real world* urgency, where there is a vote to be taken or an agenda to be embraced, and insert[ing] it into a context of *academic* urgency, where there is an account to be offered or an analysis to be performed."[1] Fish offers a number of examples to illustrate this process of academicization. For instance, rather than pose the question of whether or not George W. Bush was the worst president in U.S. history, Fish recommends a general exploration of the American obsession with ranking things—such as cities and beers—and then a more specific exploration of presidential rankings that looks at how, when, and why they came into being.[2] In short, he proposes that academics perform an analysis of the history and context of the phenomenon to understand it better, but to deliberately avoid offering up a political endorsement or condemnation.

At this point, it can likely be surmised what Fish thinks is *not* the job of college professors. However, it is important to examine this section of his discussion, for it is here that he explicitly connects his argument to September 11th. In the chapter "Don't Try to Do Someone Else's Job," he challenges universities and professors who see their missions as somehow connected to developing responsible citizens and promoting an appreciation for diversity.[3] Such endeavors, he explains, are better left to "preachers, therapists, social workers, political activists, professional gurus, [and] inspirational speakers."[4] And to those educators who view higher learning as vital to a society built on freedom and equality, he responds that "we are in the education business, not the democracy business. Democracy, we must remember, is a political not an educational project."[5] To clarify the line between what is education—or professors doing their jobs—and what belongs to the realm of politics and activism—professors doing someone else's job—Fish examines the controversies surrounding two faculty members, Ward Churchill and Kevin Barrett, in the years following 9/11.

Because of the uproar his words stirred in the media and communities beyond academic circles, the case of Ward Churchill, former professor of ethnic studies at University of Colorado at Boulder, is familiar to many. On the day after the 9/11, he published an essay entitled "'Some People Push Back': On the Roosting of Chickens," in which he argues that the

---

[1] Stanley Fish, *Save the World on Your Own Time* (New York: Oxford University Press, 2008), p. 27. Emphasis mine.

[2] *Ibid.*, pp. 27-8.

[3] *Ibid.*, pp. 10, 66.

[4] *Ibid.*, pp. 66.

[5] *Ibid.*, p. 71.

people killed in the World Trade Center attacks deserved their fate. These individuals, he acknowledges:

> were civilians of a sort. But innocent? Gimme a break. They formed a technocratic corps at the very heart of America's global   financial empire...If there was a better, more effective, or in fact any other way of visiting some penalty befitting their participation upon the little Eichmanns inhabiting the sterile sanctuary of the twin towers, I'd really be interested in hearing about it."[6]

Fish points out that although originally published in a little-known journal, Churchill's words would eventually incense countless people.[7] Churchill's invitation to speak at Hamilton College in 2005 sparked a wave of widespread public scrutiny, with his controversial views condemned by conservative talk show hosts, including Bill O'Reilly.[8] University of Colorado Chancellor Philip DiStefano responded to the uproar with a mixed pronouncement, stating that the U.S. Constitution gave Churchill the freedom to voice his personal opinions *but* that these opinions had "appalled" both the university community and the public at-large.[9] It is this mixed pronouncement that gives us a window into Fish's views on professors and provocative political statements. Essentially, Fish believes DiStefano should have stopped after backing Churchill's right to express himself. By criticizing Churchill's actual viewpoint, DiStefano wrenched his university from the realm of education and planted it in the precarious world of politics—a dangerous move, in Fish's mind. So what emerges from his discussion of Churchill's case is Fish's support of faculty to speak their "truths"—whatever those truths may be, and however controversial they may be—in their scholarship, but a warning for schools to steer clear of weighing in on matters of a political nature.

If the Churchill story helps us grasp Fish's take on the dynamics of research, school administrators, and the public, Kevin Barrett's story allows us to discern Fish's view on politics in the classroom. Barrett, who was teaching a course on Islam at the University of Wisconsin at Madison in 2006, stated on a radio program that he believed the events of 9/11 were coordinated by the U.S. government.[10] Again, the university's response to

---

[6] Ward Churchill, "'Some People Push Back': On the Justice of Roosting of Chickens," *Kerspledeb*, 2001. Accessed December 28, 2011.
http://www.kersplebedeb.com/mystuff/s11/churchill.html.
[7] Fish, *op. cit.*, p. 84.
[8] *Ibid.*
[9] *Ibid.*, pp. 84-5.
[10] *Ibid.*, p. 86.

the ensuing public upheaval provides Fish the opportunity to define the appropriate work of higher education. Patrick Farrell, the school's provost, ultimately came to Barrett's defense, as Barrett assured administrators that he planned to introduce a whole host of different opinions on 9/11, in addition to his own perspective.[11] What was Fish's verdict? Farrell "got it wrong," because he saw the situation as a matter of balancing a multitude of viewpoints.[12] According to Fish, it is not essential that different views be introduced in a class, "although it is often pedagogically useful to do so. The true requirement is that no matter how many (or few) views are presented to the students, they should be offered as objects of analysis rather than as candidates for allegiance."[13] Thus, based on Fish's logic, Barrett could have focused exclusively on 9/11 conspiracy theories, assuming that the students' assignments were confined to discussing the history, development, and reasons for such views. In determining if Barrett deserved to be kept on at University of Wisconsin, Fish states that one simple question needed to be asked: did he "separate" himself from his "partisan identity" while teaching? If not—which seems to have been the case—Barrett should have been summarily fired.[14]

The other corollary to Fish's central argument "Do your job" is "Don't let anyone else do your job," which serves as the theme for one of the last major chapters in *Save the World on Your Own Time*. In it, he guards his vision of higher education against those groups pushing to recast colleges according to their own agenda. Eventually, the discussion moves into an extended defense of postmodernism and deconstruction, and yes, further examination of controversial 9/11 moments. Postmodernism, Fish claims, is not an anything-goes worldview and, therefore, does not deserve the vicious attacks it has received from conservatives.[15] In making his case, he examines the heated words of two men: former Secretary of Education

---

[11] *Ibid.*, pp. 86-7.

[12] *Ibid.*, p. 87.

[13] *Ibid.*

[14] Pedagogical flare-ups related to 9/11 have not faded from view since these incidents; nor have they been confined to post-secondary education. In March 2013, Flour Bluff Intermediate School in Corpus Christi, Texas became a center of controversy when a parent challenged a quiz question pertaining to the reasons why terrorists have attacked the U.S. The "correct" multiple choice answer stated, "Decisions we made in the United States have had negative effects on people elsewhere." Source: "Texas School Officials: State Curriculum Had Nothing to do with Controversial 9/11 Quiz." Accessed June 28, 2013. http://www.washingtontimes.com/blog/watercooler/2013/mar/22/texas-school-curriculum-suggests-us-was-responsibl/.

[15] Fish, *op. cit.*, pp. 132-41.

William Bennett and Columbia history professor Eric Foner. Bennett, Fish says, wrote a book titled *Why We Fight: Moral Clarity and the War on Terrorism* in 2002, which excoriates the academic left for failing to lead students through an "'honest study of our history.'"[16] Foner, who presumably symbolizes things such as postmodernism, deconstruction, and multiculturalism to Bennett, is specifically targeted for having asked which was more terrifying, "'the horror that engulfed New York City [on 9/11] or the apocalyptic rhetoric emanating daily from the White house.'"[17] What was Bennett's response? It was that such words amount to nothing more than unpatriotic "atrocious rot."[18] And what was Fish's response? "Even if it were atrocious rot, it could be honest atrocious rot; that is, it could be Foner's honest attempt, as a citizen and historian, to take the truthful measure of what the events of September 11th and their aftermath mean."[19] It is important to point out that the actual context for Foner's views was the *London Review of Books*, not the college classroom.[20] Hence, Fish's stance is not surprising. For him, it is most certainly the job of academics—even those of the postmodern camp—to engage in research and scholarship that pursue the truth. However, the line is drawn at the classroom door; once these truths are bound up in heated political opinion, it is the job of the professor to detach her/himself from such positions in the presence of students. Had Foner failed to do this, Fish would most certainly condemn him as an educator who was inviting others—namely those on the right wing of the political spectrum—to step in and redefine the role of the professoriate.

Challenging Fish

Fish's proactive view has not gone unchallenged. Many academics have defended a very different vision of the college classroom, both before and after the publication of *Save the World on Your Own Time*. A number of these academics have framed their arguments against the backdrop of living in a post-9/11 world. Kurt Spellmeyer, director of the Writing Program at Rutger's New Brunswick campus, reflects on September 11th's implications to critique the state of undergraduate education in his 2003 book, *Arts of Living: Reinventing the Humanities for the Twenty-First*

---

[16] Qtd in *ibid.*, p. 142.
[17] *Ibid.*
[18] *Ibid.*
[19] *Ibid.*
[20] "Discover The Networks: A Guide to the Political Left." Accessed December 28, 2011. http://www.discoverthenetworks.org/individualProfile.asp?indid=2205.

Century. Right after the attacks, he recalls that it was "commonplace to say that nothing would ever be the same."[21] Yet, he points out that education in the U.S. has remained stubbornly the same as it was "a century ago."[22] In particular, he sees the humanities as clinging to an antiquated curriculum centered on the likes of Plato and Shakespeare.[23] Spellmeyer laments that such a course of study is ill-equipped to prepare students for the kind of problem-solving required in contemporary society.

But 9/11 and the situation it stimulated on campus, which included "teach-ins and a special lecture series," generated the political will to recreate Rutgers' English 101 as a "foundational course" for students and instructors to examine pressing issues ranging from the consequences of the terrorist attacks to the degradation of our environment.[24] To illustrate the lofty goals for the course, Spellmeyer excerpts a number of passages from the students' reader, which he labels a "manifesto": "Our problems today are not only more sweeping than humankind has encountered before, they are also more complex...The uniqueness of our time requires us to devise new understandings of ourselves and the world. One purpose of this course is to provide a place for these understandings to emerge."[25] While Spellmeyer does not directly address the debate over whether students and professors should express political positions in the classroom, it is clear that his hopes for the university stand in direct opposition to those of Fish. Spellmeyer's ideal college education is not about detached, academic analysis; rather, it is very much connected to notions of active citizenship and participation on the local and global stages. It is, in other words, an education aimed at saving the world.

The same year that Spellmeyer published his *Arts of Living*, a group of influential composition scholars put out their own manifesto of sorts entitled *Composition Studies in the New Millennium: Rereading the Past, Rewriting the Future.* This edited volume actually has its roots in an English composition conference held in 2001, less than a month after 9/11. Spellmeyer participated in that conference and contributes an article to the book, so it's not surprising that the notion of education as having an ethical responsibility to investigate the world's problems permeates many of the other essays. In fact, the shadow of September 11th figures prominently here, acting as a clarion call for instructors to reinvigorate

---

[21] Kurt Spellmeyer, *Arts of Living: Reinventing the Humanities for the Twenty-First Century* (Albany: State University of New York Press, 2003), p. 241.
[22] *Ibid.*
[23] *Ibid.*, p. 244.
[24] *Ibid.*, pp. 242-44.
[25] *Ibid.*, p. 246.

their pedagogy. Keith Gilyard claims that because of 9/11, "all pedagogy was jolted to its very foundations."[26]

That the tragedy of that day spurred educators to pause, examine their practices, and envision a new way forward is not shocking. If this new way forward consisted only of requiring students to examine the antecedents and significance of the attacks, Fish might well be on board. But the field of composition has an overtly political past; Harriet Malinowitz notes that "liberatory pedagogy, cultural studies, multiculturalism, and other socially-based teaching practices took root in composition in the last decades of the twentieth century because reading, writing, rhetoric, language, and discourse came to be seen as constituitive, rather than merely descriptive, of events in the world."[27] Thus, compositionists (at least in this volume) wish to move beyond detached "academicization" of 9/11. September 11th, to them, is another teachable moment to seize upon in order to expose forces such as corporatization and militarism. In the days following the attacks, the American mainstream media, writes Malinowitz, offered few perspectives beyond the mantra that the jihadists were jealous of U.S. democracy.[28] Moreover, she names our educational system as part of the problem because of its ties to corporate power.[29] Education, Malinowitz suggests, has combined with the media to stagnate or impair people's capacity for critical thinking that would help them resist messages of the dominant culture. In a sense, Malinowitz, along with numerous other critical pedagogues, contends that within this system, writing courses provide "equal time," a counterbalance to the years of programming to which students have been subjected.

These pedagogical arguments were issued after 9/11, but before Fish published *Save the World on Your Own Time*. When it did come out, Fish's book caused quite a stir among compositionists, as he devoted a special section to criticizing composition instructors for politicizing their pedagogy rather than doing their job—which, in Fish's eyes, is to teach writing and only writing. Two responses were printed in *College English*, a major journal for English literature and composition faculty. Given Fish's sharp criticism, one might expect a hostile rebuttal, but these

---

[26] Keith Gilyard, "Composition and the Critical Moment," in *Composition Studies in the New Millennium: Rereading the Past, Rewriting the Future*, edited by Lynn Z. Bloom, Donald A. Daiker, and Edward M. White (Carbondale: Southern Illinois University Press), pp. 227-36, 228.
[27] Harriet Malinowitz, "The Uses of Literacy in a Globalized, Post September 11th World," in *ibid.*, pp. 237-51, 251.
[28] *Ibid.*, p. 240.
[29] *Ibid.*, p. 242.

responses are a complex mixture of agreement and disagreement with the tenets of *Save the World on Your Own Time*. Ultimately, the articles, which were published six months apart during 2009, highlight another set of academic positions that see politics as an inevitable and valuable part of the learning experience.

In the first piece, Donald Lazere, professor of English at California State Polytechnic Institute in San Luis Obispo, concedes that the idea of valuing all points of view in the classroom is highly problematic. "My encouragement," he complains, "of open classroom discussions has often led to the most belligerent, ill-informed students, usually conservative, drowning out everyone else's voices, or to meandering bull-sessions among students largely ignorant about the topics under discussion ('I feel that Saddam Hussein was behind 9/11')"[30] But for the most part, his agreement with Fish stops there. Later in the article, he turns the notion of academic truth-seeking against Fish. Lazere asks, if what parades as truth in our society is actually fiction fabricated by corporations and political powers-that-be, then doesn't that mean professors should be dissecting such lies in the classroom?[31] Although he does not explicitly connect this point to 9/11, it's a safe bet that Lazere is green-lighting liberal faculty who wish to confront the narrative of the terrorist attacks put forth by George W. Bush's administration and mainstream media outlets.

Patricia Bizzell, professor of English at Holy Cross, penned the second response to Fish's book in *College English*. Her provocative title, "Composition Studies Saves the World!", implies a thorough refutation of everything embodied by Fish's pedagogy. But her answer to Fish is actually a "Yes, but—."[32] Like Fish, she endorses the concept of academicization and believes that the primary job of composition instructors is to teach writing.[33] However, she defends the idea of teaching to better the world, which is about as anti-Fish as one can get. Presumably, discussion and writing about September 11th in Bizzell's class would seek not only to describe and historicize the tragedy, but also to comprehend it, enabling students to become agents of peace and change.

---

[30] Donald Lazere, "Stanley Fish's Tightrope Act," *College English* 71 (2009): 530-31.

[31] *Ibid.*, p. 533.

[32] Patricia Bizzell, "Composition Studies Saves the World!" *College English* 72 n. 2 (2009):174-187, 181.

[33] *Ibid.*, pp. 181-82.

My Response: Academicization as a Stepping Stone
to Informed Opinion

In the spring of 2005, I was teaching a composition course focused on the analysis of popular culture. To practice our close reading skills, students and I watched a scene from Spike Lee's 2002 film *The 25th Hour*. On one level, the movie's plot and theme revolve around Monty, a convicted drug dealer who struggles to accept responsibility for his crimes. But on another level, this is Lee's 9/11 film. Set in New York City soon after the attacks, *The 25th Hour* raises controversial points related to the political implications of September 11th. In the clip my class watched, Monty's friends argue over his culpability in an apartment that overlooks Ground Zero. A friend named Jacob maintains disbelief, grappling with the fact that Monty has been caught and naively wishing that Monty could be permitted to bring his dog to prison. The other friend, the tough-talking Franc, retorts that Monty's prosperity was "paid for by the misery of other people" and that consequently, Monty "deserves" the justice meted out to him.[34] The clip closes with the camera zooming in for a closer look at Ground Zero: buildings ripped open, the American flag, workers, and construction machinery, all looking forlorn in the glow of nightime lighting. The musical score, a mournful mix of Middle Eastern vocals and Celtic pipes, swells to maximum volume. As the scene fades to black, it is difficult to escape the impression that this is not simply a drama about a drug dealer. When I asked students to respond, they were reluctant. Gradually, a few students wondered aloud what the film had to do with 9/11: Did the setting have anything to do with the plot? A number of other students said yes— one possible reading of the scene was that the convicted criminal represented America, guilty of causing suffering to others, and therefore, deserving of punishment. At that point, one or two students stated that if that was the intended message, they disagreed with it. And with that, the discussion ground to a halt.

Like other times in my teaching career, the lively debate I imagined while preparing for a class didn't happen. In this particular intance, one possible reason is the extremely sensitive nature of September 11th. The school I was teaching at was located in upstate New York, but the vast majority of undergraduates came from the New York City and Long Island area. Understandably then, students may have wished to avoid dredging up painful emotions or offending others with their opinions. However, looking back, I cannot help but think that Fish's academicization could

---

[34] Spike Lee, *The 25th Hour*, 25th Hour Productions, 2002.

have helped to spark deeper analysis and discussion. Originally, one of my reasons for showing the movie clip was to engage the kind of critical literacy that Malinowitz urges teachers to foster in the classroom—the kind of literacy that involves thinking about unpopular perspectives, "asking questions, reading skeptically, and analyzing closely."[35] But, to tap into this literacy, Fish's emphasis on historical context and examination of rhetoric may have provided the grounding necessary for productive discussion. For instance, my students and I could have explored Lee's history of provocative filmmaking, and then studied the responses to *The 25th Hour* written by film scholars instead of expecting stimulating debate to result from one short film clip. Setting the stage in this manner would have led us to a greater awareness of how others responded to 9/11.

So, yes, I do see much value in academicization for sharpening analysis and generating discussion centered around informed perspetives. Like Lazere, I have witnessed a few too many "bull sessions" or, perhaps worse, discussions like the one above that essentially stopped before they even got off the ground. But I ultimately have a major disagreement with Fish in that I see academicization as serving a pedagogy that *embraces* the expression of opinion in the classroom.

To illustrate my evolving pedagogical beliefs, I can describe the composition course I now teach. The theme of the class would make Fish shudder: writing for social justice. Remember that he argues that colleges in general and teachers in particular are not in the business of making the world a better place. But like Bizzell, I see higher education and writing instruction as very much imbricated with the lofty goals of social responsibility and citzenship. In her critique of *Save the World on Your Own Time*, Bizzell confesses that "once upon a time, I actually had the nerve to teach a seminar at Holy Cross titled Composition Studies and Social Justice."[36] As it turns out, her wording here is intentionally humorous and self-deprecating, because the rest of her response to Fish goes on to prove that she still believes in a pedagogy infused with notions of social justice. And while my first-year course does not specifically look at the intersection of the discipline of composition and social justice, it does provide a space for students to research social issues of interest to them, issues that range from 9/11-related topics like peace to questions touching on education, the environment, and the economy. The initial steps of the drafting students does involve academicization of their chosen issue: outlining the historical context and summarizing and evaluating

[35] Malinowitz, *op. cit.*, p. 249.
[36] Bizzell, *op. cit.*, p. 175.

competing viewpoints. Ultimately, though, I ask students to commit Fish's cardinal sin; that is, I ask them to "plumb"[37] for their opinions, and I do so for a number of reasons.

First, to meet Fish on his own terms, I believe that "learning how to marshall arguments" is an academic value in itself.[38] If that is the case, then what could be a more compelling way for students to grapple with this academic craft than to go through the complex process of explaining, clarifying, and defending their actual views on an issue of interest to them? Although Fish does not specifically recommend the following in his book, it is a safe bet that he would offer this in response to my question: yes, argument is an academic skill, so simply assign students positions, and teach them how to build strong supporting cases. Of course, this teaching strategy is not new, and is used in many debate-oriented courses. Teaching argument this way has the potential to help students detach themselves from emotionally-grounded positions. I certainly see the value in this pedagogy, and have used it myself on more than one occasion.

However, to restrict students to defending pre-assigned positions is to block off a primary pathway to the "examined life." Though there are various interpretations of this Socratic value, one reasonable assumption is that living the examined life means carefully probing the underpinnings of one's deeply held convictions. Fish would likely argue that students' exploration of their opinions and biases is not the real business of the classroom, and that instructors who require this kind of work are trying to do someone else's job, perhaps that of a parent or counselor. But I see no reason why students should not subject their views to Fishian academicization, tracing their evolution, seeing how they fit into the wide spectrum of perspectives, and determining effective rhetorical means for expressing said views. And yes, I do believe that such a process holds the possibility for moderating or profoundly changing one's views. But getting students to alter their opinions is not my pedagogical goal, and I side with Fish's warnings against indoctrination. Who would not? Bizell and Lazere both point out that Fish flirts with strawman logic in *Save the World on Your Own Time*. His harping on indoctrination as a highly problematic pedagogical goal seems a case in point. A course that allows students to comprehend more fully, and perhaps even change their opinions, may simply be the natural result of applying academicization to one's own convictions.

---

[37] Fish, *op. cit.*, p. 69.
[38] *Ibid.*, p. 41.

My composition course for the fall 2010 term had a capstone assignment which required students to develop a research-driven argument paper and a related letter to a public official on a political matter of their choosing. Throughout the final month, students shared their drafts, getting feedback from others in the class. Given the nature of the assignment, advice that went beyond writing suggestions regularly entered the discussion. Tensions occasionally developed around the different political issues broached, and one of the most heated moments arose from disagreements about the wars in Afghanistan and Iraq. One student expressed support for the (now defunct) policy banning the media from photographing the caskets of dead soldiers, stating that he believed such images were disrespectful to families of the deceased. Another student, a young woman whose parents are originally from Afghanistan, countered that these images are necessary to show the realities of war. The ensuing exchange of views lasted for at most one minute, but ended with the woman raising her voice to repeat her view, and then shedding a few tears. As the class ended, she crossed the room and apologized to her classmate for becoming upset. Her classmate in turn expressed sympathy and understanding.

I have no doubt that this is precisely the kind of classroom situation that perturbs Fish, and admittedly, I am not completely at ease when emotions run this high. But I also wonder to what extent these heated moments can be part of the academicization process and the lofty goal of living the examined life. While I do not have concrete information on how this classroom debate affected these two students' intellectual lives, I suspect that at the very least, it prompted them to see how their convictions play out in the public sphere, and possibly even to reexamine how to engage competing viewpoints. I should also note that I do not offer the above classroom debate as an ideal pedagogical model—the initial flare-up was not followed by formal reflection and analysis, so the possibilities for intellectual growth were, in essence, left up to chance. However, it is my hope that I can continue learning how to build more structured follow-up for these teachable moments.

Over the years, I have developed a somewhat moderate position on the question of whether instructors should weigh in with their own views during classroom discussion. A decade ago, I was a firm believer in total, constant transparency, offering up my own views for analysis and scrutiny whenever my classes became engaged in a debate. However, I eventually learned that my politics were not always a necessary ingredient for sparking debate and reflection, and that sometimes injecting my opinions derailed the momentum of a productive discussion. This is not to say that I fear sharing my views will somehow indoctrinate my classes; as Bizzell notes, students are not the docile individuals they are often thought to be. Based on my own experience, students are more than willing to challenge my opinions and ask how I arrived at them.

In my fall 2011 "Writing for Social Justice" classes, I did not spend significant time articulating and explaining my stance on matters linked to September 11th. But this reluctance is related to what Jeffrey Melnick has referred to as "9/11 fatigue,"[39] and was not a sudden aversion to expressing and inviting opinion in the classroom. In his article "Pedagogy in the Land of the Lost: Negotiating 9/11 Fatigue when Teaching 9/11", Andrew Schopp suggests that "9/11 culture and its concomitant fatigue almost demand that we address the subject indirectly, allowing those resonances to manifest on their own rather than taking the subject head on."[40] Given the media's round-the-clock coverage of the tenth anniversary of the attacks, I opted to take Schopp's pedagogical approach, not wanting to turn up the already deafening volume to which my students were subjected.

But now that the tenth anniversary coverage has waned, I grapple with a question posed by Fish's *Save the World on Your Own Time*. As much as I think Fish is off-target on the issue of personal politics in the classroom, he definitely has me wondering what perspectives have a right to be heard. Are there perspectives related to September 11th that lack academic merit, as he suggests is the case for the Evolution vs. Intelligent Design debate[41], and are therefore not entitled to time in the classroom? I'm inclined to listen to Gerald Graff, who suggests that "the truth or validity of an idea…[is not] the sole thing to consider in deciding whether it is worth presenting to students…when we measure the pedagogical merits of an idea, its usefulness in clarifying an issue or provoking students—and teachers—to *think* can be as important as its truth or validity. In some cases, even false or dubious notions can have heuristic value."[42] Perhaps my inclination is related to the fact that introductory composition courses are often focused on critical thinking, analysis, research, and most important, student-chosen writing projects. Thus, when an individual student chooses to write about views judged by many as problematic, I

---

[39] Qtd. in Andrew Schopp, "Pedagogy in the Land of the Lost: Negotiating 9/11 Fatigue when Teaching 9/11" *Modern Language Studies* 41 n. 1 (2001): 59.
[40] *Ibid.*, p. 61.
[41] Fish, *op. cit.*, pp. 124-31.
[42] Gerald Graff, "To Debate or Not to Debate Intelligent Design?," *Inside Higher Ed*, September 28, 2005. Accessed December 30, 2011.
http://www.insidehighered.com/views/2005/09/28/graf . Emphasis mine.

often see it as an opportunity for her to work carefully and thoroughly through the issue. Discussing Intelligent Design, Graff asserts that "if the goal of education is to get students to think, then just telling students their doubts about Darwin are wrong is not going to be effective."[43] For the moment, I have a similar perspective on teaching and 9/11. I can see myself telling a student that his or her view may be seen by many as inaccurate or even hateful, but my hope is that he or she would learn something valuable by subjecting it to the rigorous process of research and writing.

Implications for the Institution of Higher Learning

Ultimately, the debate over how best to frame politics in the classroom carries implications beyond students and instructors. In the final chapters of *Save the World on Your Own Time*, Fish summarizes the trend of declining financial support for higher education in the U.S. To reverse this pattern and convince the public of higher education's inherent value, he recommends an interesting strategy: don't offer an explanation.[44] Fish suggests that we:

> "embrac[e] the fact that few nonacademics: understand what we do and why we do it, and turning it into a weapon. Instead of saying, "Let me tell you what we do so that you'll love us"…say, "We do what we do, we've been doing it for a long time, it has its own history, and until you learn it or join it, your opinions are not worth listening to."[45]

While I sympathize with Fish's frustration over explaining why the life of the mind is a worthwhile pursuit, I find his arguments snobbish and likely ineffective. Drawing a line in the sand and telling the public that they don't appreciate higher education because they do not "get it" smacks of elitism. And if building persuasive arguments is something college educators are expected to teach their students, it is more than a little ironic that Fish advocates a refusal to do so on an issue with which he is so concerned.

A more compelling argument for the value of higher education is offered by Derek Bok. In *Our Underachieving Colleges: A Candid Look at How Much Students Learn and Why They Should Be Learning More*, he argues that college as a "preparation for citizenship" has a long, proud

---

[43] *Ibid.*
[44] Fish, *op. cit.*, p. 164.
[45] *Ibid.*, pp. 165-66.

history in the U.S.: "From the time of Thomas Jefferson to the present day, leaders in America have pointed to education as the key to a healthy democracy...Civic responsibility must be learned, for it is neither natural nor effortless."[46] In other words, Bok does not see college through Fish's lens of education for education's sake. Rather, he believes that college offers something concrete in return for public support—classes that prepare students to develop thoroughly informed opinions. Clinging to Fish's rigid understanding of academicization thus misses out on opportunities to help undergraduates reflect carefully on their own emerging political views. Perhaps controversies surrounding September 11th can stimulate classroom discussions, as awkward and painful as they may be, that encourage students and instructors alike to listen respectfully to and challenge divergent viewpoints.

---

[46] Derek Bok, *Our Underachieving Colleges: A Candid Look at How Much Students Learn and Why They Should Be Learning More* (Princeton, N.J.: Princeton University Press, 2006), p. 172.

CHAPTER TWELVE

TEACHING MIDDLE EAST HISTORY AFTER 9/11

NERINA RUSTOMJI

After explosions, bombings, and shootings in the United States, Middle East specialists fall silent. The story emerges. We receive brief updates, and then Internet and cable news begin to piece the events together. Unlike most readers and viewers, we are not just trying to learn the details. Instead, we are waiting to see if the perpetrator was a Muslim. In some cases, the news is of a deranged student, an accidental fire, or an unhinged parent. Shoulders relaxed, we move through our day like most others, wondering why a student would fire upon a campus or what fuels the anger of someone who seeks to explode a federal building. But sometimes the waiting is met with a different news bulletin—one that reinforces a long-standing perception that Muslims are inherently violent.

After Pearl Harbor, specialists of Japan—whether of the Tokugawa economy or courtly poetry—became experts who were expected to comment on the enemy.[1] In a similar way, Middle East specialists are ready for the questions—big and small—and contemplate how to comment upon events that involve Muslims who partake in violence. The choice to participate (or not participate) in public discourse may have begun for some before 9/11, but since then, there have been other episodes that have also challenged Middle East specialists, especially when they involve American domestic news. After the Boston Marathon attacks, how do we make sense of Tamerlan and Dzokhar Tsarnaev's plans to maim and kill? Can we explain the motivations of others, including David Headley, Anwar al-Awlaki, Major Nidal Malik Hasan, or Colleen LaRose, aka "Jihad Jane"? And is it possible to understand and address acts of violence in a political culture fueled by the Park 51 community center controversy and Representative Peter King's congressional hearings on the

---

[1] Zachary Lockman, *Contending Visions of the Middle East: The History and Politics of Orientalism* (Cambridge: Cambridge University Press, 2004), p. 122.

radicalization of American Muslims? To be fair, not everyone who studies the region takes on the job of political interpreter, but plenty of us do so in conversations with neighbors, colleagues, and family members, and I would venture that all of us do in the classroom.

When someone learns about my chosen field, I often hear the polite line that these are "interesting times." But it has always been an interesting time when it comes to the Middle East. Nonetheless, the last ten years have offered unprecedented opportunities and risks for the Middle East specialist because of national engagement in the region. It has been a time when there have been more jobs available than ever before. It has been a time of heightened scrutiny and critique. And it has been a time when what we do in professional space and how we operate in public space have constantly been in contact with each other.

I sometimes wonder what it would be like to be an academic whose day-to-day professional interests are not splashed across the front page of the newspaper. Yet, not all moments are so stark and consequential. Sometimes they are also jarring and bizarre. I am reminded of a Middle East Studies Association (MESA) meeting at the Marriott Wardman in Washington D.C. in 2005. In the lobby of the hotel was an enormous sculpture of the fireman of September 11th in *chocolate*. As the central decorative piece of the hotel lobby, it was an odd commemoration (even though it was not the only chocolate sculpture of 9/11 first responders in D.C.), and an even odder one for a national conference whose members had recently come under attack for not predicting 9/11.

If 9/11 has been a transformational event on a national and global scale, then it has been an event that has tested the Middle East specialist. After 9/11, some scholars have often felt the need to perform the role of cultural ambassador, explaining what Islam is or is not. Yet other scholars have become caught up in cases over freedom of speech. I assume that a person who chooses the Middle East as a regional focus is someone who has some political impulse. We study because it matters. Yet, our studies have had little impact. After each potential explosive event, we revisit the same questions in a media storm. Why? It is not because we (that is, specialists) have not continued to answer questions. It is because we (that is, Americans) have still not learned how to formulate good questions.

This essay explores two different critiques of Middle East Studies. The first, more political, critique emerged after 9/11. It charged that Middle East specialists were not able to develop a predictive model for the attacks and, as a result, were not working for the interests of national security. The second, more academic critique surveys the development of the Middle East textbook from the 1950s onwards and argues that the difficulties of assessing political events begins with the problems of narrative found within history textbooks. Comparing the assumptions behind these different critiques suggests that the value of studying Middle East history depends neither on immediate nationalistic nor removed academic perspectives, and it calls for reflection about how dominant historical paradigms limit our ability to interpret contemporary events. It also cautions against the current use of 9/11 as a central point for understanding the Middle East and Islam.

The "Campaign against Middle East Studies:" Martin Kramer and Daniel Pipes after 9/11

Since 9/11, Middle East academics have been on the defensive. In an effort to offer analysis and point to larger, broader themes, academics had to both assess the intentions and efforts of al-Qa'ida and also place them within religious and political contexts. Scholars drew upon disciplinary training in order to explain the motives of the hijackers and concerns for future security in what journalist David Cohen has called a "deconstructionist" mode.[2] With this aim, two kinds of stories emerged. The first was an explanation of al-Qa'ida as a fringe group that gained traction through the efforts of American support during the Afghan-Soviet struggle, and it was a story about American foreign policy. The second was a reassurance that all Muslims were not terrorists seeking to kill Americans and destroy symbols of America, and it was an argument that sought to protect American Muslims from the mistaken belief that al-Qa'ida represented Islamic or Muslim wishes and instead introduce Islam as a peaceful religion. This framework was reiterated by President Bush when he continually conveyed that Islam was not the enemy. Since then, anthropologist Mahmood Mamdani has made a powerful argument about the political implications of making distinctions between "good" Muslims and "bad" Muslims. However, in 2001, the idea that there were bad Muslims (the attackers) and good Muslims (our neighbors) was formulated as a way to stem potential hate crimes.

Instead of focusing on the singular nature of 9/11, academics were pressed to focus on continuities and disjunctions. But those ebbs and flows were difficult to elaborate since al-Qa'ida was such a recent organization. Those well versed in Islamist violent groups cautioned against seeing too broad a pattern. Yet, arguments that what we witnessed on 9/11 was the

---

[2] David Cohen, "The psyche of terror," *The Guardian.* September 28, 2001. Accessed August 7, 2011. guardian.co.uk.

last desperate effort of a terrorist network were too difficult to comprehend as the search for bodies continued on the Pile. Furthermore, there were only a few op-eds by Middle East specialists, and aside from reiterating the differences between al-Qa'ida, Islam, and Muslims, Middle East specialists initially did not offer much to written, public discourse.[3]

If academics were visible, it was not because of their contribution to the analysis of the events of September 11th, but rather the critique that they had failed their jobs. The question of failure was one that occupied many people's minds, and gave impetus to a number of assessments, the most notable being the *9/11 Commission Report*. However, while it was clear that there were both intelligence and security failures on behalf of the federal government, the failures of academics were seen as a particular kind of betrayal.

Initially, the historian and political commentator Daniel Pipes was alarmed by the prospect that professors not only did not help predict 9/11, but he also claimed they had greater sympathies with the attackers than the victims. He began a website called *Campus Watch* where he invited students to write in on the comments of their professors. This "watch-list" was to provide a database of suspect professors. The grass-roots feature of students informing on their teachers was eventually removed after a vociferous campaign by academics throughout the humanities; however, the site itself is still in operation and offers a detailed compendium of Middle East professors in the news.

A more sustained blow was delivered by Martin Kramer, the former director of the Moshe Dayan Center for Middle Eastern and African Studies, at Tel Aviv University. In his November 2001 op-ed in the *Wall Street Journal* and book *Ivory Towers on Sand: Failure of Middle Eastern Studies in America* (2001), Kramer urged Congress to remove funding for programs that award universities with Title 6 federal funds to study the Middle East. Kramer suggested that not only did professors who benefitted from Title 6 government funds fail to predict 9/11, but they also refused to work with government agencies.

In the more pointed *Wall Street Journal* op-ed, Kramer contended that professors have such liberal biases that they are unable to recognize the events of 9/11 as acts of terror. In fact, he suggested that academics will

---

[3] Exceptions include Roy Mottahedeh, "Islam and the Opposition to Terrorism," Op-Ed, *New York Times*, September 30, 2001; Fawaz Gerges, "A Time of Reckoning," Op-Ed, *New York Times*, November 8, 2001; and Shibley Telhami, "The Mideast is Changing," Op-Ed, *New York Times*, September 19, 2001. Specialists in other fields, especially in security, international law, and domestic rights, proved far more vocal.

benefit from the attacks: "Ironically, the very same professors who helped to anesthetize America to the dangers of radical Islam are enjoying a windfall: Their phones don't stop ringing, their books sell briskly, and their courses fill to overflowing." [4] As a warning to the Bush Administration, Kramer counseled that academics are part of the problem and they should not be heeded until there is a significant reform of Middle East Studies:

> But as we begin to ask why the country was so unprepared, one conclusion is inescapable: The academics are part of the problem, not its remedy…MESA's board called on "those with responsibility for U.S. Policy in the Middle East and the Islamic world to avail themselves of the insights of scholarship." Mr. President, don't waste your time. The professors don't meet the course prerequisites. Members of Congress: There is no justification for an additional penny of support for this empire of error—and no better time to reexamine the federal subsidies it already enjoys." [5]

If Daniel Pipes' Campus Watch was interpreted by academics as an assault on free speech, then Martin Kramer's critique posed a serious challenge to the enterprise of Middle East Studies. Yet, the controversy was not entirely new to the field. International Relations scholar Fred Halliday suggested in the review of Kramer's book that the "Middle Eastern community had been buffeted by controversy, much of it of dubious academic and epistemological value…" [6]

Soon after Kramer's book, there were considerations of his critique. These included a colloquy in the *Chronicle of Higher Education* [7] and numerous book reviews. In one of the more balanced critiques, political science professor Gregory Gause III suggested that Kramer's argument should be taken seriously, though his charge that academics did not work in the nation's best interests was wrong. "Besides, it is not ignorance of bin Laden that explains the tragedy of September 11; vast American intelligence efforts have been directed at him for years. The main problems lie elsewhere, in a range of domestic vulnerabilities and in a

---

[4] Martin Kramer, "Terrorism? What Terrorism?!" *Wall Street Journal*, November 15, 2001. Accessed August 11, 2011. http://www.meforum.org/96/terrorism-what-terrorism.

[5] *Ibid.*

[6] Fred Halliday, "9/11 and Middle Eastern Studies Part and Future: Revisiting Ivory Towers on Sand," *International Affairs* 80 n. 5 (2004): 955.

[7] D. W. Miller, "Middle East-Studies Programs Are Accused of Scholarly Orthodoxy," *Chronicle of Higher Education* October 26, 2001.

failure of imagination on the part of all concerned regarding specific forms such an attack may take."[8] For Gause, Kramer leveled unfair critiques, and ultimately Gause argues that the enterprise of Middle East studies has a functioning structure where students receive proper training that helps them "think for themselves."[9] International Studies professor Joel Midgal added that the field, even with its shortcomings, provided useful resources:

> To my mind, Kramer's critique is akin to dismissing seismological studies for missing the next earthquake...Practicality and relevance should be measured in Middle East studies, not by scholars' capacity to predict the next political earthquake, but by their ability to provide keys to understanding culture, politics, and society in the region as unpredictable events unfold. Kramer's disservice to the field lies in his diverting attention from a serious assessment of how well Middle East scholars have done that.[10]

In effect, reviews of Kramer's work included critiques and celebrations of scholarly successes.[11]

Kramer's scathing views appeared not just after 9/11, but also during an ongoing re-examination of the funding paradigm of the area studies approach developed during the Cold War. His book, thus, extended the question about whether the approach of area studies is a fruitful way of studying various disciplines in the academy.[12] Yet, even if Kramer's book advanced a larger argument against area studies, it effectively ushered in an era where there was a "campaign against Middle East Studies."[13] The Kramer critique was an external one based on how academics did not work closely with the government. Since it was focused on the objective of scholarly prediction, it did not consider the ways in which historians

---

[8] F. Gregory Gause III, "Review of Ivory Towers on Sand," *Foreign Affairs* 81 n. 2 (2002): 166.

[9] *Ibid.*, p. 168.

[10] Joel S. Migdal, "Review of Ivory Towers on Sand," *International Journal of Middle East Studies* 35 n. 1 (Feb. 2003), p. 203.

[11] Rex Bryen, "Cluster-Bombs and Sandcastles: Kramer on the Future of Middle East Studies in America," *Middle East Journal* 56 n. 2 (Spring 2002): 323-28.

[12] Pinar Bilgin, "Is the 'Orientalist' past the Future of Middle East Studies?" *Third World Quarterly* 25 n. 2 (2004): 423-33; Michael Young, "A Frenchman Fries Middle East Studies in the U.S.," *Reason* December 29, 2004. Accessed July 31, 2013. http://www.campus-watch.org/article/id/1485; Francis Fukuyama, "How Academia Failed the Nation: The Decline of Regional Studies," *Saisphere* (Winter 2004) as reported in http://www.campus-watch.org/article/id/1498. Accessed July 31, 2013.

[13] Lockman, *op. cit.*, p. 266.

conceived of al-Qaʻida and the place they accorded the United States in the Middle East history classroom. Kramer's position, then, constituted an external judgment rather than an internal assessment, and as a result, it was political rather than academic. Ironically, it was Pipes' *Campus Watch* that had a better sense of where the real conversation was taking place. That conversation was in the classroom.

Middle East Textbooks and the Problems with Narrative

How do we represent a singular event? In a class (such as the "Modern Middle East") that can span centuries, how do we give space to a blinding moment of violence that we have witnessed before our eyes? Today 9/11 is central to the narrative of Middle East relations with America, but the narrative of 9/11 is not deep, does not go back far, and obfuscates other significant political dynamics of the twentieth century. A review of the ways that Middle East textbooks represent political violence and terrorism against the United States suggests that lack of engagement with terrorism among academics is not due to an unwillingness to talk about al-Qaʻida and address questions about Islam; instead, the problem is with the way that the United States has figured in narratives of the Middle East. That problem with narrative continues in contemporary academic discussions about political violence. As American historian Beverly Gage asks: "How do we talk about terrorism without reinforcing the 'war on terror' or lapsing into hopeless presentism?"[14] The question of how to narrate 9/11 does not just involve ideology (as Kramer and Pipes suggest), but how we place the events of 9/11 within the larger continuum of relations between the Middle East and the United States. Before we can answer these questions or even set up predictive models (if we choose to do so), we have to make judgments about how we tell the story.

The classroom is a unique space where we consider lines of thought that are not fully explored in daily conversation. The classroom can accommodate the detailed lecture as well as questions that people no longer ask or that might have an overtly political slant. Yet if classrooms can be shaped by the instructor and students, they are still grounded in textual arguments. For the introductory history class, it is the textbook that anchors the narrative. Developed after World War II and funded during the Cold War, the field of Middle East history is fairly new. As a result, textbooks about the Modern Middle East are few, and the editions

---

[14] Beverly Gage, "Terrorism and the American Experience: A State of the Field," *Journal of American History* 98 n. 1 (June 2011): 73-94, 74.

of textbooks offer a discrete set. The earliest textbooks not only illustrate the state of the field decade by decade, but they also lend great insight into America's place in the international world order.

Initially, my aim was to read through textbooks on the history of the modern Middle East published after 1993 in North America to see how they characterize the World Trade Center bombings and then 9/11. It became clear, however, that even contemporary editions can be based on decades-old texts. As a result, I found myself going back to the earliest editions of Middle East textbooks in order to study their narrative structures since most textbooks develop over time through a layering of historical interpretations that respond to shifting markets.

In choosing the texts, I limited the field to frequently used texts in the Modern Middle East history classroom that have been revised multiples times, and as a result, offered multiple editions. These include Sidney Nettleton Fisher's *The Middle East: A History* (1959, 1960, 1968/69, 1979), later revised with William Ochsenwald (1990, 1997, 2004); Arthur Goldschmidt's *A Concise History of the Middle East* (1979, 1983, 1988, 1991), later revised with Lawrence Davidson (1996, 1999, 2002), and William Cleveland's *A History of the Modern Middle East* (1994, 2000, 2004), later revised with Martin Bunton (2008). For contemporary texts, I turned to more historically-oriented works, such as Marvin E. Gettleman and Stuart Schaar's *The Middle East and Islamic World Reader* (2003) and James Gelvin's *The Modern Middle East: A History* (2005, 2008, 2011). In the textbooks, three notable themes before 2010 emerge: the static role of the United States in foreign policy; the slight mention of the 1993 World Trade Center bombings; and the explanations of 9/11. In the following sections, I assess the narrative choices within the textbooks and then turn to an analysis of textbooks designed after 9/11.

America in the Middle East

The most striking aspect of textbooks is how little significance they assign America in narratives of twentieth-century Middle East history. If American foreign policy or military intervention is incorporated within the texts, it tends to be mentioned either in relation to the American intervention in Beirut in the 1980s or in Iraq in the 1990s. This omission of the United States from the development of the Middle East as a region is understandable given the solely regional narrative thread; nonetheless, there is a sense in the textbooks that Middle East history is a history of "out there," which may be influenced by American actions, but is not related to American foreign policy or cultural influence in any substantial way.

The most fruitful example of this isolationist tendency can be found in the *The Middle East: A History*, written in 1959 by Sidney Fisher, revised with William Oschenwald in 1997, and then taken over by Oschenwald in the 2004 version. In the first (1959) and second (1969) editions, the role of the United States becomes critical within Fisher's framing of the textbook. Yet, America is not treated as a principal political agent until the fourth (1990) edition when the topic of recent acts of terrorism over the previous twenty years is mentioned in the abstract: "Terrorism became an obsession for the United States in the 1970s and 1980s, because so many terrorist acts were undertaken against Americans."[15]

The earlier editions introduce American interest in the region principally "because of her great power and world position."[16] In Fisher's text, the United States does not have any involved self-interest: "Neither the American people nor the American government has had any imperial ambitions in the Middle East. American oil investments in the area are very extensive, estimated at more than two billion dollars, but it is doubtful if the United States would exert much pressure on their behalf."[17] In fact, understanding the Middle East is to be taken on purely educational terms: "To win the Middle East, therefore, requires winning of the Middle Eastern peoples. Like a rich girl, the people of the Middle East do not want to be wooed for wealthy oil possessions or valuable real estate. They wish to be courted for themselves. Their culture, skills, and civilization, must be understood and appreciated and their desires respected. The age of being 'natives' has passed."[18] What the first and second editions bring into high relief are two interrelated themes that emerge in Middle East history textbooks.

First, America is merely an observer of events within Middle Eastern states. That is to say, Middle East history is a history of a distant region, and that while the Middle East may be important strategically and the United States may be a world power, the intersection of the two players is not significant enough to form a history of its own. This characteristic is striking given the growing importance of the United States since World War I. Second, America can only be understood within a Cold War

---

[15] Sydney Nettleton Fisher, *The Middle East: A History*. 4th edition (New York: Knopf, 1990), p. 740.
[16] Sydney Nettleton Fisher, *The Middle East: A History*, 2nd edition (New York: Knopf, 1969), p. v.
[17] *Ibid.*, p. 744.
[18] *Ibid.*, p. 749.

paradigm that provided a frame for interpreting Arab and Iranian national reform movements in the twentieth century. This tendency continued with textbooks well after 9/11, and echoes the dominance of Cold War conflict in American strategists' planning.

When the U.S. is incorporated in Middle East history, it tends to be in reference to specific agreements, interventions, or the Arab-Israeli conflict. Yet in the twenty-first century, few texts address American prominence in the region. In one telling organizational move, William Cleveland introduces the section "America's Moment in the Middle East" in his second edition of A History of the Modern Middle East (2000), which included chapters on U.S. engagement in Iraq, political Islam, and democratization. By the third edition (2009), the section on "America's moment" was reframed as chapter 25, "America's Troubled Moment in the Middle East."

Terrorism and the 1993 bombing

Sections of Middle East textbooks that discuss the U.S. and terrorism do not become specifically labeled or developed until the 1990s. Instead, terrorism in earlier editions tends to be framed by sections on the Arab-Israeli conflict, with the 1993 bombing receiving slight attention. Because the Cold War became the principal way to frame topics such as Gamel Abdel Nasser's rise in Egypt, U.S. involvement in the Arab-Israeli conflict, and the economic problems related to the OPEC oil embargo in the 1970s, there is little elaboration of U.S. policy or events that speaks to the symbolism of the United States in the political landscape of the Middle East. Acts of political violence—from al-Otaybi's takeover of the Grand Mosque in Mecca (1979) to the Iranian hostage crisis (1979) to the landing of the American Marines in Lebanon (1982)—are mentioned only in passing within the narrative framework.

The United States is specifically named as a target in Fisher and Oschenwald's fourth edition (1990). The fifth edition (1997) elaborates the 1993 bombing, stating that: "Terrorism from the Middle East reached the United States directly in a spectacular bombing of the World Trade Center building in New York City on February 26, 1993, carried out by an Islamic fundamentalist group." The section goes on to discuss in broad strokes other targets of terrorm, such as "Palestinians, Israelis, Turks, Lebanese, and non-Middle Easterners residing in Lebanon."[19] The later

---

[19] Sydney Nettleton Fisher and William Ochsenwald, The Middle East: A History, 5th edition (New York: Knopf, 1997), p. 735.

edition mentions the 1993 World Trade Center bombing, but then situates the reference within the larger frameworks of Lebanon and the Arab-Israeli conflict. In the 2004 edition, the linkages between different terrorist events are brought together in a developed narrative where the events of 9/11 are associated with "widespread unhappiness in the Middle East" and the Arab-Israeli dispute.[20] Another section steps outside the Arab-Israeli frame and reiterates the themes of Americans living abroad.

> Terrorism became a deep concern for the United States in the 1970s and afterward, because many terrorist acts were undertaken against Americans living abroad. Terrorism from the Middle East reached the United States directly in the first attempt to destroy the World Trade Center buildings in New York City on February 26, 1993. Al-Qaʻida carried out attacks on United States embassies in Africa in 1998 and on a United States naval vessel, the U.S.S. Cole in the harbor in Aden, Yemen, on October 12, 2000. The most devastating suicide attacks took place on September 11, 2001, when members of al-Qaʻida hijacked American civilian aircrafts. One airplane flew into the Pentagon just outside Washington, D.C., one crashed in Pennsylvania, and two others crashed into the World Trade Center twin towers, thereby killing thousands of innocent civilians.[21]

The section is straightforward and descriptive, but it offers little development about the meaning of the events and what they signify. To be fair, terrorism is difficult to discuss because of the diffused nature of violence.[22] Furthermore, the textbooks are supposed to be about Middle East history and so they privilege the events that take place in the region.

However, sometimes textbooks collapse the compartmentalization of regional zones. The Goldschmidt text, for example, offers sophisticated discussions of terrorism beginning in the third edition (1988) in the section "The Terrorist Triumph." In providing a definition of terrorism, Goldschmidt not only introduces it as a topic of consideration (as opposed to mere mention), but also notes how terrorist targets are formulated: "Middle Eastern governments and peoples have been victimized by terrorists to a greater extent than American and Europeans, but the terrorists prefer to strike at the West, to get not only vengeance but also the publicity that they crave."[23] In the seventh edition (2002), Goldschmidt

---

[20] William Ochsenwald and Sydney Nettleton Fisher, *The Middle East: A History*, 6th edition (New York: Knopf, 2004), p. 723.

[21] *Ibid.*, p. 737.

[22] Gage, *op. cit.*, p. 87.

[23] Arthur Goldschmidt, *A Concise History of the Middle East*, 3rd edition (Boulder, Col.: Westview Press, 1988), p. 369.

introduces the concept of state-sponsored terrorism in the cases of Israel, Syria, and Iraq,[24] and there is mention of Osama bin Laden and the 1993 attacks:

> It even seemed that terrorism was spreading to the United States, as a group of expatriate Egyptians was accused of planting bombs that blew up part of New York's World Trade center in February 1993. An exiled Saudi millionaire, Osama bin Laden, set up terrorist cells in the Sudan and then in Afghanistan. He is widely suspected of having inspired the 1993 World Trade Center bombing and attacks on the U.S. embassies in Kenya and Tanzania in August 1998.[25]

The passage then goes on to return the Arab-Israeli conflict. The full development of the theme of terrorism is subsumed within a region-specific issue. There is place for the 1993 bombing, but it is not placed within any significant pattern or terrorism or U.S.—Jihadi dynamics. The Cleveland text, by contrast, mentions terrorism within the framework of American presidential politics. In the section on "Political Islam and Democratization," Cleveland writes, "One of the platforms in U.S. President Bill Clinton's foreign policy was combating terrorism."[26] In the third edition (2004), he broadens the discussion to mention the 9/11 attacks, but reserves the development of 9/11 to an Epilogue.

Before the 2001 attacks, there was a history of sponsored attacks on U.S. embassies, consulates, and naval ships; however, it was not seen as a dominant narrative that rivaled the Cold War themes in the textbooks. This propensity to fall back on earlier historical patterns may have been because of narrative structure and also because of lack of awareness of al-Qaʻida as an organization whose purpose was to attack the United States as a means to bring change to Muslim regions. After the 2001 attacks, however, the lack of discussion of America's role and perception in the Middle East, even by fringe groups such as al-Qaʻida, signals that the textbook narrative confined historical discussion rather than opened new avenues of analysis.

---

[24] Arthur Goldschmidt and Lawrence Davidson, *A Concise History of the Middle East*, 5th edition (Boulder, Col.: Westview Press, 1996), pp. 381-82.
[25] Arthur Goldschmidt and Lawrence Davidson, *A Concise History of the Middle East*, 7th edition (Boulder, Col.: Westview Press, 2002), p. 399.
[26] William Cleveland, *History of the Modern Middle East*, 2nd edition (Boulder, Col.: Westview Press. 2000), p. 503.

Explanations of 9/11

In textbooks formulated or revised since 9/11, the role of the United States is addressed in chapters dedicated to the United States. In the *Middle East and Islamic World Reader* (2003), Gettleman and Schaar collect primary and secondary sources for a teaching unit entitled, "9/11: Terrorism, War, and Global Responsibility." In a *History of the Modern Middle East*, William Cleveland (2009) introduces "America's Troubled Moment in the Middle East." Yet, authors derive various meanings from the 9/11 attacks. Oschenwald's 2004 edition related 9/11 to unhappiness in the region,[27] and the straight-forward descriptions of the 1993 bombings, attacks on embassies in 1998, the attack on the U.S.S. Cole in 2000, and the 9/11 attacks themselves are understood through the lens of fundamentalism: "Addressing the underlying causes of radical Islamic fundamentalism was likely to remain an even more important task for the world community of narrations than the immediate necessity to eliminate the capacity to perform more attacks such as those of September 11, 2001."[28]

While Cleveland's book mirrors the previous pattern of depending on the Cold War paradigm through the section entitled "The Policy of Dual Containment," it goes on to place al-Qaʻida within its own context and to give a full narration of the attacks of 9/11. Cleveland also ventures to build a context for the 9/11 attacks by focusing on Westernization, U.S. foreign policy, and the Palestinian-Israeli conflict. When discussing in detail the formation of al-Qaʻida and its reliance on Taliban-controlled Afghanistan, Cleveland considers the implications of globalization and American popular culture. Cleveland also introduces American intentions at the heart of the narrative of 9/11: "The attacks of Sept. 11th gave rise to a brief period of U.S. soul searching in which the predominant question was 'Why do they hate us so much?' It seemed to come as a surprise to many Americans that their country's policies could generate levels of anger and frustration sufficient to trigger such deadly retribution. Yet, as we have seen elsewhere in this book, recent history reveals a pattern of U.S. policy that was insensitive to, and largely ignorant of, Arab and Islamic public opinion."[29] After discussing these murkier forms of support and causation, Cleveland returns to the Middle East by discussing the U.S. occupation of Iraq.

---

[27] William Ochsenwald and Sydney Nettleton Fisher, *The Middle East: A History*, 6th edition (New York: Knopf, 2004), p. 723.

[28] *Ibid.*, p. 738.

[29] William L. Cleveland and Martin Bunton, *History of the Modern Middle East*, 4th edition (Boulder, Col.: Westview Press. 2009), p. 543.

Gettleman and Schaar, by contrast, cover the debate about whether to characterize the attacks on 9/11 as "acts of war" or simply as crimes worthy of vigorous police attention. Before presenting the primary sources, the editors' introduction considers new ways to configure history because of new kinds of global connections: "After September 11 no one can believe any longer in the invulnerability of the United States. In that horror we see the full reality of the interconnectedness of our planet. What happens in Kabul, Ramallah, Yemen, or in Uzbekistan's Ferghana valley will reverberate throughout the Middle East and the Islamic World generally, and beyond."[30] The differing tones of the 9/11 sections suggest that historians are unclear how to interpret the significance of the attacks and how to articulate their causes. Their consideration of the United States as an active agent and the historical patterns of globalization and popular culture that extend beyond the Cold War paradigm signal that the narrative of the Middle East is being reshaped, however.

A Cautionary Conclusion

In the second edition (1983) of his book *A Concise History of the Middle East*, Goldschmidt articulates to the unease felt by many historians about commenting on the present: "A historian who writes about the recent past walks on eggs. Things happen suddenly in the Middle East, and projections about the future are hazardous."[31] In a discipline that prizes careful research and developed analysis, weighing forth about the unknown is not a favored activity of most historians. As a result, journalists dominate the articles and books that introduce the public to the Middle East, and the major themes found in journalism frame the way we understand Islam, the Middle East, and America's influence in other regions.

Yet, there are alternative models. James Gelvin's *The Modern Middle East: A History*, first published in 2004 with a recent third edition of 2011, introduces his textbook with a remarkable essay, "9/11 in Historical Perspective." In a few pages, he details 9/11 and the decade of American wars that followed it, but he also puts the aims of al-Qa'ida within the context of Middle East history. Middle East history, for Gelvin, requires not only discussion of regional developments, but also placing the Middle

---

[30] Marvin Gettleman, and Stuart Schaar, eds., *The Middle East and Islamic World Reader* (New York: Grove Press, 2003), pp. 323-24.
[31] Arthur Goldschmidt, *A Concise History of the Middle East*, 2nd edition (Boulder, Col.: Westview Press, 1983), p. 318.

East within the larger landscape of global history: "historians specializing in the Middle East certainly have a story to tell, but it is a global story told in a local vernacular."[32]

After nearly fifty years of distancing American influence and intervention in the Middle East, textbook writers may be tempted to overemphasize al-Qa'ida and the meaning of September 11th. There is a way to teach 9/11 without lapsing into clichéd debates. A more considered account of 9/11 requires rethinking both America's place in the Middle East and al-Qa'ida's ideology in the broader framework of the late twentieth and twenty-first centuries. The events of September 11th present an important story to tell, but it is not the only story, and it may ultimately be a smaller story albeit with global consequences. The development of the Arab Spring has already intimated that the preexisting Cold War, national, and colonial paradigms do not adequately explain local and transnational yearnings for democratic processes and governments. Narrative judgment and conceptual foresight are required, and the rewards of these skills are great. Kramer and Pipes looked for results, but they only measured their objectives in terms of ideology. There is a more consequential goal, however. If Middle East specialists are able to strike the right narrative balance in the classroom and in their textbooks, then they may be able to help bring more much needed balance to public discourse as well.

---

[32] James Gelvin, *The Modern Middle East: A History*, 3rd edition (New York: Oxford University Press, 2011), p. 3.

PART FOUR:

REPRESENTING 9/11

CHAPTER THIRTEEN

A TIGHTROPE AT THE TWIN TOWERS:
PHOTOGRAPHS OF FALLING BODIES
AND JAMES MARSH'S *MAN ON WIRE*

CHRISTOPHER VANDERWEES

Figure 13.1 Falling Man. AP Photo. Richard Drew.
The photograph features a man falling headfirst, hands at his side, one leg

bent, dressed in a white shirt and black pants (fig. 13.1). His body is pointed in such a way that journalist Tom Junod describes him as "an arrow."[1] Behind the man are the vertical mullions of the World Trade Center. In *New York Sights*, Douglas Tallack likens these mullions to the stripes of the American flag: "The stripes are vertical and not horizontal stripes, and are accidentally there and not patriotically invoked."[2] The man is frozen slightly higher than the middle of the frame against this backdrop.

Like most photos of falling bodies taken during the terrorist attacks of September 11, 2001, viewers must extrapolate from Richard Drew's "The Falling Man" in order to presume the reality of a gruesome death that occurred beyond the frame. Although mainstream media outlets endlessly aired video footage of the collapsing towers in the days and months after the terrorist attacks, images of those who jumped or fell to escape the heat and smoke on the upper floors of the World Trade Center only appeared in newspapers on the day after the attacks and were never reprinted, due to public outcry and corporate self-censorship. Two years after the terrorist attacks, in a short piece for the *Los Angeles Times*, Drew briefly discusses his experience following the short-lived publication of his now notorious photograph:

> My family calls it "the picture that won't go away." Most newspaper editors refused to print it. Those who did, on the day after the World Trade Center attacks, received hundreds of letters of complaint. The photograph was denounced as coldblooded, ghoulish and sadistic. Then it vanished. Yet, two years later, I still get asked about it. I've been invited on national talk shows, interviewed by foreign TV crews and asked to speak about it at universities across the country. Esquire magazine just published a 7,000 word essay that hails it as an icon, a masterpiece and a touching work of art. All this for a single frame out of hundreds shot in haste before I was pulled to safety as the second tower of the World Trade Center tumbled toward me. My fellow photographers call it "the most famous picture nobody's ever seen."[3]

Drew's comments begin to suggest some of the paradoxes that the

---

[1] Tom Junod, "The Falling Man," *Women & Performance: A Journal of Feminist Theory* 14 n. 1 (2004): 211-227, 211.

[2] Douglas Tallack, *New York Sights: Visualizing Old and New New York* (New York: Berg, 2005), p. 176.

[3] Richard Drew, "The Horror of 9/11 That's All Too Familiar," *Los Angeles Times*, September 10, 2003. Accessed June 19, 2013. http://articles.latimes.com/2003/sep/10/opinion/oe-drew10 .

photographs of falling bodies seem to embody. These images are both attractive and repulsive, perceived as exploitative and voyeuristic, but they are also celebrated as masterful works of art and photojournalism. Despite corporate self-censorship in a post-9/11 climate of uncritical patriotism, the images of falling bodies remain "the most haunting and memorable part of the tragedy."[4] These images, especially Richard Drew's "The Falling Man," have now become iconic of September 11, 2001 for authors and artists who deal with the terrorist attacks in their works.[5]

In this essay, I argue that the need to repress Drew's photograph and other images of falling bodies rose from popular American media's desire to support and maintain what Tom Engelhardt calls "victory culture," a collective of American narratives of triumph and nationalism that only portray defeat as "a springboard for victory."[6] Engelhardt argues that victory culture is a fundamental part of American national identity, an argument that I extend in order to refer to Charles Taylor's broader concept of the "social imaginary." I contend that the various images of falling bodies disrupt the American social imaginary through, what Julia Kristeva calls, abjection, as they unsettle post-9/11 narratives of victory culture. After the terrorist attacks, corporate media producers would not only censor images of falling bodies, but would also seek to replace them with familiar and reparative nationalist narratives of victory culture and American exceptionalism.

I turn to the recent cultural resurgence of tightrope walker Philippe Petit as an example of victory culture, one that is haunted by traces of the terrorist attacks and images of falling bodies. Specifically, I examine James Marsh's documentary drama, *Man on Wire*. Although the film never explicitly acknowledges or refers to the terrorist attacks, its attempt to reproduce the familiarity of American Dream ideals in effect inverts the terror of falling bodies through Petit's masculine heroism and his triumphant tightrope walk. *Man on Wire* thus strives to operate as a nostalgic fantasy that fulfills the desire for the two towers to have never collapsed, the desire for people to have not fallen to the streets below. I maintain, however, that *Man on Wire* complicates its own portrayal of

---

[4] Mikita Brottman, "The Fascination of Abomination," *Film and Television after 9/11*, ed., Wheller Winston Dixon (Carbondale: Southern Illinois University Press, 2004), pp. 163-177, 172.
[5] Tim S. Gauthier, "Narratives about the Falling Persons of 9/11," *September 11 in Popular Culture: A Guide*, eds., Sara E. Quay and Amy M. Damico (Santa Barbara: Greenwood, 2010), p. 101.
[6] Tom Engelhardt, *The End of Victory Culture*, 2nd edition (Amherst: University of Massachusetts Press, 2007), p. 3.

American triumph and nostalgic escapism, as the film cannot help but denote the falling bodies that it is so intent on repressing. Ultimately, Marsh's documentary demonstrates a disrupted temporality, engaging two events simultaneously and thereby revealing that the events of September 11, 2001 encode any number of past and present representations of New York City.

In the days and weeks after the attacks, media producers would play and replay video footage of the twin towers' collapse, but images of falling bodies quickly became taboo to view or display. Newspapers across the United States, for example, ran Drew's photograph, "The Falling Man," on the day after the attacks, but pulled the photo from subsequent coverage due to public outcry. In his article entitled, "The Falling Man," originally published in *Esquire*, Tom Junod writes that after publishing Drew's photo "[p]apers all over the country, from the Fort Worth *Star-Telegram* to the Memphis *Commercial Appeal* to *The Denver Post*, were forced to defend themselves against charges that they exploited a man's death, stripped him of his dignity, invaded his privacy, turned tragedy into leering pornography."[7] Jeffrey Melnick also notes these gestures of self-censorship within mainstream media outlets after the attacks. He writes that there was "almost [a] complete media blackout when it came to presenting images of the dozens, and perhaps hundreds, of people who leapt (or fell) to their deaths from the World Trade Center…[M]ost mainstream media—after publishing or broadcasting an image or two—refused to offer up any other footage of bodies falling from the Twin Towers."[8] Although these moving images did not depict actual death and did not reveal the identities of those captured on film, news networks still refused to air any images of falling bodies after initial coverage of the terrorist attacks, claiming that they were maintaining the standards of "good taste."[9] In *Regarding the Pain of Others*, Susan Sontag notes that the corporate "insistence on good taste in a culture saturated with commercial incentives to lower standards of taste may be puzzling. But it makes sense if understood as obscuring a host of concerns and anxieties about public order and public morale that cannot be named."[10] While I agree with Sontag's comments, I want to explore more closely some of these concerns and anxieties in terms of the dominant nationalist

---

[7] Junod, *op. cit.*, p. 215.
[8] Jeffrey Melnick, *9/11 Culture: Under Construction* (West Sussex: Wiley-Blackwell, 2009), p. 80.
[9] Barbie Zelizer, *About to Die: How News Images Move the Public* (Oxford: Oxford University Press, 2010), p. 43.
[10] Susan Sontag, *Regarding the Pain of Others* (New York: Picador, 2003), p. 69.

narrative in the immediate aftermath of 9/11.

Here, I suggest that the repression of falling body images is more broadly connected to the maintenance of an American social imaginary based upon victory culture. I take the term "social imaginary" from Taylor who sees it as a broad and multifaceted concept that incorporates "the ways people imagine their social existence, how they fit together with others, how things go on between them and their fellows, the expectations that are normally met, and the deeper normative notions and images that underlie these expectations"[11] Taylor also writes that the social imaginary cannot really be thought of as a theory as it "has no clear limits" and "can never be adequately expressed in the form of explicit doctrines because of its unlimited and indefinite nature."[12] Taylor's understanding of the social imaginary also encompasses what many theorists call the "cultural imaginary," understood as "the available cultural repertoire of images and representations [that]...shapes our emotions, our desires, and our beliefs."[13] He writes that the social imaginary is "carried in images, stories, and legends," is "shared by large groups of people, if not the whole society," and is "that common understanding that makes possible common practices and a widely shared sense of legitimacy."[14] In *The Imaginary Institution of Society*, Cornelius Castoriadis argues that the social imaginary underlies the symbolic order of any society, grounding its system of social significations, providing social patterns and consistency:

> These patterns do not themselves exist in the form of a representation one could, as a result of analysis, put one's finger on...They can be grasped only indirectly and obliquely...as a "coherent deformation" of the system of subjects, objects and their relations; as the curvature specific to every social space; as the invisible cement holding together this endless collection of real, rational and symbolic odds and ends that constitute every society, and as the principle that selects and shapes the bits and pieces that will be accepted there.[15]

When I refer to the social imaginary, I refer to this complex and mutable

---

[11] Charles Taylor, *Modern Social Imaginaries* (Durham, N.C.: Duke University Press, 2007), p. 23.

[12] *Ibid.*, p. 25.

[13] Catriona Mackenzie, "Imagining Oneself Otherwise," in *Relational Autonomy: Feminist Perspectives on Autonomy*, edited by Catriona Mackenzie and Natalie Stoljar (New York: Oxford University Press, 2000), pp. 124-150, 143.

[14] Taylor, *op. cit.*, p. 23.

[15] Cornelius Castoriadis, *The Imaginary Institution of Society* (Cambridge, Mass.: MIT Press, 1998), p. 143.

system of common understanding that allows individuals and communities to carry out collective practices, define and maintain their identities in relation to the symbolic order, and understand certain narratives, images, social codes, and ideas as normative or factual.

In *The End of Victory Culture*, Engelhardt argues that a culture of "triumphalism" historically defines American national identity. National identity, being "a collective sentiment based upon the belief of belonging to the same nation and of sharing most of the attributes that make it distinct from other nations" and a "[b]elief in a common culture, history, kinship, religion, territory, founding moment and destiny," is a significant part of the social imaginary.[16] Engelhardt traces the origins of victory culture as far back as nineteenth-century captivity and rescue stories. These narratives typically portray victory as an act of justified revenge carried out by white European settlers against "savage" and "evil" others, usually rescuing helpless women and children in the process. Engelhardt sees a resurgence of victory culture in the aftermath of September 11, 2001, in the speeches of the Bush Administration, and in the rhetoric of mainstream media. He argues that the 2001 terrorist attacks invoked "an old tradition of American triumphalism...They brought back much of [victory culture's] language and many of its images, while promising 'victory' in a new, generations-long, Manichean struggle against 'evil' enemies."[17]

In *The Terror Dream: Fear and Fantasy in Post-9/11 America*, Susan Faludi makes a similar argument about mainstream cultural texts after the terrorist attacks. She argues that the Bush Administration and corporate media outlets reproduced "elements of a national fantasy in which we are deeply invested, our elaborately constructed myth of invincibility."[18] Like Engelhardt, Faludi traces the origins of this myth to nineteenth-century captivity narratives in which white men rescue women and children in danger from darker evil others. Faludi writes that corporate news outlets began to construct endless narratives of male heroes rescuing those in danger as news articles after the attacks, and that they "always seemed to gravitate toward the same argument: 'maleness' was making a comeback because New York City's fire*men* were heroes on 9/11, and they were heroes because they had saved untold numbers of civilians."[19]

---

[16] Montserrat Guibernau, *The Identity of Nations* (Cambridge: Polity Press, 2007), p. 11.
[17] Engelhardt, *op. cit.*, p. xi.
[18] Susan Faludi, *The Terror Dream: Fear and Fantasy in Post-9/11 America* (New York: Metropolitan Books, 2007), p. 14.
[19] *Ibid.*, p. 79.

Joan Didion also observes that after the attacks, it seemed that "[a]s if overnight the irreconcilable event had been made manageable, reduced to the sentimental, to protective talismans, totems, garlands of garlic, repeated pieties that would come to seem in some ways as destructive as the event itself. We now had 'the loves ones,' we had 'the families,' we had 'the heroes.'"[20] In *Welcome to the Desert of the Real*, Slavoj Žižek describes this as a "derealization" of the horror that took place on 9/11. Žižek writes that despite the media's report of the death toll and description of the gravity of the event:

> it is surprising how little of the actual carnage we see—no dismembered bodies, no blood, no desperate faces of dying people...in clear contrast to reporting on Third World catastrophes, where the whole point is to produce a scoop of some gruesome detail: Somalis dying of hunger, raped Bosnian women, men with their throats cut. These shots are always accompanied by an advance warning that "some of the images you see are extremely graphic and may upset children"—a warning which we never heard in the reports on the WTC collapse. Is this not yet further proof of how, even in this tragic moment, the distance which separates Us from Them, from their reality, is maintained: the real horror happens *there*, not *here*?[21]

In other words, after September 11, 2001, corporate media outlets attempted to restore America's social imaginary with the comfortable and familiar narrative of victory culture, obviously repressing images of falling bodies that might communicate notions of American vulnerability or weakness. Guarding against that was the conflation of maleness with national exceptionalism: atrocities do not happen *here*, even when they do. Tim S. Gauthier writes that "[t]he representations of the falling persons— real as well as fictionalized—continue to disturb because they offer little redemption—they refuse to be incorporated into a soothing narrative. They remain that part of the day not counteracted by stories of heroism or good luck or divine intervention."[22] The reality of falling bodies cannot assimilate the post-9/11 narrative of victory culture, which explains why their images were purged from corporate media coverage of the terrorist attacks. In other words, the social imaginary of victory culture was maintained through the repression of that which does not conform to it.

Despite these censorships efforts, anyone with a laptop computer and

---

[20] Joan Didion, *Fixed Ideas: America Since 9/11* (New York: New York Review of Books, 2003), p. 9.
[21] Slavoj Žižek, *Welcome to the Desert of the Real* (New York: Verso, 2002), p. 13.
[22] Gauthier, *op. cit.*, p. 101.

an Internet connection could, and still can, easily access dozens if not hundreds of images and videos of the falling bodies on any number of websites. In "The Movement of Vulnerability: Images of Falling and September 11," Andrew D. Fitzpatrick writes that regardless of censorship, the "images of those who fell from the towers became traumatically imprinted in people's minds," and Drew's photograph became "an image that, perhaps more than any other, epitomizes the tragedy and horror of the September 11 catastrophe in Western cultural memory."[23] Although footage of the collapsing towers might similarly communicate American vulnerability, they do not concretely depict a loss of life. By contrast, the falling bodies remain "the most salient and human representation of the suffering undergone that day."[24]

Shortly after the terrorist attacks, philosophers generally adopted the view that the events of the terrorist attacks, including and especially the images of falling bodies, were shocking and beyond interpretation. In *The Spirit of Terrorism*, Jean Baudrillard writes that the attack on Lower Manhattan "defies...any form of interpretation."[25] In *Philosophy in a Time of Terror*, Jacques Derrida similarly sees the significance of the terrorist attacks as irreducible and elusive. Derrida argues that what collapsed was not so much two architectural symbols of political, military, and capitalist power as "the conceptual, semantic, and one could even say hermeneutic apparatus that might have allowed one to see coming, to comprehend, interpret, describe, speak of, and name 'September 11.'"[26] In *Out of the Blue*, Kristiaan Versluys argues that "September 11...is ultimately a semiotic event, involving the total breakdown of all meaning-making systems."[27] Similarly, writers often describe images of those who fell from the upper floors of the two towers as "incomprehensible," "too real,"[28] or as one witness wrote when referring to the falling bodies, "[b]eyond

---

[23] Andrew D. Fitzpatrick, "The Movement of Vulnerability: Images of Falling and September 11," *Art Journal* 66 n. 4 (2007): 84-102, 85.
[24] Gauthier, *op. cit.*, p. 101.
[25] Jean Baudrillard, *The Spirit of Terrorism*, translated by Chris Turner (London: Verso, 2002), p. 13.
[26] Derrida quoted in Giovanna Borradori, *Philosophy in a Time of Terror: Dialogues with Jürgen Habermas and Jacques Derrida* (Chicago, Ill.: University of Chicago Press, 2003), pp. 93-4.
[27] Kristiaan Versluys, *Out of the Blue: September 11 and the Novel* (New York: Columbia University Press, 2009), p. 2.
[28] Claire Kahane, "Uncanny Sights: The Anticipation of the Abomination," *Trauma at Home: After 9/11*, edited by Judith Greenberg (Lincoln: University of Nebraska Press, 2003), pp. 107-16, 111.

description," and "[b]eyond words."[29]

Since Kristeva's understanding of abjection explicitly deals with the collapse of boundaries, language, meanings, and distinctions, I suggest the images of falling bodies might best be understood in relation to her theoretical interpretation of that which disrupts the symbolic order. In *Powers of Horror*, Kristeva sees abjection as the state where a subject is drawn toward its boundaries, a condition where meaning collapses and there is neither a distinct subject nor object, only the abject. What is abject must be expelled and repressed in order to maintain boundaries and allow for the "self" to be both recognized in the "other," but also constituted in opposition to that same "other." The abject is something rejected from which one cannot separate. Although death, decay, and the unclean are Kristeva's prime examples of abjection, that which is abject is not necessarily a corpse or the smell of rotten milk, but rather the thing that "disturbs identity, system, order," the thing that "does not respect border positions, rules," "[t]he in-between, the ambiguous, the composite."[30] Abjection is an experience of cognitive dissonance through conflicting impulses of attraction and repulsion. The abject is what must be repelled in order to maintain the symbolic order.

One of Kristeva's main examples of abjection, the cadaver, finds its root word in Italian, *"cadere"* or *"to fall."*[31] Falling is a complex concept, one that communicates any number of overlapping and contradictory fears, anxieties, and metaphors. I would argue, however, that the concept of free falling, much like Kristeva's example of confronting a corpse, demonstrates abjection. In "Uncanny Sights: The Anticipation of the Abomination," Claire Kahane summarizes some of the metaphorical and psychological aspects of falling in relation to trauma:

> [F]alling…is a marker of the abysslike structure of trauma. Falling: *losing ground, having the rug pulled out from under you, being pushed over the edge, catch me I'm falling.* My own free-fall thoughts suggest that archaic memory traces of infantile experiences must inhabit the metaphor, signifier of the ultimate loss of control, of loss of agency, of loss of boundaries. Compounded by a host of cultural associations, the fear of falling in all likelihood must be part of our neurobiological makeup, contributing to our survival. But there is more to the fear of falling than the fear of falling;

---

[29] Luke Howie, *Terror on the Screen: Witnesses and the Reanimation of 9/11 as Image-Event, Popular Culture, and Pornography* (Washington, D.C.: New Academia Publishing, 2010), p. 205.

[30] Julia Kristeva, *Powers of Horror: An Essay on Abjection,* translated by Leon S. Roudiez (New York: Columbia University Press, 1982), p. 4.

[31] *Ibid.*, pp. 3-4.

falling evokes not just memory but fantasy, contaminating both memory and desire with perverse wishes that push us past our limits, urge us toward risk, even toward death itself.[32]

Kahane's understanding of free falling directly reflects the experience of abjection as falling embodies similar fears and desires that "push past our limits" toward the edge of death. There is an attraction or identification associated with the concept of falling, but also a fear and a rejection of it. This "loss of control, of loss of agency, of loss of boundaries" is partly why the images of falling bodies are troubling for a social imaginary that relies heavily on a narrative of victory culture, a narrative that needs clear boundaries of "self" and "other," "us" and "them," in order to function.

Drew's "The Falling Man" is a specific example that clearly embodies the abject dimensions of free falling. Drew's image captures the last seconds of this man's life, but only implies his death. According to Roland Barthes, every photograph denotes dying and death through the image's ability to objectify. Barthes writes that when his photograph is taken, he is "neither subject nor object but a subject who feels he is becoming an object: I then experience a micro-version of death (of parenthesis): I am truly becoming a specter…Ultimately, what I am seeking in the photograph taken of me…is death: Death is the *eidos* of that Photograph."[33] For Barthes, the image in the photograph "produces Death while trying to preserve life."[34] Susan Sontag similarly claims that "[a]ll photographs are *memento mori*. To take a photograph is to participate in another person's (or thing's) mortality, vulnerability, mutability. Precisely by slicing out this moment and freezing it, all photographs testify to time's relentless melt."[35]

Of course, some photographs communicate this sense of death more concretely than others, but it is always present. Drew's photograph captures a moment where the man in the frame is on the border of life and death. Here, I might draw a comparison between Drew's image and Barthes' analysis of Alexander Gardner's 1865 portrait of Lewis Payne, who attempted the assassination of United States Secretary of State, William H. Seward. Gardner photographed Payne in his jail cell, where Payne was waiting to be hanged for his crimes (fig. 10.2). For Barthes, the aesthetic "prick" or piercing (*punctum*) produced by such a photograph,

---

[32] Kahane, *op. cit.*, pp. 110-11.
[33] Roland Barthes, *Camera Lucida* (New York: Hill and Wang, 1981), pp. 14-15.
[34] *Ibid.*, p. 92.
[35] Susan Sontag, *On Photography* (New York: Picador, 1977), p. 15.

Figure 10.2 Lewis Payne, in sweater, seated and manacled. Library of Congress.
Alexander Gardner, Washington Navy Yard, D.C.

which cognitively and affectively disrupts the more mundane experience
of viewing for interest's sake, is not only the realization that "*he is going
to die*," but in Barthes' words, this is also the acknowledgement that "*This
will be* and *this has been*; I observe with horror an anterior future of which
death is the stake. By giving me the absolute past of the pose (aorist), the
photograph tells me death in the future. What *pricks* me is the discovery of
this equivalence...Whether or not the subject is already dead, every
photograph is this catastrophe. This *punctum*, more or less blurred beneath
the abundance and the disparity of contemporary photographs, is vividly
legible in historical photographs: there is always a defeat of Time in them:
that is dead and *that* is going to die."[36] Even more than Gardner's portrait
of Payne in his cell, Drew's photograph presents the clearest example of
the abject: "It is death infecting life."[37] The photographs of falling bodies
on September 11, 2001 explicitly produce this realization without any
need for context or contemplation of the photographic medium.

---

[36] Barthes, *op. cit.*, p. 96.
[37] Kristeva, *op. cit.*, p. 4.

In *Watching the World Change*, David Friend argues that the identification which viewers of such photographs as "The Falling Man" might experience is what led to widespread corporate censorship of the falling body images: "the viewer saw himself too clearly in the frame: a man who had been propelled to his death for having chosen to go to work that morning in an American office building."[38] Friend also offers a quotation from Drew, the photographer himself, alluding to the cognitive dissonance between viewers' identification with and repulsion towards images of falling bodies:

> I think that we just identify too much with this…Think about how many times you've seen a picture of someone who might have been attempting suicide, jumping from the Brooklyn Bridge or some building. We have more curiosity than aversion…We might have to face that similar situation some time…It could be us…It's hard for people to look at because they're thinking about what comes at the end of that, when he hits the ground, and that could be them. He is you and me.[39]

The image terrifies viewers through their identification with the falling man in the frame, seeing themselves as him, him as themselves. In order to protect their sense of identity and uphold the social imaginary, viewers must reject the image, which is simultaneously an act of rejecting themselves in order to ground their sense of self. Referring to what is abject, Kristeva writes "'I' want none of that element…'I' do not assimilate it, 'I' expel it. But since [the abject] is not an 'other' for 'me'…I expel *myself*, I spit *myself* out, I abject *myself* within the same motion through which 'I' claim to establish *myself*."[40] When Dori Laub writes that the terrorist attacks, including the falling bodies, are "an encounter with something that makes no sense," they "fit nowhere," and are part of an "experience of collective massive psychic trauma," she's describing the abject, that which does not make sense within the social imaginary, that which disrupts it.[41]

In many ways, Marsh's *Man on Wire* exemplifies the popular media's attempt to repress images of falling bodies and repair the social imaginary through narratives of victory culture and American exceptionalism.

---

[38] David Friend, *Watching the World Change: The Stories Behind the Images of 9/11* (New York: I. B. Tauris & Co., 2006), p. 140.

[39] Drew qtd. in *ibid.*, pp. 140-1.

[40] Kristeva, *op. cit.*, p. 3.

[41] Dori Laub, "September 11, 2001—An Event without a Voice," *Trauma at Home: After 9/11*, ed., Judith Greenberg (Lincoln: University of Nebraska Press, 2003), pp. 204-15, 204.

Although Marsh's film does not explicitly reflect victory culture in terms of justifiable American retaliation against darker evil others, the film still reproduces some key aspects of victory culture, especially in terms of gender. The film's narrative might not feature a clearly defined enemy, but it does feature a clearly defined hero who exemplifies certain masculine ideals. *Man on Wire* emphasizes Petit's heroic masculinity in numerous scenes, as the film displays his physical prowess. Petit's career as a wire walking daredevil is documented as a hyper-masculine pursuit. Petit's accomplice, David Foreman, idealizes the wire walker's fearlessness, his masculine stoicism, recounting the first time he saw Petit on a wire cable: "I had never seen concentration like that. And I think I never have to this day. And his face became this ageless mask of concentration, I mean, he became like a sphinx. It was amazing."[42] Whether Petit is shirtless while practicing on a wire cable, or completely naked when searching for a fishing line at the top of the World Trade Center, *Man on Wire* constantly characterizes its protagonist as a highly sexual, masculine hero. This point is also made clear at the end of the film, when Petit is released from police custody only to leave on a whim his friends and girlfriend for a "magnificent explosion of pleasure"[43] with a female admirer of his tightrope walk. In this sense, the film's portrayal of Petit's behavior communicates the hyper-masculine ideals of what Marc Feigen Fasteau calls "The Male Machine":

> The male machine is a special kind of being, different from women, children, and men who don't measure up. He is functional, designed mainly for work. He is programmed to tackle jobs, override obstacles, attack problems, overcome difficulties, and always seize the offensive. He will take on any task that can be presented to him in a competitive framework, and his most important positive reinforcement is victory.[44]

Unsurprisingly, *Man on Wire*'s presentation of a masculine hero also includes a supportive, submissive female partner: Annie Allix. At one point during the film, Annie describes her relationship with Petit: "He introduced me to the wire he had set up at the end of his garden and I spent hours watching him walk. He never thought to ask me whether I had my own destiny to follow. It was quite clear I had to follow his."[45] *Man on Wire* aligns with the mainstream television and popular culture

---

[42] Quoted in *Man on Wire*, directed by James Marsh (New York: Magnolia Home Entertainment, 2008), DVD.
[43] Petit quoted in *ibid.*
[44] Marc Feigen Fasteau, *The Male Machine* (New York: Dell, 1975), p. 1.
[45] Quoted in *Man on Wire*, *op. cit.*

representations of men and women that Faludi argues were meant to comfort audiences after September 11, 2001, as the film generates "the consolations of a domestic idyll where men w[ear] all the badges and women wield...all the roasting pans."[46] Petit says at the end of the film that "it's so simple that life should be lived on the edge of life. You have to exercise rebellion. To refuse to taper yourself to rules, to refuse your own success, to refuse to repeat yourself, to see every day, every year, every idea as a true challenge and then you are going to live your life on a tightrope."[47] Like many post-9/11 media portrayals of men, *Man on Wire* presents Petit as an inspirational and ideal model for hyper-male intensity. *Man on Wire* reproduces the expectations of men and masculinity that victory culture demands.

Despite his French origins, Petit fulfills the role of a national hero, as *Man on Wire* consistently frames his story in terms of American Dream ideals. The film tells the story of Petit's beginnings in France as an unknown street performer and his perseverance to achieve a "dream" that could only be realized in America. In the film, Petit recounts his thoughts during his first visit to New York. Petit says that the first time he looked up at the Twin Towers, he felt defeated: "I knew that my dream was destroyed instantly. Impossible. Impossible. Impossible. It's clearly impossible, not only to walk across, this, I'd probably hardly thought of it, but to bring almost a ton of equipment secretly, to rig a wire for hours, to guideline it. It's clearly out of human scale."[48] Petit's story, however, is about the ability to triumph over what appears impossible. Petit's castrating feelings of defeat become the catalyst for his victory at the Twin Towers. Petit says, "I thought, 'Okay, now, it's impossible, that's sure. So, let's start working.'"[49] After the completion of the tightrope walk, Petit became a folk hero in New York City. Annie says that after the walk, she "saw Philippe discover what it meant to be famous, to be recognized, with expressions of friendliness and enthusiasm. People would cross the street to tell him, 'You gave us such a gift! It was beautiful. It was a breath of fresh air! Thank you!'"[50] In his memoir of which *Man on Wire* is partially based, Petit writes, "America has saluted me. New York City adopts me. I stay."[51] *Man on Wire* flaunts Petit's story of individual determination and

---

[46] Faludi, *op. cit.*, p. 139.
[47] Quoted in *Man on Wire, op. cit.*
[48] *Ibid.*
[49] *Ibid.*
[50] *Ibid.*
[51] Philippe Petit, *Man on Wire*, 2nd edition (New York: Skyhorse Publishing, 2008), p. 228.

ultimately his triumph as an immigrant who achieves his dream in America and who is accepted by Americans. In this way, the film reinforces the idyllic notion that immigrant success is "a function of brains and hard work rather than influence or inheritance, and that American society as a whole provides the milieu in which this can happen."[52] Since his tightrope walk, Petit has also become an enthusiastic spokesperson for the American Dream. In an interview for the PBS documentary, "New York: The Center of the World," for example, Petit emphasizes the determination that was needed to make his "dream" a reality:

> You need dreams to live. It's as essential as a road to walk and bread to eat. I would have felt myself dying if this dream had been taken away from me by reason. The dream was as big as the towers. There was no way it could be taken away from me by authority, by reason, by destiny. It was really anchored to me in such a way that life was not conceivable without doing this.[53]

In this context, Petit frames "dreams" in terms of higher aspirations, ambitions, or goals, denoting the larger concept of the American Dream. Petit also universalizes this "dream" as if it were necessary to human survival and a sense of self-purpose. Of course, there is also a romantic, but ultimately ignorant, socio-economic implication in his statement: as long as any individual struggles through the obstacles of "authority," "reason," and "destiny," any "dream" can be accomplished, anything is possible. "I know it's impossible," Petit writes in his memoir, recounting his first thought after looking down from the 110th floor of the Word Trade Center, "[b]ut I know I'll do it."[54] Petit's accomplice, Jean-Louis Blondeau, echoes these sentiments in *Man on Wire* when he says, "If you want something, nothing is impossible."[55] *Man on Wire*'s presentation of Petit, a person who so completely embodies and supports American Dream ideals, inevitably reproduces the nostalgic certainties of heroism and the American Dream through the triumphant tightrope walk. The film acts as reparative to a social imaginary shaken by the events of September 11, 2001. The film's emphasis on male heroics and American Dream ideals also obscures and distracts from the Twin Towers as symbols of American corporate power within the framework of global capitalism, the

---

[52] William A. Clark, *Immigrants and the American Dream: Remaking the Middle Class* (New York: The Gulford Press, 2003), p. 27.
[53] Quoted in "The Center of the World," *New York: A Documentary Film*, Episode 8, directed by Ric Burns (Washington: PBS, 2003), Television Show.
[54] Petit, *op. cit.*, p. 17.
[55] Quoted in *ibid.*

very reason they became the targets of terrorism. *Man on Wire* reframes this symbolism as the towers simply become the objects that enable Petit's "dream" and story of individual success.

Man on Wire also fulfils a common desire expressed in many post-9/11 cultural texts for the two towers to have not collapsed, the desire for people not to have fallen to the streets below. Marsh's film fulfils this desire for inversion, as Petit accomplishes what those who fell from the two towers on 11 September 2001 could not. In his 1982 article on Petit, "On the High Wire," Paul Auster writes that "[e]ach time we see a man walk on the wire, a part of us is up there with him. Unlike performances in the other arts, the experience of high-wire walking is direct, unmediated, simple, and it requires no explanation whatsoever. The art is the thing itself, a life in its most naked delineation. And if there is beauty in this, it is because of the beauty we feel inside ourselves."[56] If viewers identify with Petit during *Man on Wire*, this identification remains distinct from the experience of cognitive dissonance that viewers might suffer while viewing images of falling bodies. Unlike images of the falling bodies, Petit's walk ultimately does not deliver abjection. "He did it beautifully and calmly," Alan Welner says during the film, "in fact, he did it literally with his eyes closed. It was just what he does. Everything he told me was true."[57] *Man on Wire*'s post-9/11 portrayal of Petit's wire walk emphasizes the wirewalker's preparedness, his extreme sense of concentration and control, his fearlessness, his mastery of heights, of the air, and of the Twin Towers. Contrary to the falling bodies, the film allows individuals to identify with a man who defies gravity, defies what is abject.

In *Let the Great World Spin*, a novel that explicitly attempts to examine the historical connection between Petit's walk and the events of 11 September 2001, Colum McCann's narrator discusses the peculiarity of Vic Deluca's 1974 photograph of Petit's wire walk (fig. 13.3), which McCann reprints in his book and which Marsh also displays in *Man on Wire*.[58] The photograph captures Petit on the high wire between the two towers with an airplane flying directly above him at the top of the frame, looking as if it will plunge into one of the building's upper floors. McCann's narrator contemplates this image at length:

A man high in the air while a plane disappears, it seems into the edge of

---

[56] Paul Auster, "On the High Wire," *The Art of Hunger* (New York: Penguin, 1997), pp. 249-61, 253.
[57] Quoted in *Man on Wire*, *op. cit.*
[58] Colum McCann, *Let the Great World Spin* (Toronto: HarperCollins, 2009), p. 237.

the building. One small scrap of history meeting a larger one. As if the walking man were somehow anticipating what would come later. The intrusion of time and history. The collision point of stories. We wait for the explosion but it never occurs. The plane passes, the tightrope walker gets to the end of the wire. Things don't fall apart.[59]

Figure 13.3 Philippe Petit waling the tightrope between the towers of the World Trade Center, New York. July 8, 1974. Rex Features. New York Post. Vic Deluca.

Here McCann's narrator describes the appeal of Petit's walk in a post-9/11 context as it brings audiences to a place where "things don't fall apart." Not only does *Man on Wire* provide audiences with a story of the Twin Towers that avoids any explicit mention of their destruction, but the film also does not question or explore the ramifications had Petit actually fallen. Ruth Mackay is also aware of this point: "The film's structure allows very little space to consider the potential ramifications of the act, confirming that the film's creators work to distance Petit's narrative from these concerns."[60] In this sense, *Man on Wire* operates as a repressive

---

[59] *Ibid.*, p. 325.
[60] Ruth Mackay, "'Going Backward in Time to Talk about the Present': *Man on Wire* and Verticality after 9/11," *Comparative American Studies* 9 n. 1 (2011): 3-

fantasy or, in Petit's own words, "a fairytale,"[61] where nobody falls from the World Trade Center.

Deluca's photograph, however, exemplifies how *Man on Wire*'s attempt to repress and overlap images of falling bodies with an emphasis on heroism, American Dream ideals, and nostalgic fantasies is ultimately futile. It expresses a dual temporality, referring not only to Petit's walk but also to the terrorist attacks of 9/11. In "On the High Wire," Paul Auster writes that "[u]nlike the stuntman, whose performance is calculated to emphasize every hair-raising risk, to keep his audience panting with dread and almost sadistic anticipation of disaster, the good high-wire walker strives to make his audience forget the dangers, to lure it away from thoughts of death by the beauty of what he does on the wire itself."[62]

After the photographs of falling bodies, however, this statement no longer seems to make sense in the case of Petit's walk between the two towers, if it ever did in the first place. In a post-9/11 context, the photographs and portrayals of Petit's wire walk allude to danger, free falling, and death. Marsh's *Man on Wire* recounts a moment where Petit's black turtleneck sweater fell from his bag, out into the air. One of Petit's accomplices, Barry Greenhouse, says during an interview in the film, "I saw a thing falling down and I couldn't believe it. And I said to myself, 'That's it. You've been fooling yourself this whole time. He went straight down with the first step off the roof. He might be dead.'"[63] Even the photographs of Petit's walk that are shown in *Man on Wire* share uncanny similarities with photographs of the falling bodies. In many of the photographs of Petit on his tightrope, the wire is difficult to see, so it appears as if the performer is floating in mid-air. Auster describes a photograph of Petit's performance where the tightrope is "almost invisible," and Petit, standing on top of the wire, appears as if "suspended magically in space."[64] Fitzpatrick also describes Drew's "The Falling Man" in a way that could easily be transposed to describe Petit's wire walk: "the aesthetic qualities and symmetry [Drew's photograph] create a false sense of suspension: a strange buoyancy as if he is floating by a thread."[65] "Floating" and "flying" are common descriptors that writers use to describe both Petit and the falling bodies. The various post-9/11 portrayals of Petit consistently allude to falling bodies as it is inevitable for

20, 9.
[61] Quoted in *Man on Wire, op. cit.*
[62] Auster, *op. cit.* p. 253.
[63] Quoted in *Man on Wire, op. cit.*
[64] Auster, *op. cit.*, p. 251.
[65] Fitzpatrick, *op. cit.*, p. 90.

any text to refer in some way to what it intends to overlap, mitigate, or displace.

In an interview with BBC reporter Neil Smith, for example, Marsh rationalizes his decision to omit any juxtaposition or discussion of Petit's walk in light of the terrorist attacks: "It would be unfair and wrong to infect [Petit's] story with any mention, discussion or imagery of the Towers being destroyed. Everyone knows what happened to those buildings…The film has a poignancy for that reason, but not one that needs to be overstated."[66] In the same interview, Marsh hopes that audiences will be able to "enjoy those buildings for the duration of the film, hopefully without that enjoyment being too infected by an awareness of their destruction."[67] In her article about the documentary film, Mackay critiques Marsh's comments as she writes that there is no way *Man on Wire* can "stand free from its audience's awareness of 11 September."[68] She takes particular issue with Marsh's choice of words:

> Marsh's use of the words "unfair" and "wrong" are an attempt to cover the fact that he must have been acutely aware that 9/11 would at least inform, if not guarantee, the success of *Man on Wire*. More than simply disingenuous, his comments are significantly loaded; using terminology such as "wrong" implies a moral transgression on behalf of those who would see 11 September 2001 refracted in the film. Moreover, the idea that the events of that day could "infect" the film is a particularly volatile metaphor that ascribes 9/11 an animate, even viral, status. Marsh's words are so strikingly incongruous with the film's clear relationship to 9/11 that they betray an underlying anxiety to at once address and push away the horrific association of 2001.[69]

Mackay's critique of Marsh's logic demonstrates that even in the absence of references to the collapse of the World Trade Center, any text that features Petit's walk or the Twin Towers will inevitably denote the presence of September 11, 2001. It is unthinkable how an image of the Twin Towers, let alone *Man on Wire*, might exist in the contemporary cultural climate without associatively reflecting traces of the terrorist attacks. The imagery and language associated with falling bodies, like the broader events of 9/11, encode representations of Petit's tightrope walk

---

[66] Quoted in Neil Smith, "Wire-walk Film Omits 9/11 Tragedy" *BBC News*, August 2, 2008. Web. September 8, 2011.
http://news.bbc.co.uk/2/hi/entertainment/7498364.stm
[67] *Ibid.*
[68] Mackay, *op. cit.*, p. 10.
[69] *Ibid.*

regardless if the authors, artists, or directors who reproduce his story in various cultural texts intend otherwise.

Ultimately, *Man on Wire* is a single prominent example of how many representations of pre-9/11 New York City have become encoded with imagery and language that denote the events of September 11, 2001. The terrorist attacks have disrupted the temporality of certain pre-9/11 events and various representations of those events. Cultural texts released prior to the terrorist attacks often appear prophetic as if they were predicting the demise of the World Trade Center decades in advance. McCann's narrator refers to this phenomenon in Deluca's photograph of Petit: "As if the walking man were somehow anticipating what would come later."[70] E. B. White's comments about New York City in relation to post-World War II anxieties about modernized warfare are also a notable example that serves to demonstrate how the events of September 11, 2001 encode the past. This quotation appears in White's short portrait of New York City, *Here is New York*, first published in 1949:

> The subtlest change in New York is something people don't speak much about but that is in everyone's mind. The city, for the first time in its long history, is destructible. A single flight of planes no bigger than a wedge of geese can quickly end this island fantasy, burn the towers, crumble the bridges, turn the underground passages into lethal chambers, cremate the millions. The intimation of mortality is part of New York now: in the sound of jets overhead, in the black headlines of the latest edition.[71]

It becomes impossible to read White's comments without thinking of terrorism and the attacks in Lower Manhattan. The imagery of terrorism similarly encodes *Man on Wire* just as it might encode any number of portrayals of New York City or the Twin Towers. The difference, however, is that *Man on Wire* is a direct response to the aftermath of September 11, 2001, one that appears to be invested in repressing the trauma of the terrorist attacks, especially the images of falling bodies, through the familiarity of victory culture. This repression is at least a partial failure, due to the fragmented temporality of *Man on Wire*. The film, therefore, demonstrates not just the possibility for new socio-political significance to emerge from representations of pre-9/11 images and events, but also how the infectious imagery and language of the terrorist attacks may always trouble or haunt that new meaning.

---

[70] McCann, *op. cit.*, p. 325.
[71] E. B. White, *Here is New York* (New York: Little Bookroom, 2000 [1949]), p. 54.

CHAPTER FOURTEEN

A FAILURE OF IMAGINATION? PROBLEMS IN 'POST-9/11' FICTION

RACHEL SYKES

These are the days after. Everything now is measured in after.
—Don DeLillo, *Falling Man*[1]

The above epigraph, taken from Don DeLillo's 2007 novel *Falling Man*, provides an insight into the problem of history in literary depictions of September 11, 2001. To many Americans, and to many observers worldwide, the terrorist attacks on the World Trade Center and the Pentagon symbolised the start of a new era of terror, a new reality which was unfamiliar, fragmented, and marked by tragedy. Collective surprise at the attacks and the consistency with which dramatic footage was streamed and repeated implied to the public that they had been denied time to respond and interpret the events. It did not, as DeLillo illustrates, indicate the beginning of a period of change, but suggested that the world had already changed irretrievably, that "These are the days after."

Falling Man is just one example of literature which prematurely seeks to define the events of September 11, 2001 as a turning point in American history. DeLillo inherits what Aaron DeRosa has described as the "postlapsarian terms" of public trauma and thus reflects the notion of temporal rupture perpetuated in "post-9/11" discourse.[2] The novel dwells upon the physical recreation of the event itself, portraying New York as inconceivably different in the years after 2001. Yet contradictorily, DeLillo struggles to imagine a future beyond the destruction of the Twin Towers. The "falling man" of the title is a fictional performance artist who repeatedly suspends himself with a rope and harness in a recreation of

---

[1] Don DeLillo, *Falling Man* (New York: Picador, 2007), p. 13.
[2] Aaron DeRosa, "Analysing Literature After 9/11," *Modern Fiction Studies* 57 n. 3 (Fall 2011): 607-618.

Richard Drew's famous image. The artist hangs provocatively from the buildings of the city, introducing his performance and its associations into the everyday lives of New Yorkers so that the event's symbolism becomes literally inescapable. He is not merely a disruptive presence, but also a symbol of stasis; crucially, the performance consists of not falling from buildings but hanging over the city in a suspended state. DeLillo is similarly paralysed by his willingness to interpret the terrorist attacks as an objective symbol of great change. In *Falling Man*, he suggests that every American narrative must now begin and end with "9/11," that the event has not just changed but also come to encompass contemporary America.

The narrowness of this perspective has also contributed to the prolonged illusion of a cohesive body of "post-9/11" literature. Between 2005 and 2007, a number of prominent fiction writers including DeLillo, Jonathan Safran Foer (*Extremely Loud and Incredibly Close* [2005]), Claire Messud (*The Emperor's Children* [2006]), and Jay McInerney (*The Good Life* [2006]) published novels based around the events in New York. These novels have been loosely grouped as a "9/11" canon and studied as key examples of "the 9/11 novel" for their recreation either of the event or of the weeks following the attacks. Yet I would argue that each novelist fails fully to interrogate the idea of September 11, 2001 on a national or international scale. In these novels, the narrative restricts the point of view to the warring white middle-class family, and thus reflects a dominant form of realism that pre-dates the terrorist attacks.

Academics and reviewers have often fared no better in finding a language to articulate fully the limitations of these novels. The problem of imagination in both author and critic began with an immediate pressure to respond. In *9/11: The Culture of Commemoration* (2006), David Simpson suggests that "taking time" will be the ultimate challenge to sustained reflection on the terrorist attacks. "Scholarly time," he writes, "looks its best when there are no critical events going on around it: then it can reflect and project and even hope to appear prescient."[3] The speed with which "9/11" became connected with global politics and military ambition forestalled the time for reflection which the novel and its criticism require. Even DeLillo agonized over how long he should wait to respond: "Is it too soon? We seem pressed for time, all of us."[4] The novelist implies that a bleaker future lies ahead, but that the weight of the future is already "pressed" upon him. DeLillo therefore underscores the need for imperative action even in his moment of indecision; the potential for change in the

---

[3] David Simpson, *The Culture of Commemoration* (Chicago, Ill.: The University of Chicago Press, 2006), p. 11.
[4] Don DeLillo, "In the Ruins of the Future," *Harper's*, December 2001, p. 40.

present moment becomes associated only with further tragedy and the time for reflection is lost.[5]

Over the past decade, the prevailing assumption has remained: American literature must and will produce a body of novels which imposes meaning upon the attacks. This essay interrogates some of the problems surrounding the representation of September 11, 2001 in fiction and its broader categorisation as "post-9/11" or "9/11 literature." Both terms have slipped into critical discourse surrounding American fiction with little qualification of their generic or periodic distinctions. I will therefore discuss the critical response that has generated the "post-9/11" label before making a case for the relative innovation of William Gibson's 2003 novel, *Pattern Recognition*. One of the first novels to include the event in its plotline, *Pattern Recognition* places the events of September 11th into a broader network of conspiracy, terrorism, and globalisation that enables him to integrate the attacks into fiction as a moment of perceived change that diminishes its exceptional character.

The problems in "9/11 fiction" began with its terminology. Even in the initial weeks following the attacks, the symbolism of the digits 911, or the act of defining the day and month without any indication of the year, was indicative of its removal both from history and from its correspondence to the present moment. W. J. T. Mitchell foresaw the temporal loop that the event's definition indicated in October 2001 when he wrote in *Critical Inquiry*, "It is Day One of an event whose days are unnumbered, indefinite, an emergency in which the emergent order has yet to make itself clear."[6] As "9/11," September 11, 2001 became part of the future, endowed with the weight of history, of destiny, but removed from a sense of historical continuity. Jacques Derrida made a similar objection to the naming of "9/11," arguing in one interview that:

> This act of naming: a date and nothing more. When you say "September 11" you are already citing...You are inviting me to speak here by recalling, as if in quotation marks, a date or a daring that has taken over our public space and our private lives...The very impact of what is at least *felt*, in an

---

[5] Consider this connotation of change beside Barack Obama's slogan during the 2008 presidential campaign: "Change you can believe in." Obama's campaign capitalised upon the identification of change with positivity, but note the operative modifier becomes "believe"—to have not only the appearance of change but to represent tenable and identifiable change, as opposed to the negative and fictitious change the Democrats associated with George W. Bush's administration.

[6] W. J. T. Mitchell, "911: Criticism and Crisis," *Critical Inquiry*, 28 n. 2 (2002), p. 568.

apparently immediate way, to be an event that truly marks, that truly makes its mark, a singular and, as they say here, "unprecedented" event.[7]

Derrida makes an important distinction between what is "*felt*" to be singular and what is in reality "unprecedented." September 11, 2001 was presented as an immediate rupture in time so that the event "*felt*" like a turning point in history before any time had passed. The danger, as Derrida points out, is that in referring to 9/11 without quotation the speaker or writer will forget that they are citing, thereby accepting the event as an objective reality, not a temporal construct. The application of the term "9/11" to a cultural movement, then, assumes a legacy of exceptionalism which has existed discursively since the morning of September 11th.

Fiction writers voiced a similar problem with language in the days and weeks after. Many spoke of the insufficiency of words: "I have nothing to say," Toni Morrison famously wrote about "the dead of September".[8] Many novelists sat down to write on the day of the attacks. On September 24, 2001, *The New Yorker* devoted its "Talk of the Town" section to nine 700-word vignettes on the attacks earlier that month, to "reflect on the tragedy and its consequences."[9] Just a week after the terrorist attacks, Jonathan Franzen observed that "the new world" was already "a different world," its newness stemming from the shock at the penetration of U.S. soil.[10] Susan Sontag saw the alleviation of common ignorance in what she called the "monstrous dose of reality" dealt to Americans. Yet she also acknowledged its transitory nature; the public, she felt sure, had not been "asked to bear much of the burden of reality" and would soon return to its former, more comfortable existence.[11] In these first few weeks after the attacks, the writing of many novelists reflected the belief that, in some indefinable way, "9/11" had already changed everything.

---

[7] Giovanna Borradori, *Philosophy in a Time of Terror: Dialogues with Jürgen Habermas and Jacques Derrida* (Chicago, Ill.: The University of Chicago Press, 2003), pp. 85-86.

[8] Toni Morrison, "The Dead of September 11," *Vanity Fair*, November 2001, p. 48.

[9] David Remnick, ed., "Talk of the Town," *The New Yorker*, September 24, 2001. Accessed August 2, 2013.
http://www.newyorker.com/archive/2001/09/24/010924ta_talk_wtc.

[10] Jonathan Franzen, "The Talk of the Town," ed., David Remnick, *The New Yorker*, September 24, 2001, web. Accessed August 2, 2013.
http://www.newyorker.com/archive/2001/09/24/010924ta_talk_wtc.

[11] Susan Sontag, "The Talk of the Town," ed., David Remnick, *The New Yorker*, September 24, 2001, web. Accessed August 2, 2013.
http://www.newyorker.com/archive/2001/09/24/010924ta_talk_wtc.

In their own biographical responses, Don DeLillo and John Updike described how the physical destruction in Lower Manhattan seemed to threaten the fabric of reality itself. DeLillo especially suggested that all thoughts of the writer should be consumed, if only temporarily, in assigning meaning to what was left behind: "In its desertion of every basis for comparison, the event asserts its singularity...The writer tries to give memory, tenderness and meaning to all that howling space."[12] Updike elaborated that the problem of representing September 11, 2001 would be that reality itself now appeared to be reflexive, and that the lines between fact and fiction had blurred irrevocably: "there persisted the notion that, as on television, this was not quite real; it could be adjusted; the technocracy the towers symbolized would find a way to put out the fire and reverse the damage."[13] DeLillo and Updike doubted the authority of the author at a time of crisis. Yet both would accept the burden of representation, perpetuating the contradictory suggestion that "9/11" was impossible to represent and impossible to ignore.

Discussion about the failures of language in the aftermath of tragedy is by no means new. Fifty years earlier, Theodor Adorno had famously argued that "To write poetry after Auschwitz is barbaric"[14] just as Lionel Trilling suggested that "There is no possible way of responding to Belsen and Buchenwald."[15] Further, DeLillo's declaration that it is the novelist's duty to provide the reader with meaning is indicative of what Adorno described as "the drastic guilt of him who was spared."[16] Writing in 1966, Adorno identifies a cultural form of survivor's guilt which manifests in the artist who is caught between capturing an event's singularity and negotiating it into the past. Burdened by a sense of duty to those who have died and an accountability to those who remain, Adorno claims that "By way of atonement [the artist] will be plagued by dreams such as that he is no longer living at all."[17] Any event presented as a rupture in a nation's

---

[12] Don DeLillo, *op. cit.*, p. 38.

[13] John Updike, "The Talk of the Town," ed., David Remnick, *The New Yorker*, September 24, 2001, web. August 2, 2013. http://www.newyorker.com/archive/2001/09/24/010924ta_talk_wtc.

[14] Theodor W. Adorno, "An Essay on Cultural Criticism and Society," translated by Samuel Weber and Sherry Weber, *Prisms* (New York: Columbia University Press, 1981 [1955]), p. 34.

[15] Lionel Trilling, *The Liberal Imagination* (New York: Doubleday, 1953), p. 256.

[16] Theodor W. Adorno, "Meditations on Metaphysics," *Negative Dialectics*, translated by E. B. Ashton (New York: Continuum International Publishing Group, 2005 [1966; translation 1973]), p. 363.

[17] Adorno, *op. cit.*, p. 363.

narrative draws the artist into a temporal loop, unable to relegate the event's significance to the past and instead projecting its legitimacy into the future. In stasis, art is unable to evolve because the artist no longer thinks in terms of progression ("he is no longer living at all").

The tenth anniversary of the attacks renewed media interest in what "9/11 fiction" was capable of achieving. In an article for the BBC, Alizeh Kohari marked the anniversary with the question: "Is there a novel that defines the 9/11 decade?" Kohari's article quotes figures which suggest that as of 2010 there had been 164 published works of "9/11 fiction," with an additional 145 works of juvenile literature.[18] Characteristic of many articles seeking to review and group novels "about" the attacks, the author fails to specify the criteria that group the works. Of the 164 novels, Kohari notes no defining features, such as shared themes, common tropes, locations, subject matter, or even inclusion of the event itself. The article therefore provides quantitative evidence of the general vagueness that surrounds the genre. The "9/11" novel has come to include everything from a direct representation of the event (e.g., *Falling Man*) to any work of fiction interpreting the political landscape since 2001. For example, Jonathan Franzen's *Freedom* (2010) is often categorised as a "9/11 novel." Reviewing the novel for *NPR*, Guy Raz described the novel as "a masterpiece of modern, post-Sept. 11 fiction," something which Franzen directly contradicted: "I wasn't trying to wrestle with 9/11 as it was being so over-wrestled with in the media."[19] The interviewer here assumes that engagement with the contemporary means that the author must in some way address the national event. This again assumes the need for the novelistic response to the terrorist attacks without consideration of what a novel "about" September 11, 2001 actually entails.

The lack of formal, ideological, generic, spatial, or even temporal constraints has imitated the timescale with which the event has been placed nationally, implying the unlimited and oftentimes apocalyptic repercussions which the Bush Administration inferred it to entail. Further, this premature periodization by reviewers and critics alike has helped to prioritise the study of "9/11 fiction" without sufficient interrogation of its aims. Studies such as Kristiaan Versluys' *Out of the Blue: September 11 and the Novel* (2009) and *Literature After 9/11* (2008), edited by Ann

---

[18] Alizeh Kohari, "Is there a novel that defines the 9/11 decade?" *BBC News*, August 28, 2011, web. Accessed August 2, 2013.
http://www.bbc.co.uk/news/entertainment-arts-14682741.
[19] Jonathan Franzen quoted in Guy Raz, "Jonathan Franzen takes the long road to *Freedom*," *NPR*, September 11, 2010, web. Accessed August 2, 2013.
http://www.npr.org/templates/story/story.php?storyId=129799680.

Keniston and Jeanne Follansbee Quinn, analyse a wealth of texts but continually prioritise the same narrow canon. Literature concerning September 11, 2001 has also been primarily studied in isolation, with little consideration of its relative importance; the idea of its necessity, until recently, has largely gone unquestioned. However, the publication of Mohsin Hamid's *The Reluctant Fundamentalist* (2007) and Joseph O'Neill's *Netherland* (2008) was met with critical acclaim for their transnational reimaginings of the terrorist attacks. At the same time, the beginnings of a critical evolution can be traced. *Terror and the Postcolonial* (2010), edited by Elleke Boehmer and Stephen Morton, attempts to understand the phenomenon of terror as "the ground upon which sovereignty is in many cases defined in the colonial present."[20] The collected essays focus on depictions of the U.S. that reach beyond traditional boundaries of the nation-state and crucially begin to situate "9/11" beyond the original U.S. orientation of its scholarship.

Richard Gray has been particularly instrumental in reassessing the lasting impact of "9/11" on American culture. *After the Fall* (2011) is the first detailed study to bridge the gap between U.S.-centered and postcolonial studies of "9/11", presenting twenty-first century America as "a transcultural space in which different cultures reflect and refract, confront and bleed into one another."[21] Gray vastly expands what scholars have long supposed "post-9/11 literature" to be; yet even Gray's approach has vast limitations. *After The Fall* developed from Gray's 2009 essay "Open Door, Closed Minds: American Prose Writing at a Time of Crisis" which provided one of the first criticisms of the "failure of imagination" read throughout DeLillo and his contemporaries. September 11, 2001, however, still emerges as a defining force in the future of literature. "And then there are the cataclysmic events of 9/11 and their aftermath." Gray writes, "These are part of the soil, the deep structure lying beneath and shaping the literature of the American nation, not least because (these events) have reshaped our consciousness; they are a defining element in our contemporary structure of feeling."[22] The presumption that September 11, 2001 would be the defining crisis point for the twenty-first century not only suggests American exceptionalism, but reduces the task of literature

---

[20] Elleke Boehmer and Stephen Morton, "Introduction: Terror and the Postcolonial," *Terror and the Postcolonial*, edited by Elleke Boehmer and Stephen Morrton, (Oxford: Wiley Blackwell, 2010), p. 6.

[21] Richard Gray, *After The Fall: American Literature Since 9/11* (Oxford: Wiley Blackwell, 2011), p. 55.

[22] Richard Gray, "Open Doors, Closed Minds: American Prose Writing at a Time of Crisis," *American Literary History* 21 n. 1 (Spring 2009), p. 129.

to that of responding to designated points of crisis. Further, Gray fails to avoid this rhetorical minefield when discussing the terrorist attacks. Ending his address to the nation just after 8.30 p.m. EST on September 11, President George W. Bush asserted that "None of us will ever forget this day. Yet, we go forward to defend freedom and all that is good and just in our world."[23] In his speech, Bush placed the event as already part of an unforgettable past, with the "Yet" of Bush's final sentence implying that it is also part of the future, a factor in events yet to happen. Bush assumes a generic audience, and so does Richard Gray.   He uses the collective pronouns "we" and "our" throughout the essay, like Bush, supposing a generic public body standing with them to reinforce the "task" and necessity of "post-9/11 literature" as Gray sees it.

It is important at this juncture to ask what the term "post-9/11" refers to. Is this the establishment of a new genre or an attempt at periodization? Has it already conflated "9/11" and the "act of naming" referred to by Derrida? Periodization is often used as a tool by which to attribute order to a period of relative confusion. In his article "The Cultural Logic of Historical Periodization" (2003), Peter Toohey describes the need to periodize as the desire for "Regularizing, packaging and calibrating the apparent disorder of historical record."[24]   But whilst periodization is, to a certain extent, inevitable in writing a history of the contemporary moment, "9/11" has not been sufficiently defined as a period, let alone as a genre of literature. The events of "9/11" are useful as a foothold in the twenty-first century, allowing "us" to periodise the first decade of the twenty-first century in a way that distinguishes this century without the need for further specificity. But what if the same trends document the start of a new genre? The term "post-9/11 fiction" was used most frequently in reviews by Michiko Kakutani, first in her review of Ian McEwan's *Saturday* for *The New York Times* in 2005. She stated: "Mr. McEwan has not only produced one of the most powerful pieces of post-9/11 fiction yet published, but also fulfilled that very primal mission of the novel: to show how we—a privileged few of us, anyway—live today."[25] Interestingly,

---

[23] George W. Bush, *"Statement by the president in his address to the nation,"* The White House, September 11, 2001, web. Accessed August 2, 2013. http://georgewbush-whitehouse.archives.gov/news/releases/2001/09/20010911-16.html.

[24] Peter Toohey, "The Cultural Logic of Historical Periodization," *Handbook of Historical Sociology*, edited by Gerard Delanty (London: SAGE Publications, 2003), p. 209.

[25] Michiko Kakutani, "Books of the Times; A Hero with 9/11 Peripheral Vision," *The New York Times*, March 18, 2005, Books section, web. Accessed August 2,

Kakutani already groups *Saturday* within a cohesive body of "post-9/11 fiction" just four years after the attacks. She already retrospectively defines a genre of literature that is in its infancy.

So far we have talked abstractly about the literature of September 11th without looking at the texts themselves; when considering those novels which take the attacks as their direct subject matter, it is possible to identify some common themes. DeLillo writes in *Falling Man*, "These three years past since that day in September, all life had become public."[26] Typically, however, the domestic focus is contradictorily the most prevalent in the novels immediately classified as "9/11 fiction." The trope of marriage breakdown is most often paralleled with the terrorist attacks, and is at the centre of DeLillo's *Falling Man*, McInerney's *The Good Life*, and Ken Kalfus's *A Disorder Peculiar to the Country* (2007). In fact, *Falling Man*, *A Disorder Peculiar to the Country*, and McEwan's *Saturday* all focus on nuclear families, metaphorically equating the breakdown of family relationships with the distress caused by the attacks. In the cases of DeLillo and Kalfus, not only do the male protagonists escape from their offices in the World Trade Center, but their marriages had broken down prior to the event. A white middle-class context predominates, most significantly in *The Good Life* and Claire Messud's *The Emperor's Children,* which address the overindulgence of the wealthy in Manhattan who struggle to fulfil their grandiose ambitions. All adults are college educated; all families are white. But prevalent through all examples of this proposed genre is an awareness of the dissatisfaction of American life prior to September 11th, which the events of that day only exacerbate and parallel.

What might be seen as common themes, however, does not constitute a period or genre. Grouping these novels as a cohesive "9/11 literature" does not demonstrate a period of literature but rather a lack of originality. And most significantly, this list of features reads like many works of American literature published decades before the attacks of 2001. Of course, there have been exceptions to this rule, when the author looks outside the domestic scope. In John Updike's *Terrorist* (2006) or Martin Amis' short stories *The Second Plane* (2008), the focus remains entirely on the "enemy" or "other", but their characterisation in these cases doesn't develop beyond caricature. As mentioned above, Joseph O'Neill's *Netherland* geopolitically imagines the repercussions of "trauma,"

2013.
http://query.nytimes.com/gst/fullpage.html?res=9E01E0DD103CF93BA25750C0
A9639C8B63.
[26] DeLillo, *op. cit.*, p. 182.

incorporating aspects of multinationalism, yet it remains essentially concerned with similar themes of broken marriages and child protection.

One of the earliest novels to feature the terrorist attacks as a plot device, William Gibson's *Pattern Recognition* (2003) provides a more nuanced consideration of the changes implied by the events of September 11, 2001. *Pattern Recognition* is set in a world closely related but not identical to America in 2002. Gibson's protagonist, Cayce Pollard, is grieving for her father who went missing on the morning of the attacks. Her father's body has never been recovered, nor has it been explained why he was in the vicinity of the World Trade Center that morning. As such, Cayce is neither able fully to access nor to process her memories of the events of September 11th; she is both perpetually haunted by and completely removed from the events. Cayce's inability to engage with her memories necessitates a valuable narrative distance, ensuring that *Pattern Recognition* conceptualises the events with a more convincing degree of objectivity. Unable to obtain information on her father's death through global systems of conspiracy, surveillance, and distrust, Gibson's novel challenges the assumption that the terrorist attacks had brought about any great or illuminating change in American society, placing the event within a pre-existing, and ill-defined, global network of terrorism.

September 11, 2001 provides a moment only of perceived change in *Pattern Recognition*, an incident positioned as a crisis around which the anxieties of New Yorkers, and Americans, consolidate. Cayce's problems are emphasised by the climate in New York in the years after 2001, which in turn influences her interpretation of the events. They are, however, long-term problems which, along with a fear of intimacy and a dysfunctional relationship with her mother, include the mysterious condition of apophenia. This ailment leaves her paralysed by the uncontrolled identification of patterns and symbols, experiencing seizures whenever she is exposed to logos such as the Michelin Man.[27] She suffers from "the spontaneous perception of connections and meaningfulness in unrelated things" (p. 113), which heightens her experience of the terrorist attacks by a supernatural sensitivity to interpretation. September 11, 2001 does not change Cayce or the society in which she exists but provides a motif through which to communicate the problems she faces to the reader. The shock with which other characters experience September 11, 2001 parallels Cayce's own personal disconnect from society. Furthermore, the

---

[27] William Gibson, *Pattern Recognition*, (London: Penguin, 2004). All further references to this edition will be referenced as *PR*, with page numbers, in the body of the text. Cayce is also "allergic" to the Tommy Hilfiger brand, experiencing reactions to both these logos on pp. 2, 4, 164, and 188.

event is positioned not as a moment of transition but as a spectacle of illusory transformation whose extravagant performative nature echoes similar events throughout history and the contemporary world.

The trope of apophenia allows *Pattern Recognition* to divorce itself from this assumption of negative change, and instead mimic the feeling of the "unreal" discussed by many commentators. David Foster Wallace published "The View from Mrs. Thompson's" in *Rolling Stone* magazine in October 2001, describing the strange déjà vu he felt watching the live and repeated footage, the feeling that "We've Seen This Before."[28] Wallace claims that the premeditation of the TV footage is clear in everything from the news anchor's immaculately dishevelled hair to the repetitions of select parts of the programming: "the constant rerunning of horrific footage might not be just in case some viewers were only now tuning in and hadn't seen it yet."[29] He implies what Slavoj Žižek argued further: America's moment of self-perception in the events of September 11, 2001 was unavoidably repeated in the footage, but this repetition also identified that self-perception with the familiarity of its imagery. In terms of aggressive foreign policy, imperialist ambitions, and the scenes which it had previously "fantasized about" in cinema, September 11, 2001 seemed to Žižek to be a realisation of American fantasy:

> Not only were the media bombarding us all the time with talk about the terrorist threat; this threat was also obviously libidinally invested—just remember the series of movies from *Escape from New York* to *Independence Day*. That is the rationale of the often-mounted association of the attacks with Hollywood disaster movies: the unthinkable which happened was the object of fantasy, so that, in a way, America got what it fantasized about, and that was the biggest surprise.[30]

This criticism by Žižek indicates several layers by which September 11, 2001 might be interpreted as a construction. On face value, the events constitute a public experience of "trauma," yet its immediate visual power to incite fear and paranoia relied upon its underlying continuity rather than the dramatic change it was meant to imply.

In *Pattern Recognition*, the internet complicates the visual element of September 11, 2001, as the television clips of the event become the "footage" of online forums. The lives which characters build on the internet also troubles the idea of change within global communities, as

---

[28] David Foster Wallace, "The View from Mrs. Thompson's," *Consider the Lobster*, (London: Abacus, 2005), p. 140.

[29] *Ibid.*, p. 140.

[30] Slavoj Žižek, *Welcome to the Desert of the Real*, (London: Verso, 2002), p. 15.

worldwide online-communities become more identifiable than physical definitions of society. As a result, the nation-state becomes decentred. Cayce's condition singles her out from the beginning, but it is only through online communities that she is able to fall in love and bring about the resolution of her father's death, subsequently stopping the fits of her apophenia. Her online-community forms part of what Lauren Berlant describes as "an alternative present", allowing her not only a way to escape consumer culture, but also to evade the public response to September 11, 2001.[31] Her virtual community becomes "a way now, approximately, of being at home. The forum has become one of the most consistent places in her life, like a familiar café that exists somehow outside of geography and beyond time zones" (p. 4). The shrinking of perceived distances between locations also allows Gibson's text to draw consistent comparisons between geographical locations and places associated with suffering, moving quickly from the everyday Starbucks and thrift stores of New York to images of Buchenwald and Chernobyl (p. 38). September 11, 2001 acts as a pivot around which Gibson stresses the continuity that previous events can represent in contemporary life, assimilating references to past events within a living, evolving sense of history. Gibson's network of global "trauma" recognises September 11, 2001 as "an experience outside of culture" (p. 137), a statement which, rather than positioning the event as a defining element of American culture, points to the event as a point of shared reference.

Cayce's online-community forms a virtual counterculture that seeks to challenge established historiographies, even going someway to create their own. Cayce's friends and rivals are all collectors of cultural artefacts. Most often, they collect artefacts relating to instances of war and "trauma" which appear throughout the novel: artefacts from the Second World War, e.g., an excavated Stuka aircraft, Soviet calculators, etc. The most popular collectible of the novel is the mysterious internet footage created by the victim of a Russian terrorist attack, and released sporadically over an online forum: *Footage:Fetish:Forum*. The footage is a collection of short films thought to make up a cohesive body of work; the debate between the fans of this footage considers whether each clip is being broadcast as it is created, or whether they are already fragments of a whole work. At times, the debate seems to be about intention: is the film being changed as it is made, or is it following a planned trajectory? N. Katherine Hayles suggests that the footage allows both maker and viewer to break from

---

[31] Lauren Berlant, "Intuitionists: History and the Affective Event," *American Literary History* 20 n. 4 (Winter 2008): 856.

obsessive repetition and allow trauma to become a form of artistic expression.[32] However, the fans argue over production of the footage in similar ways to critics considering the footage of September 11, 2001, with a "tendency to quote Baudrillard" (p. 48), and with extended space to comment online. The footage represents an art form engaging with the contemporary moment, just as Gibson's novel is the reader's physical hold on the cultural experience of September 11, 2001.

The online community that Gibson portrays therefore understands history as essentially postmodern and continually rewritten by the society that interprets it.[33] Cayce's eventual love interest, Parkaboy, is the most vocal advocate of this philosophy:

> I only know that the one constant in history is change: the past changes. Our version of the past will interest the future about the extent we're interested in whatever past the Victorians believed in. It simply won't seem very relevant (p. 57).

Parkaboy locates the present moment in the continuum of history, stressing its pervasive subjectivity. As a follower of the anonymous footage, known only by his internet pseudonym, he claims that artefacts of a culture offer access to the experience of a moment, a stable representation of an unstable historical instance. It is the object's continued existence in the present moment which defines its enduring interest to us. History itself is an unstable element and the ability to change, to be rewritten, is "the one constant" (p. 57) of its continuum.

Gibson's idea of change as "the one constant" in history sets him apart from the event-driven narratives of "9/11" fiction. Take, for example, the claims made by Don DeLillo at the beginning of this essay. Stating that "Everything now is measured in after", *Falling Man* focusses on the aftermath of event, alluding to a now irrevocable historical shift which occurred when the planes hit the WTC. The event is not subject to revision as it is in *Pattern Recognition*, and DeLillo is fixated on the idea that something has already changed, unable to foresee how the event might be reimagined beyond the narrative present. DeLillo was caught up in writing *Cosmopolis* (2003) when the attacks occurred and would complete the

---

[32] N. Katherine Hayles, "Traumas of Code," *Critical Inquiry* 33 n. 1 (Autumn 2006): 142.

[33] The historicism of *Pattern Recognition* is more fully explored in Neil Easterbrook, "Alternate Presents: The Ambivalent Historicism of *Pattern Recognition*," *Science Fiction Studies* 33 n. 3 (2006): 483-504. Easterbrook compares the arguments of Gibson's central characters to the work of Italian philosopher Benedetto Croce.

novel before beginning *Falling Man*. Gibson, however, claimed that he was already some way through a first draft of *Pattern Recognition* when he saw the destruction of the World Trade Center on television. The novel was Gibson's first project set in the present that watched the events and led him to question his representation of the present moment: "I actually sat down at my computer and looked at the manuscript and it was like it had been sort of reverse-obsoleted or something...There's not even a word for it. It had been backcancelled."[34] Whilst there is a degree of exceptionalism in this comment, prioritising his experience of September 11th over experiences that preceded it, Gibson also identifies that it was not reality which had changed, but his perception of history itself. The events of September 11, 2001 provided Gibson with a vivid symbol of the networks of terrorism in the contemporary world. Gibson claims that the novel he was creating felt directly and physically affected by these events, that the digital form of the novel shifted and became out-dated as soon as he had watched them.

Part of the reason that *Pattern Recognition* can accept that the world has not changed irrevocably is because of Cayce Pollard, who is able to find a personal, if clichéd, resolution. Despite her apophenia, her grief, and her eventual imprisonment in a Russian prison, Gibson allows her a happy ending. He endows her character with enough cognition to see beyond the disillusionment in the society around her: although she works in advertising, she never becomes an advertiser who capitalises upon the originality and creativity of others, despite pressures to exploit the mysterious footage and the events of September 11, 2001 itself. Ultimately, Cayce is able to remove the spectre of "9/11" from her mind, not only guiding her to freedom from prison but negotiating the event into the contemporary moment:

> When her eyes have adjusted, she realizes she can see two towers of light, off in the distance, in the direction she thinks she's been walking in. They aren't like the memorial display from Ground Zero, but like the towers of her dream, in London, only fainter, further away (p. 323).

Cayce is able to assimilate the phantom of "Ground Zero" with the London skyline and in doing so draws a final comparison between present and absent spaces. By merging the now symbolic imagery of the Twin

---

[34] William Gibson, as quoted by Fiona Graham, "Finding faces in the clouds," *The Daily Telegraph*, April 30, 2003, Culture section, web. Accessed August 2, 2013. http://www.telegraph.co.uk/culture/donotmigrate/3593416/Finding-faces-in-the-clouds.html# .

Towers with her experience in the present moment, she is finally able to dispel its spectre.

In the representation of alternative forms of counterculture, Gibson reduces the potency of September 11, 2001 as a definition of crisis. The branding of "9/11" is represented by several crude attempts to commercialise the event: "the Coca-Cola logo, a crude representation of the Twin Towers, and the words "WE REMEMBER" [*PR*, p. 303]. It is the commercialised attempts to memorialise which ultimately receive the brunt of Gibson's criticism. Souvenirs of the present assimilate the originality of a culture and devalue those collectibles which represent markers of genuine moments of invention. *Pattern Recognition* asserts the individual's superiority over a homogenised public identity and in doing so negates the idea that the events of September 11, 2001 have changed the world. Instead, Gibson suggests that its place in the continuum of history renders the event manageable and less traumatic. This is where it differs from the works blithely classified as "post-9/11" fiction. September 11, 2001 has been too often represented by the idea of cataclysmic change at its core because it created a rare moment of national vulnerability which Americans wanted to escape. In *Pattern Recognition*, Gibson demonstrates not only that September 11, 2001 did not change the individual in contemporary culture, but that its strength as a subject lies in the criticism of monoculture and capitalism which might be drawn through it.

CHAPTER FIFTEEN

IMAGING ATROCITY:
THE FUNCTION OF PICTURES
IN NARRATIVES ABOUT 9/11

LILIANA M. NAYDAN

Perhaps reflecting the increasingly image- and media-driven nature of twenty-first-century American existence, numerous accounts of the events of 9/11 demonstrate the imagistic if not near-cinematic quality of the terrorist attacks on the World Trade Center. Artist Damien Hirst observed that the attacks were "devised visually" in order to realize the kind of impact they made on the American masses.[1] And American responses to what they witnessed on 9/11 suggest Hirst is right. "It was like something out of a movie," observed World Trade Center security officer Gabriel Torres in his description of what he endured while in Building 5.[2] "It could have been a Showtime movie: *Back to Queens: The Long Walk Home*," said Astoria resident Nell Mooney of what she saw first-hand: the "social rainbow of escapees from Manhattan."[3] Or, as Manhattanite Nicole Blackman suggests, it could have been "[s]ome sort of sci-fi movie where everyone female had been bombed out of Manhattan and only the men had stayed behind."[4] Even literary stalwart John Updike, who happened to witness the attacks "[f]rom the viewpoint of a tenth-floor apartment in Brooklyn Heights," framed the horrific event in terms much like those of the average observer.[5] As he explained in a short piece written for the *New*

---

[1] Rebecca Allison, "One year on: 9/11 wicked but a work of art, says Damien Hirst," *The Guardian*, September 11, 2002, p. 4.
[2] Gabriel Torres, "Gabriel Torres," *Tower Stories: An Oral History of 9/11*, edited by Damon DiMarco (Santa Monica, Cal.: Santa Monica Press, 2007), pp. 100-13, p. 103.
[3] Nell Mooney, "Nell Mooney" in *ibid.*, pp. 212-7, p. 216.
[4] Nicole Blackman, "Nicole Blackman" in *ibid.*, p. 275.
[5] John Updike, "The Talk of the Town," *New Yorker*, September 24, 2001, p. 28.

Yorker, "the destruction of the World Trade Center twin towers had the false intimacy of television, on a day of perfect reception."[6]

Why have the attacks of 9/11 been perceived and remembered in such visual terms? And how have American authors negotiated textual expression with what Julien Bringuier and Madelena Gonzalez argue is "the essentially visual dimension of [9/11]"?[7] These are the questions this essay explores by considering the way in which 9/11 resists representation, especially via the spoken and written word. Focusing on works created by once or current New Yorkers in the decade following the attacks, most notably Lynne Sharon Schwartz's *The Writing on the Wall* (2005), Jonathan Safran Foer's *Extremely Loud and Incredibly Close* (2005), and Sid Jacobson and Ernie Colón's *The 9/11 Report: A Graphic Adaptation* (2006), I argue that tempered visual phenomena provide a means by which to translate the unspeakable into at least somewhat more comprehensible terms. Indeed, by virtue of embracing "the essentially visual dimension" of 9/11 and generating visually-oriented or hybrid texts that merge word with image, American authors attempt not only to tap into a more authentic version of the kind of "false intimacy" that Updike suggests media images provide to modern-day viewers, but to move beyond the pervasive disorientation that 9/11 created.[8] They recreate the effect of the puzzled and thereby childlike gaze with which many Americans saw 9/11 and hence they effectively come to represent the *feel* of 9/11 for future generations. Moreover, they reinforce the value of reflection and understanding in a post-9/11 world that continues to desire catharsis amid increasingly polarizing and uncompromising views on religion and politics.

The Problem of Representing and Transcending Atrocity

The scale of 9/11 as atrocity in no way approaches that of the Holocaust, yet the two events bear a resemblance to one another, particularly with respect to the ways in which artists and authors responded to them. Although the two atrocities gave subject and voice to artist Art Spiegelman, creator of the Pulitzer prize-winning, two-volume comic book memoir, *Maus* (1986 and 1991), and *In the Shadow of No Towers* (2004),

---

[6] *Ibid.*

[7] Julien Bringuier and Madelena Gonzalez, "Fiction after 9/11: A Journey through the Desert of the Real," in *Generic Instability and Identity in the Contemporary Novel,* edited by Madelena Gonzalez and Marie Odile Pittin-Hédon (Newcastle upon Tyne, England: Cambridge Scholars, 2010), pp. 220-37.

[8] Updike, *op. cit.,* p. 28.

a work that marks Spiegelman's return to comix, they functioned as a stifling force for many others.[9] Theodor Adorno famously observed that "[t]o write poetry after Auschwitz is barbaric"[10], and in the immediate aftermath of the Holocaust, many survivors were unable to confront the trauma of the past by discussing it or writing about it.[11] Adorno later retracted his words,[12] but their message nevertheless appeared to ring true for post-9/11 American authors. These authors have certainly written about 9/11, an event that announces itself as existing beyond the bounds of language via its bare name date, what Marc Redfield terms "a blank little scar"[13], but they have done so by drawing attention to the extreme difficulty of the task at hand. *New York Times* journalist R. W. Apple Jr. was among the first to articulate that "mere words were inadequate vessels to contain the sense of shock and horror that people felt", but he was far from the last.[14] Jewish-American author Lynne Sharon Schwartz portrays protagonist Renata as remarking outright in *The Writing on the Wall* that no one seems able to "find the right words" in the face of "seventeen acres of tangled metal and concrete and shoes and unspeakable body parts."[15]

---

[9] As Spiegelman explains in "The Sky is Falling," which functions as a preface to *In the Shadow of No Towers*, he had "spent much of the decade before the millennium trying to avoid making comix, but from some time in 2002 till September 2003, [he] devoted [him]self to what became a series of ten large-scale pages about September 11 and its aftermath" (p. 1).

[10] Theodor Adorno, "Cultural Criticism and Society," in *Prisms*, translated by Samuel and Shierry Weber (Cambridge, Mass.: MIT Press, 1967 [1949]), pp. 17-34, p. 34.

[11] For instance, Elie Wiesel took over ten years to publish *Night* (1955), his highly acclaimed memoir of the death camps.

[12] As Adorno put it in 1966:

> Perennial suffering has as much right to expression as a tortured man has to scream; hence it may have been wrong to say that after Auschwitz you could no longer right poems. But it is not wrong to raise the less cultural question whether after Auschwitz you can go on living—especially whether one who escaped by accident, one who by rights should have been killed, may go on living.

Negative Dialectics, translated by E. B. Ashton (New York: Continuum, 1973), pp. 362-3.

[13] Marc Redfield, *The Rhetoric of Terror: Reflections on 9/11 and the War on Terror* (New York: Fordham University Press, 2009), p. 1.

[14] R. W. Apple, "Awaiting the Aftershocks: Washington and Nation Plunge into Fight with Enemy Hard to Identify and Punish," *The New York Times*, September 12, 2001, A1.

[15] Lynne S. Schwartz, *The Writing on the Wall: A Novel* (New York: Counterpoint, 2005), p. 88.

More to the point, Renata observes that image could perhaps "do [9/11] justice."[16] As she puts it, the fictionalized Italian photographer Franco Donati's photographs could potentially enable the events of 9/11 to "enter history and become a symbol of something."[17] It could help 9/11 transcend the limits of the surreal aura of the apocalyptic and the unspeakably tragic. It could help it transcend its existence as what Redfield identifies as a rhetorical "virtual trauma" that trembles "on the edge of becoming present: one that is not fully or not properly 'actual.'"[18]

Renata's metafictionally-oriented observation effectively draws attention to Schwartz's own struggle to represent atrocity—a struggle that appears ubiquitous for writers writing in 9/11's aftermath. Fiction writers failed to make sense of the attacks much like experts who analyzed 9/11 in the years that followed,[19] but their struggles manifested themselves in different ways. Like an array of other wholly textual works about 9/11, most notably Anita Shreve's *A Wedding in December* (2005), Ken Kalfus's *A Disorder Peculiar to the Country* (2006), Jay McInerney's *The Good Life* (2007), and Joseph O'Neill's *Netherland* (2008), Schwartz's novel centers almost exclusively on a domestic scenario. Readers *do* read about the attacks themselves, but as Schwartz's novel progresses, it drifts from describing 9/11, instead portraying personal traumas in Renata's family history. For the most part, Schwartz writes about Renata's inability to cope with her twin sister Claudia's premature death, which occurs

---

[16] *Ibid.*
[17] *Ibid.*
[18] Redfield, *op. cit.*, p. 2.
[19] Experts who have analyzed the attacks have been unable to agree on a specific reason for them. In *The Looming Tower: Al-Qaeda and the Road to 9/11* (2006), Lawrence Wright intimates, simply by virtue of his focus on biographies of terrorists and events that well predate 9/11, that the personal histories of al-Qaeda members, the interplay of those histories, and sheer circumstance helped cause the atrocity. By contrast, in *The Age of Terror: America and the World after September 11* (2002), Strobe Talbott and Nayan Chanda suggest that it is wholly possible that "[i]n striking against targets nearly 7,000 miles away from his Afghan lair, part of bin Laden's intention was to stir up populations closer to home" not only "against the Great Satan, but against their own repressive, corrupt, frightened rulers" (p. xv). Fred Halliday presents yet other causes in *Two Hours That Shook the World: September 11 2001, Causes and Consequences* (London: Saqi Books, 2001), arguing that the September 11th attacks were generated by what he terms "the greater West Asian crisis" (p. 26), which he views as having "three general features": a "new pattern of linkages between hitherto separate conflicts" in Iran, Afghanistan, and South Asia; "the crisis of the state in this region"; and "the emergence of a new, transnational and fundamentalist Islam" (p. 38).

eighteen years prior to the novel's 2001 present. She also depicts the ways in which her past traumas haunt her, producing in her an intense desire for a daughter who would fill the void left behind by her sister. Schwartz's discussion of twins and voids certainly alludes to 9/11, but it skirts outright representation of it, arguably because 9/11 and violent events like it transcend comprehension. It reflects Irene Kacendes's observation, in her discussion of 9/11, that "[i]n fundamental ways trauma is connected to incomprehensibility."[20]

The kind of visual as opposed to verbal representation of the day that Renata and Schwartz herself seem to desire is the kind of representation that Americans predominantly received as they watched the events of the day develop on the TV news. Of course, newscasters facilitated verbal as well as visual representations of events. As Renata concedes in Schwartz's novel, it was "[o]nly on TV" that there was "no shortage of words."[21] Nevertheless, the undeniable degree to which 9/11 was a visual spectacle inevitably drove Americans to their televisions and Internet browsers on the day of the attacks and in the weeks that followed. As evidenced by CNN's first twelve hours of coverage on the 11th, images functioned as the lifeblood of broadcast and cable news reports. According to Amy Reynolds and Brook Barnett, "CNN's first 50 minutes of coverage showed only live images of the World Trade Center towers burning and smoking from a variety of angles and distances, as well as both live and recorded images of the second plane flying into the south tower."[22] Yet a single streaming image of devastation evidently failed to suffice. As Reynolds and Barnett explain, "[a]fter the first hour of coverage, CNN used two different split-screen techniques to show viewers images simultaneously,"[23] Moreover, "CNN producers made no apparent effort to connect the information the viewers were hearing from sources on the left side of the screen to the images they were watching on the right."[24] Apparently, producers felt that these images were capable of speaking for themselves as they mesmerized the masses. Like Don DeLillo's Beryl Parmenter,

[20] Irene Kacendes, "9/11/01=1/27/01: The Changed Post-traumatic Self," in *Trauma at Home: After 9/11*, edited by Judith Greenberg (Lincoln: University of Nebraska Press, 2003), pp. 168-86, p. 171.

[21] Schwartz, *op. cit.*, p. 78.

[22] Amy Reynolds and Brooke Barnett, "'America under Attack': CNN's Verbal and Visual Framing of September 11" in *Media Representations of September 11*, edited by Steven Chermak, Frankie Y. Bailey, and Michelle Brown (Westport, Conn.: Praeger, 2003), pp. 85-101, p. 97.

[23] *Ibid.*, p. 98.

[24] *Ibid.*

who, in *Libra* (1988), watches the news footage of Lee Harvey Oswald's death "over and over" as though she is addicted to it[25], or like Lianne Glenn of DeLillo's *Falling Man* (2007), who "[keeps] on watching" videotaped 9/11 footage despite her efforts to stop[26], historical news viewers "repeatedly watched images of commercial airplanes crash into the World Trade Center towers."[27]

Given that the millennially-charged year 2000 had passed without a literal bang despite extensive fear and anticipation of it,[28] Americans may very well have been subconsciously craving apocalyptic images just as readers, according to Frank Kermode, crave the apocalyptic endings that narratives provide.[29] Yet in the years following the attacks and the hyper-visually-oriented news reports of them, cultural critics have questioned the value of graphic—meaning image-based—renderings of the apocalyptic events of 9/11 that are *overly* graphic—meaning explicit. Observing that "[o]n September 11th, more people clicked on documentary news photographs than pornography for the first (and only) time in the history of the Internet", David Levi Strauss intimates that there exists something

---

[25] Don DeLillo, *Libra* (New York: Penguin, 1991 [1988]), p. 445.

[26] As DeLillo puts it, "[e]very time she saw a videotape of the planes she moved a finger toward the power button on the remote. Then she kept on watching." *Ibid.*

[27] Reynolds and Barnett, *op. cit.*, p. 85.

[28] The millennium as I refer to it—with a lowercase "m" as opposed to a capital "M"—involves the end of the second thousand-year period of Common Era history, not the prophesied thousand-year period of Christ's reign as Revelation 20 describes it. However, because these theological and secular definitions of the word "millennium" are so easily conflated, it is not surprising to see that apocalyptic anxiety can accompany millennial anticipation, as it did throughout the 1990s, a decade during which media outlets of all kinds infused the seminal year with mystical import. Americans witnessed news coverage of end-times oriented events like the 1993 siege in Waco, Texas, and the 1997 Heaven's Gate mass suicide, and they heard discussion of the millennium in popular television shows and movies. For instance, late-night talk show host Conan O'Brien would perform his "In the year 2000" sketches and movies like Arnold Schwarzenneger's *Terminator 2: Judgment Day* (1991) and Bruce Willis's *Armageddon* (1998) overtly alluded to the apocalypse. Moreover, Americans feared technological apocalypse via what we came to know as the Y2K computer crisis.

[29] According to Frank Kermode's *The Sense of an Ending* (Oxford: Oxford University Press, 2000 [1967]), the structures of fictional narratives mimic the structure of the Bible, which moves from Genesis to Revelation, toward a dramatic ending that satisfies what Kermode characterizes as the reader's inherent "hunger for ends and for crises" (p. 55).

pornographic about the violence and atrocity of the event.[30] Moreover, there perhaps exists a risk to *fixate* on the reality of the atrocious images that emerged on 9/11. Although Hollywood movies about 9/11, including Paul Greengrass's *United 93* (2006) and Oliver Stone's *World Trade Center* (2006), generally received critical acclaim, critics questioned the effect of the realism of these movies, particularly given that the real events of 9/11 were cinematic in and of themselves—simulations of the kind of apocalyptic violence that most Americans only know through Hollywood.[31] A. O. Scott suggests both movies "represent a return to the literal" and "revisit the immediate experience of Sept. 11" via "maximum detail."[32] For Scott, *World Trade Center* is "*almost* unbearably moving."[33] Manohla Dargis more explicitly questions the tolerability of a realistic Hollywood rendering of 9/11 in her *New York Times* review of *United 93*: She wonders "why, notwithstanding the usual (if shaky) commercial imperative, this movie was made. To jolt us out of complacency? Remind us of those who died? Unite us, as even the film's title seems to urge? Entertain us?"[34] As she continues, she observes that she "didn't need a studio movie to remind [her] of the humanity of the thousands who were murdered that day or the thousands who have died in the wars waged in their name."[35] Dargis believes we need "something more from our film artists than another thrill ride and an emotional pummeling."[36] She

---

[30] David Levi Strauss, *Between the Eyes: Essays on Photography and Politics* (New York: Aperture, 2003), p. 184.

[31] As A. O. Scott puts it in his August 9, 2006 review of *World Trade Center*:
[i]t was impossible to banish the thought, even in the midst of that day's horror and confusion, that the attacks themselves represented a movie scenario made grotesquely literal. What other frame of reference did we have for burning skyscrapers and commandeered airplanes? And then our eyes and minds were so quickly saturated with the actual, endlessly replayed images—the second plane's impact; the plumes of smoke coming from the tops of the twin towers; the panicked citizens covered in ash— that the very notion of a cinematic reconstruction seemed worse than redundant. Nobody needed to be told that this was not a movie. And at the same time nobody could doubt that, someday, it would be. (E1)

[32] A. O. Scott, "Film Review: Pinned Under the Weight of Shattered Towers, and 9/11 History," *New York Times,* August 9, 2006: E1+.

[33] *Ibid.*: E2, my emphasis.

[34] Manohla Dargis, "Defiance Under Fire: Unbounded Bravery in Unfriendly Skies," *New York Times*, April 28, 2006: E1+.

[35] *Ibid.*

[36] *Ibid.*

believes Americans need "catharsis"—an experience that an overly realistic portrayal may be incapable of providing.[37]

Ordering Disorder through Image in Jonathan Safran Foer's *Extremely Loud and Incredibly Close*

In that 9/11 manifested itself in such visual terms—in that the day left a vast visual void in America's best known city skyline—visual media appear necessary for adequate artistic commemoration, but only when they are emotionally bearable and foster reflection, understanding, and, eventually, the kind of catharsis about which Dargis writes. In *Extremely Loud and Incredibly Close* (2005), Jonathan Safran Foer attempts to include this kind of visual commemoration as a complement to the text of his novel, thereby skirting the limits of linguistic representation that authors like Schwartz encounter. Foer's work—about nine-year-old protagonist Oskar Schell's attempt to cope with his father's death in the World Trade Center—suggests that Oskar's effort to make sense of atrocity as it impacted his personal life is akin to the efforts of Holocaust and World War II survivors like Oskar's own grandfather, who survived the 1945 firebombing of Dresden. Moreover, his effort resembles to America's effort to make sense of 9/11 and recover from it. Although two years pass since his father's death, Oskar cannot move beyond it. He becomes obsessed with finding the matching lock to a key he discovers in his father's closet, and, while searching for it, he creates *Stuff that Happened to Me*, a journal composed of magazine images. Despite the journal's title, the images it includes represent not so much what actually happens to Oskar, but Oskar's evolving emotions in 9/11's wake. Critics like Updike have attacked Foer's novel for his "picto-/typographical antics",[38] but I posit that like text, image is, as Roland Barthes suggests in "Rhetoric of the Image," a thing to be read and interpreted, not just "an extremely rudimentary system in comparison with language."[39] As Philippe Codde argues, the images that rupture Foer's text attempt to render "the condition of the traumatized mind"[40]—a mind that, according

---

[37] *Ibid.*

[38] John Updike, "Mixed Messages," *The New Yorker*, March 14, 2005, p. 138.

[39] Roland Barthes, "Rhetoric of the Image." *Image–Music–Text*, trans. Stephen Heath (New York: Hill and Wang, 1978), pp. 32-51, p. 32.

[40] Philippe Codde, "Philomela Revisited: Traumatic Iconicity in Jonathan Safran Foer's *Extremely Loud & Incredibly Close*" *Studies in American Fiction* 35 n. 2 (2007): 241-54, p. 248.

to Cathy Caruth, is "possessed by an image or event."[41] These images sometimes complement Foer's text, but, inevitably, they also interrupt it. Albeit to a lesser degree, they recreate the jolting feeling of interruption that 9/11 created in America. They force the reader to pause, shift mental gears, and think in visual as opposed to textual terms. Text that follows a page or several pages of image then forces the reader to return to thinking in textual terms.

The images Foer includes throughout the novel do, in several cases, make explicit reference to 9/11, but more often than not, the reference is implicit, suggesting that in post-9/11 America, anything and everything have the capacity to connect in some way to the terrorist attacks and the residual wound that remains at the heart of the American psyche. For instance, the falling cat and the descending roller coaster cars pictured in the novel may remind Foer's reader of Richard Drew's now famous falling man photograph, also pictured by Foer.[42] Likewise, the image of a skeleton hand and that of an actor playing Hamlet holding Yorick's skull are inevitably evocative of the human remains of victims unearthed in the aftermath of the attacks.[43] Even the image of procreating turtles and another of reflections of tourists on the windows of the observation deck of the Empire State Building have the capacity to remind Foer's reader of the cycle of life and death and of the transience of existence.[44] Whereas the images of the actual events of 9/11 were, according to Sara Ahmed, both "images of trauma" and "traumatic images"[45], these images, at least superficially, appear wholly innocent. They neither represent trauma nor attempt to induce it.

However, by strategically inviting his reader to thematize the images in his novel, Foer recreates an altogether familiar psychological experience. For the reader, repeatedly seeing thematically similar images is akin to ruminating over the attacks in a perpetual condition of post-traumatic stress. As Stephen Regel and Stephen Joseph explain, "intrusive thoughts/images of the traumatic incident...can appear to come 'out of the blue'"—much like the planes on the clear day of September 11, 2001—for

---

[41] Cathy Caruth, *Trauma: Explorations in Memory* (Baltimore, Md.: Johns Hopkins University Press, 1995), p. 5.

[42] Jonathan Safran Foer, *Extremely Loud and Incredibly Close* (Boston: Houghton Mifflin, 2005), pp. 191, 148, 59, 62, 205.

[43] *Ibid.*, pp. 155, 55.

[44] *Ibid.*, pp. 57, 246.

[45] *Ibid.*, p. 95.

those who suffer from Post-Traumatic Stress Disorder.[46] According to Mardi Horowitz's information processing theory, "active memory tends to repeat its representations of the traumatic event, causing emotional distress."[47] Just as "[t]he subsequent replaying of the Twin Towers' collapse (every few minutes on the first day; every few hours for months afterwards, and then every six months) seemed to enact the compulsion to repeat that characterizes post-traumatic stress"[48], so, too, does the experience of encountering the thematically similar images prompt Oskar and the reader to remember and relive 9/11 toward less than positive ends. Oskar and reader alike enter into a seemingly inescapable and potentially devastating loop as 9/11 comes to pervade all of existence in somewhat unexpected ways.

Although images may prompt victims to relive their traumatic experiences, they also sustain the capacity to provide therapeutic relief, enabling the trauma victim to reach what Horowitz conceptualizes as "a relative equilibrium" that signifies that the victim has effectively "worked through the experience."[49] Indeed, Oskar sees positive results emerge through his ruminations. He lists "looking through *Stuff That Happened to Me*" as one of his favorite things—in the same category as "playing the tambourine," "spoiling [his cat] Buckminster," and "arranging [his] collections."[50] Perhaps Oskar enjoys perusing the journal because pain brings him a degree of some strange pleasure. More likely, however, he enjoys perusing it specifically because creating it and looking through it resembles the act of arranging his collections. Connecting images with one another, for Foer's reader as for Oskar, enables at least some semblance of order to emerge out of the disordered, post-9/11 American world. Making order out of chaos in a journal clearly fails to remake the world at large, yet it effectively remakes Oskar's private and subjective reality during moments when he is immersed in looking at it. Like Oskar's "favorite book"[51], Stephen Hawking's *A Brief History of Time*, *Stuff That Happened to Me* attempts to encompass a universe of sorts. As Oskar puts it in the

---

[46] Stephen Regel and Stephen Joseph, *Post-traumatic Stress* (Oxford: Oxford University Press, 2010), p. 4.

[47] *Ibid.*, p. 16.

[48] Marusya Bociurkiw, "Homeland (In)Security: Roots and Displacement, from New York, to Toronto, to Salt Lake City," *Reconstruction: An Interdisciplinary Culture Studies Community* 3 n. 3 (2003): 21. Accessed August 3, 2013. http://reconstruction.eserver.org/033/bociurkiw.htm.

[49] Regel and Joseph, *op. cit.*, p. 16.

[50] Foer, *op. cit.*, p. 288.

[51] *Ibid.*, p. 11.

final pages of the novel's text when he looks through the book, "I saw maps and drawing, pictures from magazines and newspapers and the Internet, pictures I'd taken with Grandpa's camera. *The whole world was in there.*"[52]

Oskar's focus on images as opposed to text and his work of connecting images with one another in his journal have a metafictional function: they resembles the work of real-life authors of hybrid works about 9/11. Personal images appear to represent a personal connection to history for Oskar just as they do for Spiegelman, who, in *In the Shadow of No Towers*, struggles and fails, by his own account,[53] to capture fully as "[t]he Pivotal image from [his] 9/11 morning—one that didn't get photographed or videotaped into public memory but still remains burned onto the inside of [his] eyelids several years later."[54] Just as creating *Stuff That Happened to Me* enables Oskar to cope with what he sees, the act of writing and illustrating *In the Shadow of No Towers* allows Spiegelman to create "a slow-motion diary of what [he] experienced while seeking some provisional equanimity" after 9/11.[55] Moreover, Oskar bears a striking resemblance to Foer, his creator. In an interview with Kristofer Collins, Foer describes composition as Oskar might, observing that he "'think[s] of [the process of writing] visually…as a weird accumulation of objects,' rather than a strictly linear narrative."[56] Much like composing the journal helps Oskar make sense of 9/11, writing helps Foer, who, in an interview with Ted Siefer, "explain[s] that [when he writes,] he doesn't set out to convey a specific idea. Rather, he uses the process of writing to 'figure it out.'"[57]

Notably, both Foer's and Oskar's respective books and the pages of paper-based images contained in them ultimately draw attention to the palpability of the void that America sustains in the wake of 9/11. Despite Oskar's effort to remake order via constructing and rereading his

---

[52] *Ibid.*, p. 325, my emphasis.

[53] Art Spiegelman observes that he "repeatedly tried to paint this" particularly affective image "of the looming north tower's glowing bones just before it vaporized," but "with humiliating results" (*In the Shadow of No Towers* [New York: Pantheon Books, 2004], "The Sky is Falling", p. 2). Eventually, he observes that "came close to capturing the vision of disintegration digitally on [his] computer" even if he failed to capture it fully (p. 2).

[54] *Ibid.*

[55] *Ibid.*

[56] Jonathan Safran Foer, Interview with Kristofer Collins, "Foer Extremely Modest about Storytelling," *Pittsburgh Post–Gazette,* October 9, 2005, region ed.: J4.

[57] *Idem.*, Interview with Ted Siefer. "Foer's new novel looks at Sept. 11," *The Jewish Advocate*, April 14, 2006, p. 19.

scrapbook, the post-9/11 world cannot *actually* return to a secure and ordered pre-9/11 innocence. History cannot run in reverse, as it does in both Oskar's and Foer's books—works that end with a flipbook-like series of reverse-order photographs of the falling man, a figure that rises up and back into the sky. Although Oskar reflects on the potential benefit of "more pictures," photographs will not turn back time so that "[w]e would have been safe"[58]; they will only underscore the kind of "impossibility of closure" to which the novel's end, according to Codde, draws attention.[59] Yet in that Oskar's book, like Foer's, is made of burnable paper akin to "[a]ll of those notepads, and Xeroxes, and printed e-mails, and photographs of kids, and books, and dollar bills in wallets, and documents in files" that served as "fuel" for the burning towers, it gives readers a sort of figurative fuel to persevere beyond emptiness and trauma.[60] Ultimately, both authors may well be prompting their readers to embrace what emptiness and impossibility afford as substantial to existence and hence the metaphorical key—akin to the literal key Oskar finds—to transcending the effects of trauma and the disordered, post-9/11 condition.

Simplifying and Complicating Atrocity in Sid Jacobson and Ernie Colón's *The 9/11 Report: A Graphic Adaptation*

Much in the way that images in Foer's text enable readers to create order out of disorder, the images in Jacobson and Colón's *Graphic Adaptation* of the 9/11 report aim to help Americans make better sense of the attacks. Although critics lauded the lucidity of the best-selling[61] government inquiry, Colón had the impulse to create the graphic adaptation because, upon his attempt to read the original, he found it "well written" but "hard to follow—lots of Arabic names, and a lot of things going on at the same time in different places."[62] Both Jacobson and Colón wanted to "attract young readers and others who might be overwhelmed by the original document."[63] And based on responses to their work, they have succeeded. The original text's authors, though initially "dubious" about the version[64],

---

[58] Foer, *Extremely Loud and Incredibly Close*, pp. 325-26.

[59] Codde, "Philomela Revisited", p. 250.

[60] Foer, *Extremely Loud and Incredibly Close*, p. 325.

[61] The report sold over one million copies.

[62] Bob Minzesheimer, "9/11 gets a graphic retelling—Style makes official report 'accessible,'" *USA Today*, August 22, 2006, final ed.: D1.

[63] Sid Jacobson and Ernie Colón, *The 9/11 Report: A Graphic Adaptation* (New York: Hill and Wang, 2006).

[64] Minzesheimer, "9/11 gets a graphic retelling": D1.

praised the graphic work for its "close adherence" to the original's textual content in the adaptation's "Foreword", and claimed it helped to advance the "national conversation about the recommendations of *The 9/11 Commission Report*."[65] Likewise, reviewers like John A. Lent saw the *Graphic Adaptation* as a success. According to Lent, who, like many other Americans, failed to read the original report "all the way through"[66], the *Graphic Adaptation* is "more dramatic, more understandable, more compelling and no less authentic than the original, all-text edition."[67] As Lent continues, "[t]he format, layout, ultra-realistic portrait-like art work [...], and to-the-point text allow you—no, encourage, *demand* you understand what is going on as our country, our civilization is being attacked."[68] The work resists the kind of escapism that many works in its genre facilitate,[69] representing an underground network and its clandestine plot by visually animating bygone years and more recent moments for which Americans lack clear literal and metaphorical pictures.

As commentary on the *Graphic Adaptation* suggests, the illustrations strike a careful balance between simplifying an all-but-incomprehensible moment in American history and revealing complexity in that moment. At the start of the first chapter, "WE HAVE SOME PLANES," readers see the simplification toward which the *Graphic Adaptation*'s creators strive in eerily innocent-looking cartoon mug shots of the nineteen terrorists responsible for hijacking the planes. They see small, sketchy, black and white line drawings that represent these terrorists, and each terrorist is identified by name in all capital letters beneath his respective illustration. Readers learn exactly which terrorist was responsible for which hijacking, and, as the *Graphic Adaptation* proceeds, readers see the chaos of the day simplified into a comfortingly comprehensible timeline of events. Rows

---

[65] Thomas H. Kean and Lee H. Hamilton, "Foreword" in Jacobson and Colón, *op. cit.*, pp. ix-x, p. ix.

[66] As Lent puts it, "Did you read the original 9/11 Report? All the way through? Without skipping? More important, did you understand it? Liar. I read all of it...O.K., I skimmed here and there...and when I was through, I wasn't all that clear about where we were." John A. Lent, "[The 9/11 Report]," *International Journal of Comic Art* 11 n. 1 (2009): pp. 524-26, p. 524.

[67] *Ibid.*, p. 525.

[68] *Ibid.*

[69] In his *This Book Contains Graphic Language: Comics As Literature*, (New York: Continuum, 2007), Rocco Versaci "[b]y and large, 'escapism' is associated with the most 'pop' of our popular culture: the entertainment that is designed for mass appeal and minimal thinking" (p. 2). Versaci concedes that "some comic book creators embrace the 'escapist' label for their work" (p. 3), but he posits that "'escapism' and 'literature' are not mutually exclusive" (p. 5).

marked by timestamps run parallel across the *Graphic Adaptation*'s
opening pages, representing the simple, straight flight paths of the four
hijacked airplanes and ending, one-by-one, with the devastation that
transpired when each hijacked plane reached its final destination.[70]
Although "scenes of chaos and destruction" likely continue to dictate the
ways in which Americans remember 9/11, the adaptation illuminates with
great clarity the degree to which the attacks were "astonishingly well-
coordinated."[71]

The apparent simplicity of these illustrations prompts readers to recall
the historical, less complicated, essentially innocent world that many
Americans managed to sustain before the attacks. As the degree of shock
Americans experienced at the sight of the burning towers demonstrates,
Americans had seemingly grown accustomed to feeling a sense of security
that citizens of colonized and war-torn nations may never feel; they had
grown accustomed to the apparent benefits of America's position of
dominance during the American Century. Like Foer, who invites his
reader to see through a child's perspective in his novel, Jacobson and
Colón ask their readers to view their narrative through younger eyes,
thereby embracing an ethos of graphic novels against which graphic
novelists generally struggle. To put it another way, instead of resisting the
notion that graphic novels are designed for an audience of adolescents,[72]
Jacobson and Colón exploit the implications of addressing such an
audience. Like Foer, they suggest that Americans living in the aftermath of
9/11 must start at what Art Spiegelman in his introduction to *In the
Shadow of No Towers* terms a "Year Zero."[73] They see post-9/11 America

---

[70] Jacobson has observed that when he read the original report, he "had trouble
following what was happening on the four (hijacked) flights, and it hit [him].
Wow! You could show this as a timeline. You could really, really explain it."
Minzesheimer, *op. cit.*: D1.
[71] R. W. Apple, "Awaiting the Aftershocks: Washington and Nation Plunge into
Fight with Enemy Hard to Identify and Punish," *The New York Times*, September
12, 2001: A1.
[72] As Matthew Pustz puts it, "most Americans view comic books with contempt,
especially when read by adults. Adult fans and collectors are seen as geeks and
worse. Reading material supposedly aimed at children is somehow seen as a sign
of psychological maladjustment or arrested development." Matthew Pustz, *Comic
Book Culture: Fanboys and True Believers* (Jackson: University Press of
Mississippi, 1999), pp. 208-9.
[73] As Spiegelman puts it, "[a]t first, Ground Zero had marked a Year Zero as well.
Idealistic peace signs and flower shrines briefly flourished at Union Square, the
checkpoint between lower Manhattan and the rest of the city" (*op. cit.*, p. 2).

as post-apocalyptic in that it has moved past 9/11 as an apocalyptic moment and into a new beginning.

Paradoxically, however, the very simple images that comprise the *Graphic Adaptation* add significant and sophisticated depth to the story of 9/11—depth that simultaneously requires a mature audience and concomitantly produces it. While perhaps disconcerting to Americans who prefer to juxtapose American innocence with the evil violence of fanaticism seen on 9/11, these images humanize the terrorists, who look ordinary, not evil. In their respective mug shots, Fayez Banihammad and Majed Moqed look relaxed; they may even be smiling. Other mug shots and images throughout the adaptation further underscore the humanity of figures who many Americans might more readily demonize as monsters. For instance, Ziad Jarrah is portrayed as obtaining his "single-engine private pilot certificate"[74], and in the illustration, he appears as an average American, pointing to his license and grinning with sincere pride for his achievement. He appears to be living the American Dream, attaining success through his hard work. Along the same lines, many of the terrorists portrayed in the "Assembling the Teams" illustration opt against traditional Arabic garb and look altogether like ordinary Americans in their jeans and collared shirts.[75] Before the *Graphic Adaptation* comes to a close, readers encounter humanizing caricatures of the elusive bin Laden himself, smiling, shaking hands with friends, and moving freely from frame to frame as we now know he moved "freely throughout [Afghanistan]" while plotting his attacks.[76] Americans who view these illustrations are no longer confronted with a faceless enemy who lurks in a hidden underground network of Others. They are no longer confronted with fathomless evil that negates the reality of human agency, conscience, and reasoned intention. Instead, they see al-Qaeda hijackers who, for reasons that transcend mere malicious intent, seem to have blended into the mythologized melting pot of American society with relative ease, and they are invited if not forced to struggle with what exactly it means to be what Versluys terms the "ultimate Other"[77]: the terrorist. Americans must, at least on some level, contemplate the wholly human origins of seemingly inhuman acts of terror that forever changed America. They must contemplate the possibility of extant affinities between themselves and terrorists.

---

[74] Jacobson and Colón, *op. cit.*, p. 70.

[75] *Ibid.*, p. 71.

[76] *Ibid.*, p. 38.

[77] Kristiaan Versluys, *Out of the Blue: September 11 and the Novel* (New York: Columbia University Press, 2009), p. 176.

Bridging Modes of Representation, Bridging Post-9/11 Divides

Hybrid works that merge image with text like Jacobson and Colón's and Foer's as well as others including Spiegelman's *In the Shadow of No Towers* and Nancy Lee, Lonnie Schlein, and Mitchel Levitas's *A Nation Challenged: A Visual History of 9/11 and Its Aftermath* (2002) present nothing altogether new to the post-9/11 world. Image and text have accompanied one another throughout human history. We see them paired in ancient and medieval illuminated manuscripts, the most famous of which are medieval illuminated Bibles or portions of the Bible like the Book of Kells and the Lindisfarne Gospels. We also still see them in contemporary and ever-evolving new media platforms, which, according to Mary E. Hocks and Michelle R. Kendrick, create a fertile ground for a "dynamic interplay that *already exists* and has *always existed* between visual and verbal texts."[78] Yet in their apparently age-old form, contemporary hybrid works about 9/11 implicitly address the most pressing problems and questions of the post-9/11 era. According to Mieke Bal, "[n]arrative and image need each other as much as cultures need them"[79], and in the post-9/11 world, disparate cultures may well need the hybridized interplay between narrative and image in order to understand one another and thus transcend the divides that now define the times.

The attacks of 9/11 invite conceptualization via visual terms by authors, artists, and Americans in general because images have the potential not only to commemorate the events of the day, but to allow for the kind of literal speechlessness produced by the experience of witnessing 9/11. These works implicitly manage to capture the degree to which the devastation Americans felt was simply beyond words, and they allow audiences to re-experience the trauma of 9/11 on a visceral, emotional level that potentially helps produce the kind of catharsis that Dargis and other Americans certainly need. If survivors of 9/11 and those who sympathize and empathize with them seek to record the terrorist attacks and the suffering they caused on a non-material, personal, and emotional register, these works perhaps provide a way to begin that process of recording. As in earlier illuminated bibles, images in post-9/11 works illuminate something transcendent—something that deserves and demands

---

[78] Mary E. Hocks and Michelle R. Kendrick, "Introduction: Eloquent Images," *Eloquent Images: Word and Image in the Age of New Media*, edited by Mary E. Hocks and Michelle R. Kendrick (Cambridge, Mass.: MIT Press, 2003), pp. 1-36, p. 1.
[79] Mieke Bal, "Figuration," *PMLA* 119 n. 5 (2004): 1289-92, p. 1291.

a near-religious reverence because it sustains a religious aura around an event when perceived in apocalyptic terms.[80]

Moreover and more generally, these works reinforce the value of understanding and compromise as opposed to the extremism and intolerance that emerged in the post-9/11 world. Amid newspaper reports of plans for ceremonial Quran burnings[81] and resistance to building an Islamic center[82] in the vicinity of Ground Zero, Americans might benefit from a sort of middle ground—not only between modes of representation like image and text, but between the hostile and at times extremist perspectives that divide them from one another and from the Islamic world. As DeLillo expresses it in "In the Ruins of the Future," his December 2001 *Harper's Magazine* essay on 9/11, "[t]he sense of disarticulation we hear in the term 'Us and Them' has never been so

---

[80] American newspaper stories reflected the ways in which the popular American imagination connected the terrorist attacks with the biblical end of time. In *The Christian Science Monitor*, Joe Stein, a construction worker in Los Angeles watching the events of the day unfold on CNN at a breakfast eatery, is quoted as observing that "[t]his really does look like the apocalypse." Ann Scott Tyson, "From London to Los Angeles, the world stood still," *Christian Science Monitor*, September 12, 2001: 1+, p. 3. Similarly in the lead story of *The New York Times* on Wednesday, September 12th, journalist Serge Schmemann associated the vision of chaos in New York with late medieval Dutch paintings that portray biblical subjects such as the Last Judgment, noting that "[s]cenes of chaos and destruction evocative of the nightmare world of Hieronymus Bosch, with smoke and debris blotting out the sun, were carried by television into homes and workplaces across the nation." Serge Schmemann, "President Vows to Exact Punishment for 'Evil'," *New York Times*, September 12, 2001: A1+. Likewise, Geraldine Baum and Paul Lieberman of the *Los Angeles Times* suggested that "[p]eople likened [the terrorist attacks in New York] to a bomb, to midnight, to a hurricane and finally, when the air was choked with soot and smoke, to hell." Geraldine Baum and Paul Lieberman, "A Struggle to Escape Fiery Chaos," *Los Angeles Times*, September 12, 2001, natl. ed.: A1+.

[81] Terry Jones, a pastor at the Christian Dove World Outreach Center in Gainesville, Florida, had planned, for the ninth anniversary of the September 11th terrorist attacks, to burn copies of the Quran. The burning was to be part of what he termed "International Burn a Koran Day," but Jones cancelled the event largely due to widespread protest in the U.S. For more information about Jones's plan and opposition that emerged to it, see Damien Cave's "Far From Ground Zero, Obscure Pastor Is Ignored No Longer," published in the *New York Times* on August 25, 2010.

[82] Controversy over the construction of Cordoba House, which was eventually renamed Park 51 and is sometimes referred to as the "W.T.C. mosque" or the "Ground Zero mosque," emerged in May 2010.

striking, at either end" as it is in 9/11's aftermath.[83] It is image as it functions alongside text that, to appropriate Israeli author Amos Oz's phrase, allows us to "imagine each other" better and thereby undo the disarticulation DeLillo describes.[84] Hence it is image as it functions alongside text—with the objective of communicating what may be incommunicable—that may well prove to sustain at least some capacity to help cure ubiquitous fanaticisms[85] that threaten genuine understanding and lasting peace in the twenty-first century.

---

[83] Don DeLillo, "In the Ruins of the Future," *Harper's*, December 2001: 33-40, p. 34.

[84] *Ibid.*, p. 36.

[85] According to Oz, "[f]anaticism is older than Islam, older than Christianity, older than Judaism, older than any state or any government, or political system, older than any ideology or faith in the world." Amos Oz, *How to Cure a Fanatic* (Princeton, N.J.: Princeton University Press, 2006), p. 41. And, as Oz suggests, "fanaticism is almost everywhere, and its quieter, more civilized forms are present all around us and perhaps inside of us as well" (p. 50).

CHAPTER SIXTEEN

THE LANGUAGE OF EXPECTATION AND LAMENT: THE CIVIL WAR TO SEPTEMBER 11

JENNIFER TRAVIS

On the first anniversary of September 11, 2001, George W. Bush read Abraham Lincoln's "Address at the Dedication of the National Cemetery at Gettysburg, Pennsylvania." Lincoln's dedication on November 19, 1863 at the battlefield turned graveyard remembered some 50,000 soldiers who were killed or wounded. Just as Lincoln spoke of a nation "conceived in Liberty" and tested by conflict, Bush's reading of the "Gettysburg Address" on September 11, 2002 declared that day a defining moment which would once again "test" the nation's resolve and change the course of the nation's history.[1] Unlike Lincoln, who had stood over a battlefield strewn with bodies, Bush stood over the ruins of a terrorist attack from which so few bodies have been recovered that any human remains, argues David Simpson in *9/11: The Culture of Commemoration* (2006), have achieved the status of relics.[2]

Indeed, Bush's invocation of Gettysburg on September 11, 2002 rendered the site of the World Trade Center hallowed ground so that he might ask, as Lincoln did, whether those who perished there had "died in vain." Bush summoned Lincoln's words as a challenge: would "our principles of democracy and freedom endure"? On the tenth anniversary of

---

[1] Abraham Lincoln, "Gettysburg Address," Electronic Text Center, University of Virginia. Accessed August 2, 2013.
http://etext.virginia.edu/etcbin/toccernew2?id=LinGett.sgm&images=images/mode ng&data=/texts/english/modeng/parsed&tag=public&part=1&division=div1.
All future citations from this text.
[2] David Simpson in *9/11: The Culture of Commemoration* (Chicago, Ill.: University of Chicago Press, 2006), p. 29.

September 11th, we can read the great irony of these words, given the
Patriot Act, Abu Ghraib, and Guantanamo Bay, among other restrictions
on civil liberties. Bush's incantation of Lincoln's speech—a somber
meditation on a nation's grief—mimicked its battle cry, insisting that
combatants on non-native battlefields, from Afghanistan to Iraq, were like
their historic Civil War forebears: soldiers sacrificing their lives so that the
United States of America might "endure."[3] Invoking Lincoln's words if
not his spirit, George W. Bush used "The Gettysburg Address" as a call to
war, although the years following his September 11th memorial showed
what little unity existed in a country divided over the "global war on
terror" and "weapons of mass destruction." As "sites and moments of
violence" are transformed into "markers of national purpose," as Robert
Fanuzzi and Michael Wolfe write in their introduction to this collection,
the anniversary of September 11th and its memorialization demand that we
ask: What uses or misuses do the legacies of the past serve? "What kinds
of political mischief will be wrought from mourning?"[4]

2011 marked the tenth anniversary of September 11, 2001 and the
150th anniversary of the start of the Civil War. Although the
correspondence of these dates is coincidental, the way in which the Civil
War has been invoked to memorialize and, in turn, militarize, September
11th is not. How do we, a nation divided by decade-long wars, "endure"?
On the tenth anniversary of September 11th, as on the very first
anniversary memorial service, the Civil War once again set the tone. If
Bush's 2002 gesture toward historical consciousness was a precursor to
hegemonic purpose—justifying and condoning more bloodshed rather than
pausing and reflecting on atrocities perpetrated in the nation's past—from
slavery to Indian removal—that often provoked violence and war, the
Lincoln letter that George W. Bush read on the tenth anniversary of
September 11th could barely contain the deeply conflicted place in which

---

[3] On the "Gettysburg Address" and the national imaginary, see Robert Ferguson
who write: "The final long sentence of Lincoln's peroration, 'that government of
the people, by the people, for the people, shall not perish from the earth'…[is] so
moving and so memorable because they give the solution needed in celebrated
affirmation. They give final assurance against the naked fear expressed earlier that
the nation might not 'long endure.'" Ferguson, "Hearing Lincoln," *American
Literary History* 21 n. 4 (Winter 2009), pp. 687-724, p. 704.
[4] Peter Brooks, on the "failure of our mourning", write: "I mean the political
failure of our mourning and thus its failure to bring us the right, sobering lessons
about our global responsibilities." Peter Brooks, "If You Have Tears," in *Trauma
at Home After 9/11*, edited by Judith Greenberg (Lincoln and London: University
of Nebraska Press, 2003), pp. 48-51.

we find ourselves as a nation ten years later. If, after September 11th, the desecration on our "sacred" soil, our "national sacrifice," became an occasion to script the homeland violated, as Donald Pease and others have argued, the Civil War must also be an occasion to reflect on America's illusions of national innocence and the violence and violations in the nation's past.[5] In other words, rather than a patriotic call to war in the name of national unity and endurance, the invocation of the Civil War must remind us that we are a nation that continues to be embroiled in conflict, grappling with the frequent breakdown of democratic ideals at home and abroad; a nation of people who grieve not only for the losses on September 11th, but also for these failures.

On the ten-year anniversary of September 11th, George W. Bush, no longer Commander-in-Chief but emissary of a decade long legacy of war, returned to Abraham Lincoln and the Civil War by reading what has become known as the Lincoln-Bixby letter, dated November 21, 1864. In the letter, Lincoln writes to console a mother who purportedly lost five children in battle: "I feel how weak and fruitless must be any word of mine which should attempt to beguile you from the grief of a loss so overwhelming. But I cannot refrain from tendering you the consolation that may be found in the thanks of the Republic they died to save."[6] Lincoln called their deaths "a sacrifice upon the altar of freedom." In this letter, Lincoln recognized a mother's suffering and offered consolation. Although there is dispute over the authorship of the words and the historical accuracy of the occasion (did Lincoln write the letter and did Mrs. Bixby lose five children?), the letter offers an occasion to reflect on the Civil War as a touchstone for national memory and mourning.

If the Bixby letter is employed in political speech to console and to justify continued bloodshed, its resonance also exceeds its initial intention.

---

[5] See Donald Pease, *The New American Exceptionalism* (Minneapolis: University of Minnesota Press, 2006): "Myths normally do the work of incorporating events into recognizable national narratives. But traumatic events precipitate states of emergency that become the inaugural moments in a different symbolic order and take place on a scale that exceeds the grasp of the available representations from the national mythology. Before a national myth can narrate events of this magnitude, the state fantasy that supplies the horizon of expectations orienting their significance must have already become symbolically effective," p. 5. See also Christopher Merrill, "A Kind of Solution," *Virginia Quarterly Review* 80 n. 4 (Fall 2004): 68-83.

[6] Abraham Lincoln's letter to Mrs. Bixby, 1864. Accessed August 2, 2013. http://www.fordham.edu/halsall/mod/1864lincoln-bixby.asp. All future references are to this text.

Indeed, the letter's language is prescient in the sense that it expresses recognition of the failure of its very words adequately to describe a mother's pain, loss, and grief.[7] The Bixby letter reflects a sense of impasse; even its questionable provenance—the uncertainty as to the authenticity of the words themselves—enhances these qualities. The Bixby letter's meditation on the inadequacy of language is an apt metaphor for the nation's anxiety about the failure of language in the face of tragedy. This essay draws another resemblance, one that does not have to do solely with letters but also with literature. It questions, much like Lincoln's Gettysburg Address, the capacity of letters or any form of literature to console and comfort, as well as our expectations that they do so. Instead, we must wrest the parallelism between the Civil War and September 11th from the hegemonic use and misuse of national memory by rethinking some of the criticisms leveled against the failure of language and metaphor in the decade following September 11, 2001.

From a literary perspective, one of the most striking features of the tenth anniversary of September 11th is the consensus, voiced at that milestone, of our own inadequacy and failure to imagine and illuminate its import aptly. "How weak and fruitless must be any word," wrote Abraham Lincoln to Mrs. Bixby. One hundred fifty years later, we hear a similar lament: critics loudly decry that after more than a decade following September 11, 2001, art has resolutely failed to make meaning of it, citing the dearth of notable artistic monuments and significant literature, though the expectation for its production is pronounced. Writing about September 11th, Christopher Merrill sums up the expectation this way: "It is up to writers to redeem the individual from the collective tragedy, to discover the mythic underpinnings of what may seem unimaginable, to bear witness to loss with such empathy and precision that we glimpse how to navigate our way into the future."[8] Or consider what Richard Gray writes in his essay "Open Doors, Closed Minds: American Prose Writing in a Time of Crisis": September 11th and its aftermath "are part of the soil, the deep structure lying beneath and shaping the literature of the American nation...they have reshaped our consciousness; they are a defining element in our contemporary structure of feeling and they cannot help but impact profoundly on American writing."[9] The expectation for "the literature of the American nation" is great, indeed.

---

[7] For more on the culture of mourning in nineteenth century America, see Dana Luciano, *Arranging Grief: Sacred Time and the Body in Nineteenth-Century America* (New York: New York University Press, 2007).

[8] Merrill, *op. cit.*, p. 70.

[9] Richard Gray, "Open Doors, Closed Minds: American Prose Writing in a Time of

Readers have come to presume that literary narratives will provide voice for what is sometimes described, recalling Lincoln's words, as the inexpressible. Traditionally, writes Claire Kahane in "Uncanny Sights," "this has been one of the tasks of literature: to provide us with narratives that can articulate the inchoate, that can give us metaphors to contain the seemingly unspeakable as it assaults us from within and without."[10] Yet September 11th continues to be unspeakable according to literary and cultural critics. Kristiaan Versluys's 2009 book *Out of the Blue: September 11th and the Novel*, describes the discursive responses to 9/11, the instantaneity of its horror and its far-flung repercussions, calling its magnitude seemingly "unpossessable." "It is a limit event," he writes, that shatters the symbolic resources of the culture and defeats the normal processes of meaning making."[11] Resisting what he calls the "primal terror" of 9/11, Don DeLillo argues that "living language is not diminished," even though the falling towers are a "phenomenon so unaccountable and yet so bound to the power of objective fact that we can't tilt it to the slant of our perception."[12] DeLillo, like Jonathan Safran Foer, Joseph O'Neill, and others who have written fiction in the decade following September 11th, recognizes that it must to some degree be possessed and named. "There is no way," confirms Versluys, "that the events on that sunny September morning can stay out of the reach of symbol and metaphor."[13] In an interview about his September 11th novel *The Good Life* (2006), novelist Jay McInerney tells the story of his conversation with Norman Mailer, who cautioned McInerney to wait "ten years before [writing] about September 11."[14] Although McInerney ignored the advice and published *The Good Life*, a novel that I address later in this essay, this work, like many of the other novels mentioned above, was received poorly; Mailer's caution proved prescient.

On the eve of the ten-year memorial, *The New York Times* book critic

---

Crisis," *American Literary History* 21 n. 1 (Spring 2009): 128-48, p. 129.

[10] Claire Kahane, "Uncanny Sights: The Anticipation of the Abomination", in *Trauma at Home After 9/11*, edited by Judith Greenberg (Lincoln and London: University of Nebraska Press), 2003, pp. 107-16, p. 112.

[11] Kristiaan Versluys, *Out of the Blue: September 11 and the Novel* (New York: Columbia University Press, 2009), p. 1.

[12] Don DeLillo, "In The Ruins of the Future: Reflections on Terror and Loss in the Shadow of September," *Harper's Magazine* (December 2001): 33-40.

[13] Versluys, *op. cit.*, p. 3.

[14] Jay McInerney, "Interview: The Browser." Accessed August 2, 2013. http://thebrowser.com/interviews/jay-mcinerney-on-essential-new-york-novels?page=full.

Michiko Kakutani asked why September 11th remains stubbornly "resistant" to artistic treatment in an article entitled "Outdone by Reality." In *The New York Times* series "The 9/11 Decade: Artists respond to September 11th," Kakutani argues that ten years later, "it is even clearer that 9/11 has not provoked a seismic change in the arts"[15] Compelling as some individual works might be, "none were game-changing. Most September 11th works, she writes, "feel like blips on the cultural landscape—they neither represent a new paradigm nor suggest that the attacks were a cultural watershed."[16] Critics in newspapers and journals over the past decade have been largely unkind to the majority of books written about September 11. Versluys, who wrote one of the early full length studies, describes the characters in DeLillo's *Falling Man* as "so thin that their whole existence boils down to mere nomenclature" and suggests that the novel allows "no narrative momentum to develop"; Foer's *Extremely Loud and Incredibly Close* (2005) fares little better.[17] "It is a triumph of evasion", writes one reviewer, "whose net effect is to distract the reader (and Foer) from harsh truths."[18] The great September 11th novel has yet to be written, and perhaps it never will. No writer has yet captured the magnitude of the event or the shock it produced; the unsayable, decry critics, remains unsaid. With titles like "A Failure of Imagination?" and "Imagining Atrocity," several essays in Versluys's *Out of the Blue* also address the challenges of representing September 11th, both textually and visually. Will American literature be diminished if it fails to produce what critics hail as a quintessential "9/11 novel"? What meaning can we make of this critical lament?

The literary legacy of the Civil War was also one of expectation and lament. Indeed, the grievances of Kakutani, Versulys, Gray, and numerous others sound surprisingly familiar to a scholar of nineteenth-century U.S. literature and culture. William Dean Howells, an influential editor and novelist in the post-Civil War years, repeatedly bemoaned what he saw as the failure of literature to make meaning of the Civil War: "Every author who deals in fiction feels it to be his duty to contribute towards the payment of the accumulated interest in the events of our national tragedy"; yet, the war, Howells proclaimed, "not only left us the burden...of a national debt," but left a debt that the nation's literature, staggering

---

[15] Michiko Kakutani, "Outdone by Reality," *The New York Times*, September 1, 2011. Accessed August 2, 2013. http://www.nytimes.com/2011/09/01/us/sept-11-reckoning/culture.html?pagewanted=all.
[16] *Ibid.*
[17] Versluys, *op. cit.*
[18] *Ibid.*

"lamely," has scarcely repaid. [19] Anticipating Kakutani's requiem for September 11th literature, a nineteenth-century *New York Times* editor would ask, "Is this tremendous epic we are now living to bring forth naught but unutterable trash and bombast?"[20] Few of the many authors who rushed to write of the war, Howells and others repeatedly regretted, "treat the War really."[21]

Even close to a century after Howells's requiem, scholars continued to mourn the lack of "great" literature to emerge from what was then the nation's most definitive conflict. [22] It was not until the publication of Stephen Crane's short novel *The Red Badge of Courage* in 1895 that critics applauded the appearance of an authentic Civil War narrative, one written by an author who was not even born at the time. Literary critic T. W. Higginsons's 1896 description of Crane's success is emblematic: "The wonder is that this young writer, who had no way of getting at it all except by the gossip—printed or written…should be able to go behind them all, and give an account…not only more vivid…but more accurate."[23] Stephen Crane enjoyed this appraisal, more so because he, too, declared his dissatisfaction with Civil War literature after reading a series of first-person accounts of battle experiences published in *Century Magazine* titled "Battles and Leaders of the Civil War": "I wonder that some of these fellows don't tell how they felt in those scraps!" [24] Crane defines meaningful writing as emotional, requiring "feeling"; a story about psychic pain of the kind that Crane longed for, one that was not "emotionless as rocks," seemed missing from the literary landscape.[25]

The recent lament over literature in the decade following September 11, 2001 suggests that the psychic wounds so expressively imagined by Crane through his character Henry Fleming may now risk ubiquity. If one

[19] William Dean Howells, "Reviews and Literary Notices," *Atlantic Monthly*, July 1867, p. 121.

[20] Charles B. Dew, "Rally Round the Flag," *New York Times*, February 1, 2001, p. 29. Accessed August 2, 2013. http://www.nytimes.com/books/01/02/25/reviews/010225.25dewlt.html.

[21] Edmund Wilson, *Patriotic Gore: Studies in the Literature of the American Civil War* (Boston, Mass.: Northeastern University Press, 1995), p. iii.

[22] See, for example, Daniel Aaron, *Unwritten War: American Writers and the Civil War* (New York: Alfred A. Knopf, 1973).

[23] T. W. Higginson, "A Bit of War Photography," *The Philistine* 3 n. 2 (July 1896): 33-8, p. 35.

[24] Stephen Crane, *The Red Badge of Courage* (New York, 1895), p. 251.

[25] For more on Crane's *The Red Badge of Courage*, see Travis, "Soldier's Heart" in *Wounded Hearts: Masculinity, Law, and Literature in American Culture* (Chapel Hill: University of North Carolina Press, 2005).

of the "tragedies" of the Civil War, to recall William Dean Howells's terminology, was the failure of literature to capture individual emotion and psychic pain, critics now decry that in our "post-traumatic culture" representations of individual and collective traumas often overreach and ultimately fail to represent the larger socio-political landscape.[26] Indeed, trauma may today falter as an explanatory vocabulary precisely because its lexicon sunders individual and domestic events from their global repercussions. Although Stephen Crane successfully wrote about the traumatized Civil War psyche well before there was a formal language or label for his imaginings, the language of trauma now risks being either so particularized as to miss its larger meanings or so generalized as to rise to the status of an anthropomorphic condition: aren't we all "traumatized" by September 11th?[27]

These criticisms do not deny that survivors and witnesses suffer trauma. Rather, they suggest that extending the lexicon of trauma to the nation at this particular time may unwittingly undermine the gravity and complexity of the events on September 11th and the subsequent decade. This is a point that has been made by critics such as Richard Gray and Michael Rothberg in their 2009 exchange in *American Literary History*. September 11th novels, they agree, fail to move beyond the simplistic register that "something traumatic has happened" and this "failure of the imagination" means that some of the global impact of September 11th is underrepresented.[28] Both critique contemporary writers' reliance on the domestic and the pedestrian, with Gray writing that most literature post-9/11 "simply assimilate[s] the unfamiliar into familiar structures. The crisis is, in every sense of the word, domesticated."[29] Novels in their focus on domestic interiors, we see "are measured purely and simply in terms of their impact on the emotional entanglements of their protagonists."[30]Gray calls for deterritorialization (through immigrant writing) and Rothberg extra-territorialization (internationalization) to counter this trend. "Once

---

[26] For a good description of this argument, see Sabine Sielke, "Why '9/11 is [not] unique' or Troping Trauma," *Amerikenstudien* 55 n. 3 (2010): 385-410. The term "post–traumatic culture" is from Kirby Farrell, *Post-Traumatic Culture: Injury and Interpretation in the Nineties* (Baltimore, Md.: Johns Hopkins University Press, 1998).

[27] Sielke, *op. cit.*, pp. 287-8.

[28] Michael Rothberg, "A Failure of the Imagination: Diagnosing the Post-9/11 Novel: A Response to Richard Gray," *American Literary History* 21 n. 1 (Spring 2009): 152-8.

[29] Richard Gray, op. cit., p. 134.

[30] *Ibid.*

writers have acknowledged the shock and trauma of 9/11, an intellectually and politically mature literature must leave national—domestic space behind for riskier 'foreign' encounters."[31]

To lament the failure of literature post September 11th because of its domestic entanglements, however, risks repeating and valorizing hegemonic ways of reading passed down from the nineteenth century; it is to hazard the very historical and cultural amnesia that these critics would otherwise denounce. To say that domestic dramas are inadequate in scope is to ignore how the "domestic novel" throughout American literary history has been immersed in political and cultural thought and has helped to shape cultural memory. From the perspective of U.S. literary history, this lamentation about the "domestic novel" recalls the same kinds of critiques that initially led to the wholesale erasure of women's literature and the point of view of the "deterritorialized other." What scholars have learned from the recovery of the nineteenth-century domestic novel is that it is often the longing to reclaim the "small, fragmentary human stories," as Catherine Morely has argued of September 11th novels that "alone can illuminate the wider picture."[32]

I want to conclude this essay with one such domestic drama, albeit one written by one of the "bright lights" of the New York literary scene. Jay McInerney's *The Good Life* (2006) does not bring memories of the Civil War and events of September 11th together with triumphal political rhetoric but instead mires them in a shared moral ambiguity. The novel's curious recollection of the Confederate defeat in the Civil War as an evocation of the sorrow of September 11th calls into question the process of memory work and memorialization itself. The novel chronicles an extramarital relationship that smolders on the ashes, quite literally, of the September 11th dead. Corrine Calloway and Luke McGavok meet as volunteers at a rescue and recovery center in Lower Manhattan and begin an affair. Their first encounter occurs on September 11th, when Luke emerges out of the ashes of the towers and, in a chance meeting with Corrine, accepts her offer of a bottle of Evian water.[33] They are strangers, and the scene evokes the kindness of strangers in the days following the tragedy—the very spirit that, many lament, failed to endure. The Civil War references begin with this encounter. Emerging out of the "soot" and "debris," Luke looks to Corrine like a "statue commemorating some

---

[31] Rothberg, *op. cit.*, p. 157.
[32] Catherine Morely, "'How Do We Write About This?' The Domestic and the Global in the Post-9/11 Novel," *Journal of American Studies* 45 n. 4 (2011): 717-31, p. 724.
[33] Jay McInerney, *The Good Life* (New York: Knopf, 2006), p. 70.

ancient victory, or, more likely, some noble defeat—a Confederate general, perhaps."[34] This first impression is confirmed when she hears his southern twang.[35] Although Corrine, the New Englander, and Luke, a native of Tennessee, part after this small act of kindness, they later reconnect as volunteers in Lower Manhattan, where she spends her nights gratefully away from her husband Russell, and he escapes from his wife Sasha and the escalating problems with their daughter.

Corrine and Luke's initial impulse toward service quickly becomes an occasion for an illicit romance, and their generosity of spirit turns toward the pursuit of individual pleasures and self-serving prevarications. The novel ends with them going their separate ways—perhaps too tidy a resolution—and, in some respects, reproduces precisely the kind of domestic drama that has garnered so much ire. Indeed, critics have called the novel "crass" (*The Economist*), "unstable" (*The Guardian*), and "empty" (*The New York Times*). But few have moved beyond the narrow individual interiors of its two admittedly flawed and often unlikeable characters to look at how the novel's fragments of historical consciousness and gestures toward memory-work offer a cautionary tale for New York and for the nation in the post September 11th era.

One of the few critics to analyze the abundant parallelism between the Civil War and September 11th in McInerney's novel, Fiorenzo Luliano, argues that the South "acquires a central role in elaborating a national fantasy after September 11," "rehabilitating" Southern history in a vulgar effort at post-September 11th nation-building: "Almost entirely overlooking any trace of the African-American heritage, Tennessee becomes the place where America can start a new course in its history."[36] While the novel first likens September 11th to the Southern defeat in the Civil War through Corrine's initial thought upon seeing Luke, the narrative's efforts at nation-building become crucially compromised by their continuing fraught juxtaposition as the novel progresses. For example, the fateful start of Corrine and Luke's affair leads to Luke's first memory of the post-Civil War South. Will everything "just go back to the way it was?" Corrine asks Luke as they drive down the FDR Drive toward his studio in the days after the attacks. Luke tells Corrine that he supposes it will:

> The town I grew up in," Luke said, "is one of the sleepiest, most
> picturesque burgs you could hope to find. Think Mayberry RFD. It was the

---

[34] *Ibid., p. 69.*
[35] *Ibid.*, p. 70.
[36] Fiorenzo Luliano, "Falling from the Past: Geographies of Exceptionalism in Two Novels by Jay McInerney," *Altre Modernità*, special issue, (2011), p. 103.

site of one of the bloodiest battles of the Civil War. Thousands died in the course of a few hours. My great-great-grandmother's house was a field hospital and she had hundreds of wounded under her roof that night. There were four dead Confederate generals laid out on her porch out of the fifteen who fell that day. Nearly fifteen hundred soldiers are buried in what used to be the family cemetery, fourteen hundred and eighty one to be exact, and they say that my great great grandmother wrote a letter to the mothers of every single one of them. When I was a kid, I used to count the bloodstains on the floorboards.[37]

This reverie recalls many things: the "ground zero" gravesite, with so few human remains, near which Corrine and Luke now work; the efforts, then and now, at remembering and memorializing lives lost; and the glimpses of historical awareness, only now emerging both in Luke's mind and in the novel, of the nation's history of bloodshed if not of its occasions—slavery and racism. That Luke retrieves a family story passed down through generations rather than invoking the event's larger political context is hardly surprising, nor is Luke's suggestion that despite the permanent bloodstains on the floorboards of his ancestral home, his ancestors, like others, have continued to walk over this ground; they return to their way they have always been, foreshadowing the novel's conclusion.[38] The floorboards, with their literal traces of blood, can be read, or they can be mere marks underfoot, forgotten. Corrine lauds Luke's memory: "You haven't forgotten, even a hundred and fifty years later."[39] Luke aligns his meditation with what he describes as the South's "collective memory," a capacity he claims that New Yorkers lack; but even this remonstration reveals to readers his inability to move beneath the surface, to unearth the skeletons of his past. Luke's memories are without their true referents: at their most personal, his Civil War rememberance is merely an archive of his mother's affair, which he will grapple with later

---

[37] McInerney, *op. cit.*, p. 214.

[38] Louis Menand reads *The Good Life* as suggesting that "after September 11 anything seemed possible to the survivors," in "The Earthquake: A Manhattan Affair," *The New Yorker*, February 6, 2006. Accessed August 2, 2013. http://www.newyorker.com/archive/2006/02/06/060206crbo_books1?currentPage= all. Yet Benjamin Strong writes that *The Good Life* might be the most evocative novel about September 11th because it "dares to suggest that most of us weren't changed at all," *Village Voice,* January 24, 2006. See also, Arin Keeble, "Marriage, Relationships, and 9/11: The Seismographic Narratives of *Falling Man, The Good Life*, and *The Emperor's Children,*" *Modern Language Review* 106 n. 2 (April 2011): 355-73.

[39] McInerney, *op. cit.*, p. 214.

on; in its collective iteration, it is a convenient forgetting of the socio-
political atrocities for which such blood was spilled. Corrine's and Luke's
exchange encourages readers to question the uses to which historical
memory is put and the convergences and divergences of individual and
collective memories.[40]

It is Corrine and Luke's rejection of the concept of collective memory
and their ability to forget—they, too, walk over bloodstained ground and
ask little of its larger meaning—that allows them to embark on their affair.
These characters even obliquely acknowledge that if given the
opportunity, they would not turn back the clock prior to September 11th;
they most likely would not sacrifice their newfound happiness at the cost
of thousands of lives. "I think about that. It's terrible. I think I must be a
terrible person," says Corrine.[41] By way of comfort, Luke tells her,
"Maybe you should just try to live in the moment," and they do, for a very
brief time, until Luke's daughter disappears only to turn up at his
Tennessee childhood home.[42]

When Luke returns south to retrieve his daughter in the final section of
the novel, satirically titled "Holiday," he is forced to confront the past, this
time with a bit more rigor. Again, it is the referent of Confederate history
that sparks his personal memories and occasions painful recollections of
his mother's affair, his perception of her familial betrayal, and their
subsequent decades' long estrangement. "The year after the [Confederate
dead] had been hastily interred on the battlefield," his great-great-
grandmother "had supervised their re-internment on her own property and
kept a meticulous log of the names, which after a winter had already begun

---

[40] See David Simpson, *9/11: The Culture of Commemoration* (Chicago, Ill.:
University of Chicago Press, 2006), as well as scholarship on memory work such
as Ester Võsu and Ene Kõresaar and Kristin Kuutma, "Preface. Mediation of
Memory: Towards Transdisciplinary Perspectives in Current Memory Studies,"
Trames 12 n. 2 (2008): 243–63 and Susannah Radstone, "What Place is This?:
Transcultural Memory and The Location of Memory Studies," *Parallax* 17 n. 4
(October-December 2011): 109-23. For a discussion of racialization in the U.S.
pre- and post-September 11, see Ali Behdad, who argues that "viewed from a
historical perspective, one begins to doubt claims that the 9/11 attacks precipitated
the emergence of a *new* racial formation in the U.S.; it seems more accurate to say
that recent events have simply provided an occasion for remarking upon
longstanding ideas and practices pertaining to the positioning of various
marginalized groups, including Middle Easterners." Ali Behdad, "Critical
Historicism," *American Literary History* 20 n. 1-2 (Spring/Summer 2008): 286-
99, p. 287.
[41] McInerney, *op. cit.*, p. 215.
[42] *Ibid.*

to fade on the wooden crosses."[43] Luke remembers himself as a young boy running out to this graveyard, wanting the "dead to communicate" and to offer him some answers or solace for his mother's actions. Yet, what he hears from among the gravestones, as he recites to himself Tate's "Ode to the Confederate Dead", are not the voices of the past but rather his mother's cries of sexual ecstasy. Here again, the narrative presents historical memory as quickly displaced by the present and what Luke begins to see, in a moment of self-reflection, as his own "selfish desire."[44]

The escape from New York and the "holiday" in Tennessee encourage Luke to unearth past skeletons: he confronts his mother about her past affair and comes to recognize the end of his own. For his teenage daughter Ashley, her grandmother's house offers an escape from the stifling competition and demands of growing up affluent in New York City. Embracing the South is Ashley's way of disentangling herself from a suffocating social world of private school dramas. Yet this identification and her similar efforts at historical consciousness also climax in a way that is strangely out of context. As the novel shows individuals in the act of remembering, it also denies a sense of shared social memory. Back in New York, members of Luke's family reunite at The 21 Club for their annual Christmas lunch. As Luke chides himself for his "selfish desire" and ruminates about the "lost family of his childhood and the broken promise of this one," the uniformed Salvation Army Choir sings "Silent Night," "The Battle Hymn of the Republic," and, lastly, "Dixie" for the tony crowd.[45] Ashley, sullen in her surroundings, suddenly stands in allegiance, her naive salute another way to mortify her mother and to rebel. More than this, Ashley's defiance of her parents—"look away indeed," Luke thinks—and her embrace of their Confederate "heritage" is another reminder that how we choose to remember and what we choose to forget defines us. Even if Jay McInerney's characters often fail in their reckoning, their small domestic dramas recall our own. In the days, weeks, and years after September 11th, the novel reminds of that how we observe and memorialize the bloodstains on our floorboards make meaning of this and a still more distant past.

---

[43] *Ibid.*, p. 289.
[44] *Ibid.*, p. 330.
[45] *Ibid.*

BIBLIOGRAPHY

"2006 Winner: Carlos Delgado, New York Mets." *Roberto Clemente Award.* Accessed July 30, 2013. http://mlb.mlb.com/mlb/official_info/community/clemente_history.jsp.

9/11 Memorial. Accessed May 31, 2012. http://www.911memorial.org.

9/11 Memorials. Accessed July 31, 2013. http://911memorials.org/?p=39.

"9/11 Memorial Room." *New York City Fire Museum.* Accessed May 20, 2012. http://www.nycfiremuseum.org/gallery_page.cfm?alias=permanent-ex-911.

"9/11 Remembered: Day of Prayer." *YES Network.* Accessed July 30, 2013. http://web.yesnetwork.com/media/video.jsp?content_id=18988991&topic_id=&tcid=vpp_copy_18988991&v=3.

Aaron, Daniel. *Unwritten War American Writers and the Civil War.* New York: Alfred A. Knopf, 1973.

Adorno, Theodor W. "An Essay on Cultural Criticism and Society." In *Prisms,* translated by Samuel Weber and Sherry Weber. New York: Columbia University Press, 1981 (1955).

—. "Meditations on Metaphysics." In *Negative Dialectics,* translated by E. B. Ashton. New York: Continuum International Publishing Group, 2005 (1966; translation 1973)).

Allison, Rebecca. "One year on: 9/11 wicked but a work of art, says Damien Hirst." *The Guardian.* Sept. 11, 2002. Accessed August 2, 2013. http://www.theguardian.com/uk/2002/sep/11/arts.september11.

Anderson, Charles M. and Marian M. MacCurdy. *Writing and Healing Towards an Informed Practice.* Urbana, Ill.: National Council of Teachers of English, 2000.

Ando, Tadao. "*Toward New Horizons* in Architecture." In *Theorizing a New Agenda for Architecture: An Anthology of Architectural Theory 1965-1995,* edited by Kate Nesbitt. 456-61. New York: Princeton Architectural Press, 1996.

Apple, R. W. "Awaiting the Aftershocks: Washington and Nation Plunge into Fight with Enemy Hard to Identify and Punish." *The New York Times,* Sept. 12, 2001. Accessed August 2, 2013. http://www.nytimes.com/2001/09/12/us/a-day-of-terror-news-analysis-awaiting-the-aftershocks.html

Arad, Michael Arad and Peter Walker. "World Trade Center Site Memorial Competition: Reflecting Absence." Accessed May 20, 2012. http://wtcsitememorial.org/fin7.html.

Attridge, Derek. *The Singularity of Literature*. London: Routledge, 2004.

Auster, Paul. "On the High Wire." *The Art of Hunger*. New York: Penguin, 1997.

Bahktin, Mikhail. "Discourse in the Novel." In *The Dialogic Imagination*, edited by Michael Holquist and translated by Caryl Emerson. 259-422. Austin: University of Texas Press, 1981.

Bal, Mieke. "Figuration." *PMLA* 119 n. 5 (2004): 1289-1292.

Barry, Dan. "A Repository for Remains of the Dead," *New York Times*. September 4, 2011. Accessed July 30, 2013. www.nytimes.com/2011/09/04/us/sept-11-reckoning/dna.html?_r=1&hp.

Barthes, Roland. "Rhetoric of the Image." In *Image–Music–Text*, translated by Stephen Heath. 32-51. New York: Hill and Wang, 1978.

—. *The Eiffel Tower and Other Mythologies*, translated by Richard Howard. Berkeley: University of California Press, 1979.

—. *Camera Lucida*. New York: Hill and Wang, 1981.

Barton, David. *Literacy: An Introduction to the Ecology of Written Language*. Malden, Mass.: Blackwell Publishing, 1994 (2007).

Baudrillard, Jean. *The Spirit of Terrorism*, translated by Chris Turner. London: Verso, 2002.

Baum, Geraldine and Paul Lieberman. "A Struggle to Escape Fiery Chaos." *Los Angeles Times*. September 12, 2001. A1+.

Behdad, Ali. "Critical Historicism." *American Literary History* 20 n. 1-2 (Spring/Summer 2008): 286-99.

Beigbeder, Frédéric Beigbeder. *Windows on the World*, translated by Frank Wynne. New York: Miramax, 2005.

Bender, Thomas. *Unfinished City: New York and the Metropolitan Idea*. New York: The New Press, 2002.

Benhabib, Seyla. *Another Cosmopolitanism*. Oxford: Oxford University Press, 2006.

Berger, Peter L. and Thomas Luckmann. *The Social Construction of Reality: A Treatise in the Sociology of Knowledge*. New York: Doubleday, 1966.

Berlant, Lauren. "Intuitionists: History and the Affective Event." *American Literary History* 20 n. 4 (2008): 845-860.

Bilgin, Pinar. "Is the 'Orientalist' past the Future of Middle East Studies?" *Third World Quarterly* 25 n. 2 (2004): 423-433.

Bizzell, Patricia. "Composition Studies Saves the World!" *College English* 72 n. 2 (2009):174-187.

Blackman, Nicole Blackman. "Nicole Blackman." In *Tower Stories: An Oral History of 9/11*, edited by Damon DiMarco. 275. Santa Monica, Cal.: Santa Monica Press, 2007.

Blais, Alison and Lynn Rasic. *A Place of Remembrance: Official Book of the National September 11 Memorial*. Washington, D.C.: National Geographic Society, 2011.

Bociurkiw, Marusya. "Homeland (In)Security: Roots and Displacement, from New York, to Toronto, to Salt Lake City." *Reconstruction: An Interdisciplinary Culture Studies Community* 3 n. 3 (2003): 21. Accessed August 3, 2013. http://reconstruction.eserver.org/033/bociurkiw.htm.

Boehmer, Elleke and Stephen Morton. "Introduction: Terror and the Postcolonial." In *Terror and the Postcolonial*, edited by Elleke Boehmer and Stephen Morton. 1-24. Oxford: Wiley Blackwell, 2010.

Bok, Derek. *Our Underachieving Colleges: A Candid Look at How Much Students Learn and Why They Should Be Learning More*. Princeton, N.J.: Princeton University Press, 2006.

Bonnabeau, Richard F. *The Promise Continues: Empire State College, the First Twenty Five Years*. Albany, N.Y.: SUNY Empire State College 1996.

Booth, Ken and Tim Dunne. *Terror in Our Time*. New York: Routledge, 2012.

Borges, Ron. "Don't Boo Delgado for Iraq Protest," *NBC Sports*. July 22, 2004. Accessed July 30, 2013. http://nbcsports.msnbc.com/id/5482059/.

Borradori, Giovanna. *Philosophy in a Time of Terror: Dialogues with Jürgen Habermas and Jacques Derrida*. Chicago, Ill.: University of Chicago Press, 2003.

Brady, Erik. "Continuity of Sports Helped Heal the Times," *USA Today*, September 11, 2002. Accessed July 30, 2013. http://www.usatoday.com/sports/sept11/2002-09-10-ccover_x.htm.

Bretón, Marcos and José Luis Villegas. *Away Games: The Life and Times of a Latin Baseball Player*. Albuquerque: University of New Mexico Press, 1999.

Bringuier, Julien and Madelena Gonzalez. "Fiction after 9/11: A Journey through the Desert of the Real." In *Generic Instability and Identity in the Contemporary Novel*, edited by Madelena Gonzalez and Marie Odile Pittin-Hédon. 220-237. Newcastle upon Tyne, England: Cambridge Scholars, 2010.

Briton, Dee. "Comfort in Cloth: The Syracuse University Remembrance Quilt." *Voices: The Journal of New York Folkore* 34 n. 3 (2008): 3-6.

Brooks, Peter. "If You Have Tears." In *Trauma at Home After 9/11*, edited by Judith Greenberg. 48-52. Lincoln and London: University of Nebraska Press, 2003.

Brottman, Mikita. "The Fascination of Abomination." *Film and Television after 9/11*, edited by Wheller Winston Dixon. 163-177. Carbondale: Southern Illinois University Press, 2004.

Brown, Robert S. "Sport and Healing America." *Society* 42 (2004): 37-41.

Brown, Wendy. *Regulating Aversion: Tolerance in the Age of Identity and Empire*. Princeton, N.J.: Princeton University Press, 2006.

Brynen, Rex. "Cluster-Bombs and Sandcastles: Kramer on the Future of Middle East Studies in America." *Middle East Journal* 56 n. 2 (2002): 323-328.

Burdick, Eugene and William Lederer. *The Ugly American*. W.W. Norton & Company, 1999.

Bush, George W. *"Statement by the president in his address to the nation."* The White House. September 11, 2001. Accessed August 2, 2013.
http://georgewbush-whitehouse.archives.gov/news/releases/2001/09/20010911-16.html.

Butler, Judith. *Giving an Account of Oneself*. New York: Fordham University Press, 2005.

—. *Frames of War: When is Life Grievable?* London: Verso, 2009.

Caputi, Jane. "Guest Editor's Introduction: Of Towers and Twins, Synchronicities and Shadows: Archetypal Meanings in the Imagery of 9/11." *Journal of American Culture* 28 n. 1 (2005): 1-10.

Carocci, Max. "Textiles of Healing: Native American AIDS Quilts." *Textile: The Journal of Cloth and Culture* 8 n. 1 (2010): 68-85.

Caruth, Cathy. *Trauma: Explorations in Memory*. Baltimore, Md.: Johns Hopkins University Press, 1995.

Castoriadis, Cornelius. *The Imaginary Institution of Society*. Cambridge, Mass.: MIT Press, 1998.

Cave, Damien. "Far From Ground Zero, Obscure Pastor Is Ignored No Longer." *The New York Times*. August 25, 2010. Accessed August 9, 2013. http://www.nytimes.com/2010/08/26/us/26gainesville.html

Chidester, David. "The Church of Baseball, the Fetish of Coca-Cola and the Potlatch of Rock 'n' Roll: Theoretical Models for the Study of Religion in American Popular Culture." *Journal of the American Academy of Religion* 64 n. 4 (1996): 743-765.

Churchill, Ward. "'Some People Push Back': On the Justice of Roosting of Chickens." *Kerspledeb*. 2001. Accessed December 28, 2011. http://www.kersplebedeb.com/mystuff/s11/churchill.html.

Citizens Budget Commission and the Federal Reserve Bank of New York, "Encouraging Small Business Success in New York City and Northern New Jersey: What Firms Value Most." Federal Reserve Bank of New York. Accessed August 2011, http://www.newyorkfed.org/regional/smallbiz_survey.pdf.

Clark, William A. *Immigrants and the American Dream: Remaking the Middle Class.* New York: The Gulford Press, 2003.

Cleveland, William L. *History of the Modern Middle East.* 2nd edition. Boulder, Col.: Westview Press. 2000.

Cleveland, William L., and Martin Bunton. *History of the Modern Middle East.* 4th edition. Boulder, Col.: Westview Press. 2009.

Codde, Philippe. "Philomela Revisited: Traumatic Iconicity in Jonathan Safran Foer's *Extremely Loud & Incredibly Close.*" *Studies in American Fiction* 35 n. 2 (2007): 241-254.

Cohen, David. "The psyche of terror." *The Guardian.* September 28, 2001. Accessed August 7, 2011. http://www.theguardian.com/education/2001/sep/28/internationaleducationnews.highereducation.

Collins, Kristofer. "Foer Extremely Modest about Storytelling." *Pittsburgh Post–Gazette,* October 9, 2005, region ed.: J4.

Cordoba Initiative: Improving Muslim-West Relations. Cordoba Initiative, 2008. Accessed September 16, 2011. http://www.cordobainitiative.org/about/imam-feisal/.

Crain's New York Business. *Number of Small Businesses.* Accessed July 30, 2013. http://mycrains.crainsnewyork.com/stats-and-the-city/2011/small-business/number-of-small-businesses.

Crane, Stephen. *The Red Badge of Courage* (1895).

Dargis, Manohla. "Defiance Under Fire: Unbounded Bravery in Unfriendly Skies." *New York Times.* April 28, 2006. Accessed August 9, 2013. http://query.nytimes.com/gst/fullpage.html?res=9F06EED9133FF93B A15757C0A9609C8B63.

DeLillo, Don. *Libra.* New York: Penguin, 1991 (1988).

—. "In The Ruins of the Future: Reflections on Terror and Loss in the Shadow of September." *Harper's Magazine* (December 2001): 33-40.

—. *Falling Man.* New York: Scribner, 2007.

Denzin, Norman K. "The Art and Politics of Interpretation." In *Collecting and Interpreting Qualitative Materials,* edited by Norman K. Denzin and Yvonna S. Lincoln. 319-344. Thousand Oaks, Cal.: Sage, 1998.

DeRosa, Aaron. "Analysing Literature After 9/11." *Modern Fiction Studies* 57 n. 3 (Fall 2011): 607-618.

Derrida, Jacques. *Positions,* translated by Alan Bass. Chicago, Ill.: The University of Chicago Press, 1981.

—. *On Cosmopolitanism and Forgiveness*, translated by Michael Hughes. London: Routledge, 2010.

Dew, Charles B. "Rally Round the Flag." *New York Times.* February 1, 2001. Accessed August 9, 2013.
http://www.nytimes.com/books/01/02/25/reviews/010225.25dewlt.html.

Dewey, John and Arthur Bentley, *Knowing and the Known.* Boston, Mass.: Beacon, 1949.

Didion, Joan. *Fixed Ideas: America Since 9/11.* New York: New York Review of Books, 2003.

"Discover The Networks: A Guide to the Political Left." Accessed December 28, 2011.
http://www.discoverthenetworks.org/individualProfile.asp?indid=2205.

Doss, Erika. *Memorial Mania: Public Feeling in America.* Chicago, Ill.: University of Chicago Press, 2010.

Drew, Richard. "The Horror of 9/11 That's All Too Familiar," *Los Angeles Times.* September 10, 2003. Accessed June 19, 2013.
http://articles.latimes.com/2003/sep/10/opinion/oe-drew10.

Dunlap, David W. "Tribute center, an 'Interim Destination' Memorial, Gets Set to Open." *New York Times on the Web.* September 6, 2006. Accessed May 20, 2012.
http://query.nytimes.com/gst/fullpage.html?res=9F05EFD91631F935A3575AC0A9609C8B63.

Durand, Alain-Philippe."Beyond the Extreme: Frédéric Beigbeder's *Windows on the World.*" In *Novels of the Contemporary Extreme*, edited by Alain-Philippe Durand and Naomi Mandel. 109-120. New York: Continuum, 2006.

Dwyer, Jim, David Kocieniewski, Deidre Murphy, and Peg Tyre, editors. *Two Seconds under the World: Terror Comes to America—The Conspiracy behind the World Trade Center Bombing.* New York: Crown, 1994.

Dwyer, Jim, and Kevin Flynn. *102 Minutes: The Untold Story of the Fight to Survive inside the Twin Towers.* New York: Times, 2005.

Easterbrook, Neil. "Alternate Presents: The Ambivalent Historicism of *Pattern Recognition.*" *Science Fiction Studies* 33 n. 3 (2006): 483-504.

Elias, Robert. *The Empire Strikes Out: How Baseball Sold U.S. Foreign Policy and Promoted the American Way Abroad.* New York: The New Press, 2010. Kindle edition.

Eliot, Justin. "How the 'Ground Zero Mosque' Fear Mongering Began."
    Salon. Salon.com. August 16, 2010. Accessed September 16, 2011.
    http://www.salon.com/2010/08/16/ground_zero_mosque_origins/.
Elkind, David. *Images of the Young Child: Collected Essays on
    Development and Education.* Washington, DC: National Association
    for the Education of Young Children, 1993.
Ellison, Keith. "Keith Ellison's Testimony at the Muslim Radicalization
    Hearing." *The Atlantic.* March 10, 2011. Accessed March 22, 2011.
    http://www.theatlantic.com/politics/archive/2011/03/keith-ellisons-
    testimony-at-the-muslim-radicalization-hearing/72294/.
Engelhardt, Tom. *The End of Victory Culture.* 2nd edition. Amherst:
    University of Massachusetts Press, 2007.
Espada, Martín. "Alabanza: In Praise of Local 100." In *Alabanza: New
    and Selected Poems 1982-2002.* 231-232. New York: W. W. Norton
    and Company, Inc., 2003.
Evans, Christopher H. and William R. Herzog II, editors. *The Faith of
    Fifty Million: Baseball, Religion and American Culture.* Louisville,
    Ken.: Westminster John Knox Press, 2002.
Faludi, Susan. *The Terror Dream: Fear and Fantasy in Post-9/11
    America.* New York: Metropolitan Books, 2007.
*FAO in Emergencies Guidance Note: Accountability to Affected
    Populations.* United Nations Food and Agricultural Organization:
    Rome, 2012.
Farrell, Kirby. *Post-Traumatic Culture: Injury and Interpretation in the
    Nineties.* Baltimore, Md.: Johns Hopkins University Press, 1998.
Fass, Mark. "Last Seen on September 10th." *New York Magazine.* June 18,
    2006. Accessed July 30, 2013. http://nymag.com/news/features/17336/.
Fasteau, Marc Feigen. *The Male Machine.* New York: Dell, 1975.
Ferguson, Robert. "Hearing Lincoln." *American Literary History* 21 n. 4
    (Winter 2009): 687-724.
Fish, Stanley. *Save the World on Your Own Time.* New York: Oxford
    University Press, 2008.
Fisher, Sydney Nettleton. *The Middle East: A History.* 2nd edition. New
    York: Knopf, 1969.
—. *The Middle East: A History.* 4th edition. New York: Knopf, 1990.
Fisher, Sydney Nettleton, and William Ochsenwald. *The Middle East: A
    History.* 5th edition. New York: Knopf, 1997.
Fitzpatrick, Andrew D. "The Movement of Vulnerability: Images of
    Falling and September 11." *Art Journal* 66 n. 4 (2007): 84-102.
Flores, Juan. *From Bomba to Hip-Hop: Puerto Rican Culture and Latino
    Identity.* New York: Columbia University Press, 2000.

Flores-Rodríguez, Ángel G. "Baseball, 9/11, and Dissent: The Carlos Delgado Controversy." *OAH Magazine of History* 25 v. 3 (2011): 55.

Foer, Jonathan Safran. *Extremely Loud and Incredibly Close.* New York: Houghton Mifflin, 2005.

Foote, Kenneth E. *Shadowed Ground. America's Landscapes of Violence and Tragedy.* Austin: University of Texas Press, 2003.

Forbes, Charles. "'Twin Towers' Icons Transend [sic] Commercial Appeal, Memorialize 9-11." *Think & Ask.* September 2003. Accessed April 19, 2012. http://www.thinkandask.com/news/neon.html.

Fox, Renée C., Victor M. Lidz, Helen E. Sheehan, Barrett P. Brenton, and Heike Thiel de Bocanegra, "Safe Horizon after September 11, 2001: A Study of Organizational Stress and Change." Final report submitted to the *Solomon Asch Center for Study of Ethnopolitical Conflict and the Mellon Foundation.* 2004.

Fox, Renée C., and Victor M. Lidz, Helen E. Sheehan, Barrett P. Brenton, and Heike Thiel de Bocanegra, "Heroic action and its discontents: Safe Horizon's response to 9/11." *Social Science and Modern Society* 46 n. 4 (2009): 308-318.

Francis, Lynn. "The Empire State Building: The Construction and Aging of a Metaphor." *Journal of American Culture* 10 n. 2 (1987): 83-90.

Fredman, Samuel G. "Muslims and Islam were Part of Twin Towers' Life." *The New York Times.* September 10, 2010. Accessed September 16, 2011. http://www.nytimes.com/2010/09/11/nyregion/11religion.html?pagewanted=all&_r=0.

Friend, David. *Watching the World Change: The Stories Behind the Images of 9/11.* New York: I. B. Tauris & Co., 2006.

Fry, Gladys-Marie. *Stitched from the Soul: Slave Quilts from the Ante-Bellum South.* New York: Penguin Books, 1990.

Fukuyama, Francis. "How Academia Failed the Nation: The Decline of Regional Studies." *Saisphere* (Winter 2004). Accessed July 31, 2013. As reported in http://www.campus-watch.org/article/id/1498.

Gage, Beverly. "Terrorism and the American Experience: A State of the Field." *Journal of American History* 98 n. 2 (June 2011): 702-726.

Gálvez, Alyshia. *Guadalupe in New York: Devotion and the Struggle for Citizenship Rights among Mexican Immigrants.* New York: New York University Press, 2009.

Gause III, F. Gregory. "Who Lost Middle Eastern Studies?" [review essay]. *Foreign Affairs* 81 n. 2 (2002): 164-168.

Gauthier, Tim S. "Narratives about the Falling Persons of 9/11."
    September 11 in Popular Culture: A Guide, edited by Sara E. Quay
    and Amy M. Damico. 114. Santa Barbara: Greenwood, 2010.
Gee, James Paul. *An Introduction to Discourse Analysis: Theory and
    Method*. New York: Routledge, 2005.
Gelvin, James. *The Modern Middle East: A History*. 3rd edition. New
    York: Oxford University Press, 2011.
Gerges, Fawaz A. "A Time of Reckoning," Op-Ed. *New York Times*.
    October 8, 2001. Accessed August 9, 2013.
    http://www.nytimes.com/2001/10/08/opinion/08GERG.html
George Mason University. *Center for History and New Media*. George
    Mason University.
    http://911digitalarchive.org/repository.php?collection_id=12438.
Gettleman, Marvin and Stuart Schaar, editors. *The Middle East and
    Islamic World Reader*. New York: Grove Press, 2003.
Gibson, William. *Pattern Recognition*. New York: Putnam, 2003.
Gilroy, Paul. *Postcolonial Melancholia*. New York: Columbia University
    Press, 2005.
Gilyard, Keith. "Composition and the Critical Moment." In *Composition
    Studies in the New Millennium: Rereading the Past, Rewriting the
    Future*, edited by Lynn Z. Bloom, Donald A. Daiker, and Edward M.
    White. 227-236. Carbondale: Southern Illinois University Press.
Glantz, James and Eric Lipton. *City in the Sky: The Rise and Fall of the
    World Trade Center*. New York: Holt, 2003.
Goizueta, Roberto S. "Fiesta: Life in the Subjunctive." In *From the Heart
    of Our People: Latino/a Explorations in Catholic Systematic Theology*,
    edited by Orlando O. Espín and Miguel H. Díaz. 84-99. Maryknoll,
    N.Y.: Orbis Books, 1999).
Goldberg, Howard G. "Windows on the World: The Wine Community's
    True North." *The Wine News*. October-November, 2001. Accessed July
    30, 2013. www.thewinenews.com/oct-nov01/comment.html.
Goldschmidt, Arthur. *A Concise History of the Middle East*. 2nd edition.
    Boulder, Col.: Westview Press, 1983.
—. *A Concise History of the Middle East*. 3rd edition. Boulder, Col.:
    Westview Press, 1988.
Goldschmidt, Arthur, and Lawrence Davidson. *A Concise History of the
    Middle East*. 5th edition. Boulder, Col.: Westview Press, 1996.
Kenniston, Ann and Jeane Follisbee Quinn. *Literature after 9/11*. New
    York: Routledge, 2008.
Lawrence Davidson. *A Concise History of the Middle East*. 7th edition.
    Boulder, Col.: Westview Press, 2002.

Graff, Gerald. "To Debate or Not to Debate Intelligent Design?" *Inside Higher Ed.* September 28, 2005. Accessed December 30, 2011. http://www.insidehighered.com/views/2005/09/28/graf.

Graham, Fiona. "Finding faces in the clouds." *The Daily Telegraph.* April 30, 2003. Accessed August 2, 2013. http://www.telegraph.co.uk/culture/donotmigrate/3593416/Finding-faces-in-the-clouds.html#.

Gray, Richard. *After The Fall: American Literature Since 9/11.* Oxford: Wiley Blackwell, 2011.

—. "Open Doors, Closed Minds: American Prose Writing in a Time of Crisis." *American Literary History* 21 n. 1 (2009): 128-48.

Greenberg, Miriam. "The Limits of Branding: The World Trade Center, Fiscal Crisis and the Marketing of Recovery." *International Journal of Urban and Regional Research* 27 n. 2 (2003): 386-416.

Greenhouse, Steven. "Windows on the World Workers Say Their Boss Didn't Do Enough." *New York Times*, June 4, 2002. Accessed July 30, 2013. www.nytimes.com/2002/06/04/-nyregion/windows-on-the-world-workers-say-their-boss-didn-t-do-enough.html?src=pm.

Grider, Sylvia. "Spontaneous Shrines: A Modern Response to Tragedy and Disaster." *New Directions in Folklore* 5 (2001): 1-10.

Grigg, William N. "The Civil Religion and the Seventh-Inning Stretch." *Pro Libertate Blog.* July 7, 2009. Accessed July 30, 2013. http://freedominourtime.blogspot.com/2009/07/civil-religion-and-seventh-inning.html.

Gschwandtner, Sabrina. "Passage Quilts." *Fiberarts.* November/December (2008): 48-51.

Guibernau, Montserrat. *The Identity of Nations.* Cambridge: Polity Press, 2007.

Hall, James with Barbara Kevles. *In Opposition to Core Curriculum: Alternative Models for Undergraduate Education.* Westport, Conn: Greenwood Press, 1982.

Halliday, Fred. *Two Hours That Shook the World: September 11 2001, Causes and Consequences.* London: Saqi Books, 2001.

—. "9/11 and Middle Eastern Studies Part and Future: Revisiting Ivory Towers on Sand." *International Affairs* 80 n. 5 (2004): 953-962.

Harper, Jennifer. "Texas School Officials: State Curriculum Had Nothing to do with Controversial 9/11 Quiz." *The Washington Times.* March 22, 2013. Accessed June 28, 2013. http://www.washingtontimes.com/blog/watercooler/2013/mar/22/texas-school-curriculum-suggests-us-was-responsibl/.

Hartocollis, Anemona. "9/11, a Man Went to Work: His Fate Is a Mystery." *New York Times.* May 9, 2002. Accessed July 30, 2013. www.nytimes.com/2002/05/09/nyregion/9-11-a-man-went-to-work-his-fate-is-a-mystery.html.

Harvey, David. *Cosmopolitanism and the Geographies of Freedom.* New York: Columbia University Press, 2009.

Haulley, Fletcher. *Critical Perspectives on 9/11: Critical Anthologies of Nonfiction.* New York: Rosen Publishing Group, 2005.

Hawkins, Peter S. "Naming Names: The Art of Memory and the NAMES Project AIDS Quilt." *Critical Inquiry* 19 n. 4 (1993): 752-79.

Hayles, N. Katherine. "Traumas of Code." *Critical Inquiry* 33 n. 1 (Autumn 2006):136-157.

Healy, Josh. "Martín Espada—'Alabanza: In Praise of Local 100.'" *The Progressive*, September 2010. Accessed July 30, 2013. http://progressive.org/video092010.html.

Hershberg, Eric. *Critical Views of September 11: Analyses from around the World.* New York: New Press, 2002.

Higginson, T. W. "A Bit of War Photography." *The Philistine* 3 n. 2 (July 1896): 33-38.

Hiss, Tony. "The New York Region Had Found a Centering Point." *New York Times.* September 16, 2001. Accessed via ProQuest Historical Newspapers: http://search.proquest.com/docview/431871289?accountid=12084.

Hocks, Mary E. and Michelle R. Kendrick, editors. *Eloquent Images: Word and Image in the Age of New Media*, edited by Mary E. Hocks and Michelle R. Kendrick. Cambridge, Mass.: MIT Press, 2003.

Howells, William Dean. "Reviews and Literary Notices." *Atlantic Monthly.* July 1867, p. 121.

Howie, Luke. *Terror on the Screen: Witnesses and the Reanimation of 9/11 as Image-Event, Popular Culture, and Pornography.* Washington, D.C.: New Academia Publishing, 2010.

Inglis, Ken S. "The Homecoming: The War Memorial Movement in Cambridge, England." *Journal of Contemporary History* 27 n. 4 (1992): 583-605.

Jacobson, Sid and Ernie Colón. *The 9/11 Report: A Graphic Adaptation.* New York: Hill and Wang, 2006.

"Joe Torre: MLB Denial of Mets' 9/11 First Responder Caps 'A Unanimity Thing'." *CBS New York.* September 12, 2011. Accessed July 30, 2013. http://newyork.cbslocal.com/2011/09/12/joe-torre-mlb-denial-of-mets-911-first-responder-caps-a-unanimity-thing/

Jones, Cleve and Jeff Dawson. *Stitching a Revolution: How the Quilt Put a Human Face on AIDS and Brought Healing to a Nation.* San Francisco, Cal.: Harper San Francisco, 2000.

Junod, Tom. "The Falling Man." *Women & Performance: A Journal of Feminist Theory* 14 n. 1 (2004): 211-227,

Jurs, Laurie. "Community Columnist: Remember Everybody from the 9/11 Tragedy." *Green Valley News and Sun.* September 10, 2011. Accessed July 30, 2013. http://www.gvnews.com/opinion/letters_to_editor/community-columnist-remember-everybody-from-the-tragedy/article_ad9313d0-dc03-11e0-ba38-001cc4c002e0.html.

Kacendes, Irene Kacendes. "9/11/01=1/27/01: The Changed Posttraumatic Self." In *Trauma at Home: After 9/11*, edited Judith Greenberg. 166-186. Lincoln: University of Nebraska Press, 2003.

Kahane, Claire. "Uncanny Sights: The Anticipation of the Abomination." In *Trauma at Home: After 9/11*, edited by Judith Greenberg. 107-116. Lincoln: University of Nebraska Press, 2003.

Kakutani, Michiko. "Books of the Times; A Hero with 9/11 Peripheral Vision." *The New York Times.* March 18 2005. Accessed August 2, 2013. http://query.nytimes.com/gst/fullpage.html?res=9E01E0DD103CF93B A25750C0A9639C8B63.

Kantz, Barbara. "Promises Kept: Empire State College on its Twenty-Fifth Anniversary." *Long Island Historical Journal* 10 n. 1 (1997): 56-70.

Kauffman, Linda S. "World Trauma Center." *American Literary History* 21 n. 3 (2009): 647-659.

Keeble, Arin. "Marriage, Relationships, and 9/11: The Seismographic Narratives of *Falling Man, The Good Life,* and *The Emperor's Children.*" *Modern Language Review* 106 n. 2 (April 2011): 355-73.

Keh, Andrew. "A 9/11 Gesture Curtailed." *New York Times.* September 11, 2011. Accessed July 30, 2013. http://bats.blogs.nytimes.com/2011/09/11/a-911-gesture-curtailed/.

Kermode, Frank. *The Sense of an Ending.* Oxford: Oxford University Press, 2000 (1967).

Klein, Alan M. *Baseball on the Border: A Tale of Two Laredos.* Princeton, N.J.: Princeton University Press, 1997.

Klingmann, Anna. *Brandscapes: Architecture in the Experience Economy.* Cambridge, Mass.: MIT Press, 2007.

Kohari, Alizeh Kohari. "Is there a novel that defines the 9/11 decade?" *BBC News.* August 28, 2011. Accessed August 2, 2013. http://www.bbc.co.uk/news/entertainment-arts-14682741.

Knowles, M. S. *Andragogy in Action: Applying Modern Principles of Adult Education*. San Francisco, Cal.: Jossey Bass, 1984.

Kramer, Martin. "Terrorism? What Terrorism?!" *Wall Street Journal*. November 15, 2001. Accessed August 11, 2011. http://www.meforum.org/96/terrorism-what-terrorism.

Krase, Jerome. "Polish and Italian Vernacular Landscapes in Brooklyn." *Polish American Studies* 54 n. 1(1997): 9-31.

—. "Navigating Ethnic Vernacular Landscapes Then and Now." *Journal of Architecture and Planning Research* 19 n. 4 (2002): 274-81.

—. *Seeing Cities Change: Local Culture and Class*. Aldershot, UK: Ashgate, 2012.

Krieger, Susan. *Social Science and the Self: Personal Essay as Art Form*. New Brunswick, N.J.: Rutgers University Press, 1991.

Kristeva, Julia. *Powers of Horror: An Essay on Abjection*, translated by Leon S. Roudiez. New York: Columbia University Press, 1982.

Krone, Carolyn H. and Thomas M. Horner. "Quilting and Bereavement: Her Grief in the Quilt." *Uncoverings* 13 (1992): 109-126.

Kurkjian, Tim. "Wearing Hats Symbolic Gesture by Mets." *ESPN New York*. September 11, 2011. Accessed September 12, 2011. http://espn.go.com/new-york/mlb/story/_/id/6957532/new-york-mets-symbolic-gesture-united-people-sept-11

Labriola, John. *Walking Forward, Looking Back: Lessons from the World Trade Center—A Survivor's Story*. Irvington, N.Y.: Hylas, 2003.

La Marche, Jean. "The Familiar and the Unfamiliar in Twentieth-Century Architecture." *Visual Studies* 19 n. 2 (2005): 195-99.

Latour, Bruno with Albena Yaneva. "Give Me a Gun and I Will Make All Buildings Move: An Ant's View of Architecture." In *Explorations in Architecture: Teaching, Design, Research*, edited by R. Geiser. 80-89. Basel: Birkhäuser, 2008.

Laub, Dori. "September 11, 2001—An Event without a Voice." In *Trauma at Home: After 9/11*, edited by Judith Greenberg. 204-2015. Lincoln: University of Nebraska Press, 2003.

Lazere, Donald. "Stanley Fish's Tightrope Act." *College English* 71 n. 5 (2009): 530-531.

Lent, John A. "[The 9/11 Report]." *International Journal of Comic Art* 11 n. 1 (2009): 524-526.

Levinas, Emmanuel. *Time and the Other*, translated by Richard A. Cohen. Pittsburgh, Penn..: Duquesne University Press, 1987.

Lincoln, Abraham. "Gettysburg Address." *Electronic Text Center*. University of Virginia. Accessed August 9, 2013.

http://etext.virginia.edu/etcbin/toccernew2?id=LinGett.sgm&images=i
mages/modeng&data=/texts/english/modeng/parsed&tag=public&part
=1&division=div1. Accessed August 2, 2013.

Lindner, Christoph. "New York Vertical: Reflections on the Modern Skyline." *American Studies* 47 n. 1 (2006): 31-52.

Living Memorials Project. Accessed July 31, 2013. http://www.livingmemorialsproject.net/.

Lockman, Zachary. *Contending Visions of the Middle East: The History and Politics of Orientalism.* Cambridge: Cambridge University Press, 2004.

Lopresti, Mike. "New York Athletes, Coaches Remember 9/11." *USA Today.* September 1, 2011. Accessed July 30, 2013. http://www.usatoday.com/sports/story/2011-08-31/New-York-athletes-coaches-remember911/50208244/1.

Lower Manhattan Development Corporation. *World Trade Center Site Memorial Competition Guidelines.* New York: 2003.

Luciano, Dana. *Arranging Grief: Sacred Time and the Body in Nineteenth Century America.* New York: New York University Press, 2007.

Luft, Rachel E. "Looking for Common Ground: Relief Work in Post-Katrina New Orleans as an American Parable of Race and Gender Violence." *NWSA Journal* 20 n. 3 (2008): 5-31.

Luliano, Fiorenzo. "Falling from the Past: Geographies of Exceptionalism in Two Novels by Jay McInerney." *Altre Modernità* (2011), 103.

Mackay, Ruth Mackay. "'Going Backward in Time to Talk about the Present': *Man on Wire* and Verticality after 9/11." *Comparative American Studies* 9 n. 1 (2011): 3-20.

Mackenzie, Catriona. "Imagining Oneself Otherwise." In *Relational Autonomy: Feminist Perspectives on Autonomy*, edited by Catriona Mackenzie and Natalie Stoljar. 124-150. New York: Oxford University Press, 2000.

Malinowitz, Harriet. "The Uses of Literacy in a Globalized, Post September 11th World." In *Composition Studies in the New Millennium: Rereading the Past, Rewriting the Future*, edited by Lynn Z. Bloom, Donald A. Daiker, and Edward M. White. 237-251. Carbondale: Southern Illinois University Press.

Man on Wire. DVD. Directed by James Marsh. 2008. Magnolia Home Entertainment. New York.

Mayhew, Lewis. *Legacy of the Seventies.* San Francisco, Cal.: Jossey-Bass Publishers, 1977.

McCann, Colum. *Let the Great World Spin.* New York: Random House, 2009.

McGeehan, Patrick. "Bill Would Provide Federal Funds for 9/11 Memorial." *New York Times on the Web.* September 13, 2011. Accessed May 20, 2012. http://cityroom.blogs.nytimes.com/2011/09/13/bill-would-provide-federal-funds-for-911-memorial/.

McInerney, Jay. *The Good Life.* New York: Knopf, 2006.

—. "Interview: The Browser." Accessed August 2, 2013. http://thebrowser.com/interviews/jay-mcinerney-on-essential-new-york-novels?page=full.

Melnick, Jeffrey. *9/11 Culture: Under Construction.* West Sussex: Wiley-Blackwell, 2009.

"Memorial service set for Ground Zero." *CNN.com/U.S,* October 28, 2001. Accessed May 20, 2012. http://edition.cnn.com/2001/US/10/28/rec.giuliani.memorial/index.html.

Menand, Louis. "The Earthquake: A Manhattan Affair." *The New Yorker.* February 2006. http://www.newyorker.com/archive/2006/02/06/060206crbo_books1?currentPage=all. Accessed August 2, 2013.

Merrill, Christopher. "A Kind of Solution." *Virginia Quarterly Review* 80 n. 4 (Fall 2004): 68-83.

"Mets Plan Special Night as Baseball Returns to NYC." Accessed July 30, 2013. http://www.gameops.com/features/essay-writers/mets-911.

"Mets/Phillies Fans Learn of Osama Bin Laden's Death, Erupt in 'USA' Chants." *CBS New York.* May 2, 2011. Accessed July 30, 2013. http://newyork.cbslocal.com/2011/05/02/fans-erupt-in-usa-chants-during-metsphillies-game-after-learning-of-osama-bin-laden-killing/.

Migdal, Joel S. "Review of Ivory Towers on Sand." *International Journal of Middle East Studies* 35 n. 1 (February 2003): 203.

Miller, D. W. "Middle East-Studies Programs Are Accused of Scholarly Orthodoxy." *Chronicle of Higher Education.* October 26, 2001.

Minzesheimer, Bob. "9/11 gets a graphic retelling—Style makes official report 'accessible.'" *USA Today.* August 22, 2006, final ed.: D1.

Mitchell, W. J. T. "9/11: Criticism and Crisis." *Critical Inquiry* 28 n. 2 (2002)67-572.

"MLB World Series: Cardinals v. Tigers" *ASAP Sports.* October 24, 2006. Accessed July 30, 2013. http://www.asapsports.com/show_interview.php?id=39774.

Mooney, Nell. "Nell Mooney." In *Tower Stories: An Oral History of 9/11*, edited by Damon DiMarco. 112-117. Santa Monica, Cal.: Santa Monica Press, 2007.

Morely, Catherine. "'How Do We Write About This?' The Domestic and the Global in the Post-9/11 Novel." *Journal of American Studies* 45 n. 4 (2011): 717-31.

Morrison, Toni. "The Dead of September 11." *Vanity Fair.* November 2001. 48.

Mottahedeh, Roy. "Islam and the Opposition to Terrorism." Op-Ed. *New York Times.* September 30, 2001. Accessed August 9, 2013. http://www.nytimes.com/2001/09/30/opinion/islam-and-the-opposition-to-terrorism.html

Museum of the City of New York. *Online Collections.* Accessed July 7, 2013 http://collections.mcny.org.

Nanko-Fernández, Carmen. *Theologizing en Espanglish: Context, Community and Ministry.* Maryknoll, N.Y.: Orbis, 2010.

—. "Creation: A Cosmo-politan Perspective." In *In Our Own Voices: Latino/a Renditions of Theology,* edited by Benjamin Valentin. 41-63. Maryknoll, N.Y.: Orbis, 2010.

—. *¡El Santo! Baseball and the Canonization of Roberto Clemente.* Macon, Ga.: Mercer University Press, forthcoming.

National September 11 Memorial and Museum. Accessed July 30, 2013. http://names.911memorial.org/#lang=en_US&page=search.

Nelson, Marla, Marla, Renia Ehrenfeucht, and Shirley Laska. "Planning, Plans, and People: Professional Expertise, Local Knowledge, and Governmental Action in Post-Hurricane Katrina New Orleans." *Cityscape: A Journal of Policy Development and Research* 9 n. 3 (2007): 23-52.

New York: A Documentary Film. Directed by Ric Burns. 2003. PBS Television. Washington, D.C.

New York Public Library. *Digital Gallery.* Accessed April 23, 2012 and July 7, 2013, http://digitalgallery.nypl.org.

New York Public Library. *Lewis Wickes Hine: The Construction of the Empires State Building, 1930-1931.* Accessed July 7, 2013. http://www.nypl.org/research/chss/spe/art/photo/hinex/empire/empire.html

Nussbaum, Martha. *For Love of Country?* Boston, Mass.: Beacon, 1996.

"NYC 9/11 Memorial Popular Among Tourists." *NJ.com.* December 29, 2011. Accessed March 22, 2012. http://www.nj.com/news/index.ssf/2011/12/nyc_911_memorial_popular_among.html.

Ochsenwald, William and Sydney Nettleton Fisher, *The Middle East: A History.* 6th edition. New York: Knopf, 2004.

"On 9/11 and the Politics of Language: An Interview with Martín Espada."
Solidarity. September/October, 2011. Accessed July 30, 2013.
http://www.solidarity-us.org/node/3350.

"Opening Day rosters feature 241 players born outside the U.S." *MLB Press Release.* April 1, 2013. Accessed July 30, 2013.
http://mlb.mlb.com/news/article.jsp?ymd=20130401&content_id=4361
8468&vkey=pr_mlb&c_id=mlb.

Oz, Amos. *How to Cure a Fanatic.* Princeton, N.J.: Princeton University Press, 2006.

"Past Exhibitions: September 11, 2001: The Bellevue Wall of Prayer."
Museum of the City of New York. Accessed May 20, 2012.
http://www.mcny.org/exhibitions/past/453.html.

Pattison, Mark. "Papal Masses at Baseball Stadiums Not New to U.S. Catholics." *Catholic News Service.* April 17, 2008. Accessed July 30, 2013. http://www.catholicnews.com/data/stories/cns/0802087.htm.

Pease, Donald. *The New American Exceptionalism.* Minneapolis: University of Minnesota Press, 2006.

Petit, Philippe. *Man on Wire.* 2nd edition. New York: Skyhorse Publishing, 2008.

Post Robert."I ntroduction." In *Another Cosmopolitanism*, edited by Seyla Benhabib. 1-9. Oxford: Oxford University Press, 2006.

Prichard, Sue. *Quilts 1700-2010: Hidden Histories, Untold Stories.* London: V&A Publishing, 2010.

Pustz, Matthew. *Comic Book Culture: Fanboys and True Believers.* Jackson: University Press of Mississippi, 1999.

Radstone, Susannah. "What Place is This?: Transcultural Memory and The Location of Memory Studies." *Parallax* 17 n. 4 (Oct-Dec 2011): 109-23.

Rauf, Feisal Abdul. "Interview by Narayan Lakshman." *The Hindu*, 2011.

Rawls, John. *A Theory of Justice.* Cambridge, Mass.: Belknap-Harvard, 1971.

Raz, Guy. "Jonathan Franzen takes the long road to *Freedom*," *NPR.* September 11 2010. Accessed August 2, 2013.
http://www.npr.org/templates/story/story.php?storyId=129799680.

Redfield, Marc. *The Rhetoric of Terror: Reflections on 9/11 and the War on Terror.* New York: Fordham University Press, 2009.

Regel, Stephen and Stephen Joseph. *Post-traumatic Stress.* Oxford: Oxford University Press, 2010.

"Relief and Reconstruction: The Year in Review, Part I." *Center for Economic and Policy Research.* January 7, 2011. Accessed July 1,

2012. http://www.cepr.net/index.php/blogs/relief-and-reconstruction-watch/relief-and-reconstruction-the-year-in-review-part-i.

"Remembering 9/11: Ten Years Later." *National Association of Independent Colleges and Universities.* Accessed July 31, 2013. http://www.naicu.edu/special_initiatives/remembering-911-ten-years-later.

Remembering Vietnam: The Wall at 25. Produced and Written by Lynn Kessler. 2007. A Smithsonian Channel Production.

Remen, Rachel Naomi. *Kitchen Table Wisdom: Stories That Heal.* New York: Riverhead Books, 1996.

Remnick, David, editor. "Talk of the Town." *The New Yorker.* September 24, 2001. Accessed August 2, 2013. http://www.newyorker.com/archive/2001/09/24/010924ta_talk_wtc.

Reynolds, Amy and Brooke Barnett. "'America under Attack': CNN's Verbal and Visual Framing of September 11." In *Media Representations of September 11*, edited by Steven Chermak, Frankie Y. Bailey, and Michelle Brown. 85-101. Westport, Connecticut: Praeger, 2003.

Rhoden, William. "Delgado Makes a Stand by Taking a Seat." *New York Times.* July 21, 2004. Accessed July 30, 2013. http://www.nytimes.com/2004/07/21/sports/baseball/21rhoden.html.

Rising: Rebuilding Ground Zero. Written by Jessica Lyne de Ve and Kate Cohen. Directed by David Nutter. Discovery Channel. August 25, 2011.

Robbins, Bruce W. *Cosmopolitanism from the Viewpoint of Violence.* Durham, N.C.: Duke University Press, 2012.

Roberts, Elise Schebler, et. al. *The Quilt: History and Celebration of an Art Form.* Minneapolis, Minn.: Voyageur Press, 2007.

Rosenblatt, Louise. *The Reader, the Text, and the Poem.* Carbondale: Southern Illinois Press, 1978.

Rothberg, Michael. "A Failure of the Imagination: Diagnosing the Post-9/11 Novel: A Response to Richard Gray." *American Literary History* 21 n. 1 (2009): 152-158.

Rubin, Adam. "Delgado Meets the Mets in PR." *New York Daily News.* January 14, 2005. Accessed July 30, 2013. http://articles.nydailynews.com/2005-01-14/sports/18292674_1_agent-david-sloane-jeff-wilpon-mets-gm.

Ruiz, Albor. "Time is Right to Revive Post-9/11 Attack Solidarity." *New York Daily News.* May 4, 2011. Access July 30, 2013. http://articles.nydailynews.com/2011-05-04/local/29523635_1_undocumented-immigrants-attacks-families

Ruskin, Cindy. *The Quilt: Stories from the NAMES Project.* New York: Pocket Books, 1988.

Safe Horizen. Accessed July 1, 2012. www.safehorizon.org.

Saussure, Ferdinand de. *Course in General Linguistics,* translated by Roy Harris. *(New* York: The Philosophical Library Inc., 1959 (1998).

Savage, Kirk. *Monument Wars: Washington D.C., the National Mall and the Transformation of the Memorial Landscape.* Berkeley: University of California Press, 2009.

—. "Faces of the dead." *kirksavage.pitt.edu.* August 6, 2011. Accessed May 20, 2012. http://www.kirksavage.pitt.edu/?p=209.

Scheper-Hughes, Nancy. "Katrina: The Disaster and its Doubles." *Anthropology Today* 21 n. 6 (2005): 2-4.

Schmemann, Serge. "President Vows to Exact Punishment for 'Evil'." *New York Times.* September 12, 2001: A1+.

Schopp, Andrew. "Pedagogy in the Land of the Lost: Negotiating 9/11 Fatigue when Teaching 9/11." *Modern Language Studies* 41 n. 1 (2011): 59.

Schuetz, Albert. "Common-sense and Scientific Interpretation of Human Action." In *Collected Papers. Vol. 1 The Problem of Social,* edited by Albert Schuetz. 3-47. Reality. The Hague: Martinus Nijhoff, 1971.

Schuller, Mark. "Haiti's Disaster after the Disaster: The IDP Camps and Cholera." *The Journal of Humanitarian Assistance.* December 13, 2010. Accessed July 15, 2013. http://sites.tufts.edu/jha/archives/869.

—. *Mèt Kò Veye Kò: Foreign responsibility in the failure to protect against cholera and other man-made disasters.* January 22, 2011. Accessed July 15, 2013. http://ijdh.org/wordpress/wp-content/uploads/2011/01/Report-met-ko-veye-ko-final.pdf

Schwartz, Lynne S. *The Writing on the Wall: A Novel.* New York: Counterpoint, 2005.

Scott, A. O. Scott. "Film Review: Pinned Under the Weight of Shattered Towers, and 9/11 History." *New York Times.* August 9, 2006. Accessed August 2, 2013. http://movies.nytimes.com/2006/08/09/movies/09worl.html?pagewante d=all&_r=0

Scott, Janny and Howell Raines, editors. *Portraits: 9/11/01.* 2nd edition. New York: Times, 2003.

Scranton, Philip. *Beyond September 11: An Anthology of Dissent.* London: Pluto Press, 2002.

Segovia, Fernando F. *Decolonizing Biblical Studies: A View from the Margins.* Maryknoll, N.Y.: Orbis Books, 2000.

Sen, Rinku with Fekkak Mamdouh, *The Accidental American: Immigration and Citizenship in the Age of Globalization*. San Francisco, Cal.: Berrett-Koehle, 2008.

"September 11: Bearing Witness to History: The Collection." *Smithsonian Institute*. September 29, 2011. Accessed May 20, 2012. http://americanhistory.si.edu/september11/collection/about.asp.

Shaler, Robert C. *Who They Were: Inside the World Trade Center DNA Story: The Unprecedented Effort to Identify the Missing*. New York: Free, 2005.

Shanker, Andrew M. "Planning Memory: Living Memorials in the United States during World War II." *The Art Bulletin* 84 n. 1: (2002): 130-47.

Siefer, Ted. "Foer's new novel looks at Sept. 11," *The Jewish Advocate*. April 14, 2006. 19.

Sielke, Sabine. "Why '9/11 is [not] unique' or Troping Trauma." *Amerikanstudien* 55 n. 3 (2010): 385-410.

Silver, Lauren J. "Spaces of Encounter: Public Bureaucracy and the Making of Client Identities." *ETHOS* 38 n. 3 (2010): 275-296.

Simpson, David. *9/11: The Culture of Commemoration*. Chicago, Ill.: University of Chicago Press, 2006.

Sims, Ami. *Alzheimer's: Forgetting Piece by Piece*. Flint, Mich..: Mallory Press, 2007.

Smith, Neil. "Wire-walk Film Omits 9/11 Tragedy." *BBC News*. August 2, 2008. Accessed September 8, 2011. http://news.bbc.co.uk/2/hi/entertainment/7498364.stm,

Sontag, Susan. *On Photography*. New York: Picador, 1977.

—. *Regarding the Pain of Others*. New York: Picador, 2003.

Sorel, Edward. "The Towering Insanity." *New York Magazine*. December 30, 1975.

Spalding, Albert G. *America's National Game: Historical Facts Concerning the Beginning, Evolution, Development and Popularity of Base Ball*. New York: American Sports Publishing Company, 1911. Accessed July 30, 2013. http://archive.org/details/cu31924029949579.

Spiegelman, Art. *In the Shadow of No Towers*. New York: Viking Adult, 2008.

Spellmeyer, Kurt. *Arts of Living: Reinventing the Humanities for the Twenty-First Century*. Albany: State University of New York Press, 2003.

Stevens, Quentin and Karen A. Franck. *Memorials as Spaces of Engagement: Memorial Design, Use and Meaning*. London: Routledge, forthcoming.

Strauss, David Levi. *Between the Eyes: Essays on Photography and Politics*. New York: Aperture, 2003.

Street, Jim. "Emotions Flowed as Games Returned" September 9, 2002. Accessed July 30, 2013. http://mlb.mlb.com/news/article.jsp?ymd=20020909&content_id=1245 85&vkey=news_mlb&fext=.jsp&c_id=null.

Sullivan, Neil J. *The Diamond in the Bronx: Yankee Stadium and the Politics of New York*. New York: Oxford University Press, 2001.

Szymanski, Stefan and Andrew Zimbalist, *National Pastime: How Americans Play Baseball and the Rest of the World Plays Soccer*. Washington, D.C.: Brookings Institute Press, 2005.

Talbott, Strobe and Nayan Chanda. *The Age of Terror: America and the World after September 11*. Basic Books: New York, 2002.

Tallack, Douglas. *New York Sights: Visualizing Old and New New York*. New York: Berg, 2005.

Taylor, Charles. *Modern Social Imaginaries*. Durham, N.C.: Duke University Press, 2004.

Telhami, Shibley. "The Mideast is also Changed." Op-Ed. *New York Times*. September 19, 2001. Accessed August 9, 2013. http://www.nytimes.com/2001/09/19/opinion/the-mideast-is-also-changed.html

"Ten Years Later, 9/11 remembered on WUSTL campus is a variety of ways." *Washington University in St. Louis*. Accessed July 31, 2013. http://news.wustl.edu/news/Pages/22648.aspx.

The 25ᵗʰ Hour. Directed by Spike Lee. 2002. 25ᵗʰ Hour Productions. 2002.

Thomson Reuters. "New York Set for Record 50 Million Tourists." December 20, 2011. Accessed March 22, 2012. http://www.reuters.com/article/2011/12/20/us-travel-newyork-idUSTRE7BJ1WQ20111220.

Thomson Reuters. "Plan for 9/11 remains disturbs relatives of the dead." *msnbc.com*. March 9, 2012. Accessed May 20, 2012. http://today.msnbc.msn.com/id/41741280/ns/today-entertainment/t/plan-remains-disturbs-relatives-dead/#.T9jUFu1-S20.

Toohey, Peter. "The Cultural Logic of Historical Periodization." In *Handbook of historical sociology*, edited by Gerard Delanty. 208-220. London: SAGE Publications, 2003.

Torres, Alissa. *American Widow*, illustrated by Sungyoon Cho. New York: Villard, 2008.

Torres, Gabriel. "Gabriel Torres." In *Tower Stories: An Oral History of 9/11*, edited by Damon DiMarco. 100-111. Santa Monica, Cal.: Santa Monica Press, 2007.

Travis, Jennifer. *Wounded Hearts: Masculinity, Law, and Literature in American Culture.* Chapel Hill: University of North Carolina Press, 2005.

Trilling, Lionel. *The Liberal Imagination.* New York: Doubleday, 1953.

Tyson, Ann Scott. "From London to Los Angeles, the world stood still." *Christian Science Monitor.* September 20, 2001: 1+.

Updike, John. "The Talk of the Town." *New Yorker.* September 24, 2001.

—. "Mixed Messages." *The New Yorker.* March 14, 2005.

USS New York LPD-21. 2011. Accessed May 20, 2012. www.ussnewyork.com.

Vanderlinden, Lisa K. "Left in the Dust: Negotiating Environmental Illness in the Aftermath of 9/11." *Medical Anthropology: Cross-Cultural Studies in Health and Illness* 30 n. 1 (2011): 30-55.

Versaci, Rocco. *This Book Contains Graphic Language: Comics As Literature.* New York: Continuum, 2007.

Versulys, Kristiaan. *Out of the Blue: September 11 and the Novel.* New York: Columbia University Press, 2009.

Voices of September 11th. Accessed July 31, 2013. http://voicesofseptember11.org/dev/content.php?idtocitems=1,6

Võsu, Ester and Ene Kõresaar and Kristin Kuutma. "Preface. Mediation of Memory: Towards Transdisciplinary Perspectives in Current Memory Studies." *Trames* 12 n. 3 (2008): 243–263.

Vygotsky, Lev S. *Mind in Society: The Development of Higher Psychological Processes,* edited by Michael Cole, Sylvia Scribner, Ellen Soubermann, and Vera John-Steiner. Cambridge, Mass.: Harvard University Press, 1978.

Wallace, David Foster. "The View from Mrs. Thompson's," *Consider the Lobster.* 128-140. London: Abacus, 2005.

Weiss, Elliot. "Packaging Jewishness: Novelty and Tradition in Kosher Food Packaging." *Design Issues* 20 n. 1 (2004): 48-61.

White, Andrea. *Windows on the World: The UpCity Chronicles.* South Hampton, N.H.: Namelos, 2011.

White, E. B. *Here is New York.* New York: Little Bookroom, 2000.

Whitmore, William R. "The Vicar of Christ and the House that Ruth Built: Papal Masses at Yankee Stadium." Senior Thesis, Princeton Theological Seminary, 2013.

Wilson, Edmund. *Patriotic Gore: Studies in the Literature of the American Civil War.* Boston: Northeastern University Press, 1995.

World Trade Center. Directed by Oliver Stone. 2006. Paramount Pictures.

Willimon, Will. "How Evangelical Leaders Have Changed Since 9/11." *Christianity Today.* September, 5, 2011. Accessed July 30, 2013.

http://www.christianitytoday.com/ct/2011/september/howleaderschang
ed.html?start=5.%20Accessed

World Trade Center in Movies. Accessed April 19, 2012.
http://wtcinmovies.tripod.com.

Wright, Lawrence. In *The Looming Tower: Al-Qaeda and the Road to 9/11*. Vintage: New York, 2006.

Yellon, Al. "MLB Forbids Mets To Wear New York Tribute Caps." *Baseball Nation*. September 11, 2011. Accessed July 30, 2013. http://mlb.sbnation.com/2011/9/11/2419367/mlb-forbids-mets-nypd-nyfd-tribute-caps.

Young, Michael. "A Frenchman Fries Middle East Studies in the U.S." *Reason*. December 29, 2004. Accessed July 31, 2013. http://www.campus-watch.org/article/id/1485.

Zarroli, Jim. "Memorial Service at Ground Zero," *npr.org*. October 28, 2001. Accessed May 20, 2012. http://www.npr.org/templates/story/story.php?storyId=1132260.

Zelizer, Barbie, *About to Die: How News Images Move the Public*. Oxford: Oxford University Press, 2010.

Zirin, Dave. "The Silencing of Carlos Delgado." *The Nation*. December 7, 2005. Accessed July 30, 2013. http://www.thenation.com/article/silencing-carlos-delgado#.

Žižek, Slavoj. *Welcome to the Desert of the Real*. London: Verso, 2002.

Zolecki, Todd. "Philadelphia Freedom: Game Takes Backseat." May 2, 2011. Accessed July 30, 2013. http://mlb.mlb.com/news/article.jsp?ymd=20110501&content_id=1847 9234&vkey=news_nym&c_id=nym.

Zraly, Kevin. *Windows on the World Complete Wine Course: 2003 Edition—A Lively Guide*. New York: Sterling, 2003.

CONTRIBUTORS

Barrett P. Brenton is Professor of Anthropology and is a Senior Research Fellow in the Vincentian Center for Church and Society as well as Director of the Center for Global Development at St. John's University. In addition to his work on social justice and food sovereignty issues, he has conducted fieldwork on the response of organizational cultures to disaster and the forensic anthropology of landscapes of violence.

Joseph Donica is an Assistant Professor of English at Wiley College. He received his Ph.D. candidate in English at Southern Illinois University. His dissertation explored the subject of existential utopia after 9/11 and Hurricane Katrina. He has published articles on 9/11 fiction, American architecture after 9/11, and the fiction of Edward P. Jones.

Robert Fanuzzi is Associate Professor of English at St. John's University. He received his Ph.D. from Northwestern University. His main area of research is the American and trans-Atlantic antislavery movements of the eighteenth and nineteenth centuries. His many scholarly articles and essays have appeared in such journals as *American Literature and American Literary History*, and in the essay anthology, *The Black Press: New Literary and Historical Essays*. His book, *Abolition's Public Sphere* (Minnesota University Press, 2003), is a study of William Lloyd Garrison, Frederick Douglass, Henry David Thoreau, and the print culture of the New England abolition movement.

Karen A. Franck is Professor of Architecture in the College of Architecture and Design at the New Jersey Institute of Technology where she also serves as Director of the Joint Ph.D. Program in Urban Systems. Her books include *Architecture from the Inside Out* (Wiley, 2007), *Loose Space* (Routledge, 2007) *Ordering Space* (Van Nostrand Reinhold, 1994) and most recently, with Teresa Howard, *Design through Dialogue: A Guide for Clients and Architects* (Wiley, 2010). She is working on a book with Quentin Stevens about the design and people's experience of contemporary memorials.

Anne M. Galvin is Assistant Professor of Anthropology at St. John's University. Her research interests include grassroots community-based development; entrepreneurialism; urban poverty; and neoliberal globalization.

Barbara Kantz is a Professor of Community and Human Services at Empire State College. She holds a Ph.D. in Latin American history and an M.S.W. in social welfare. Her scholarly interests include social change and social criticism, disaster and disaster management, Latin America, international inequality, popular culture studies, cultural diversity, family studies, oral and visual history, the public school system, special education, child development, and Gestalt Therapy.

Jerome Krase is Emeritus and Murray Koppleman Professor at Brooklyn College, CUNY, where he teaches courses on urban sociology and inter-ethnic group relations. For three decades he has worked as a community activist-scholar and has (co)authored and/or (co)edited *Self and Community in the City, Ethnicity and Machine Politics, Italian Americans in a Multicultural Society*, as well as many articles on urban life and culture.

Inga Meier is a Ph.D. student in theatre history and performance studies at the University of Pittsburgh, where she also completed a film studies certificate. She specializes in the theatre of violence and trauma and is currently working on a dissertation focusing on performances related to 9/11. She has presented papers at conferences throughout the United States and in England, including at Film and History, MMLA, SETC and the Shaw Society. She also holds an MFA in Dramaturgy with a certificate in Cultural Studies from Stony Brook University.

Sean Murray is Assistant Professor of English Composition at St. John's University's Institute for Writing. His current pedagogical and research interests include academic service-learning and the politics of higher education.

Carmen Nanko-Fernández is Associate Professor of Pastoral Ministry and director of the Ecumenical Doctor of Ministry degree program at Catholic Theological Union in Chicago. A past president of the Academy of Catholic Hispanic Theologians of the United States (ACHTUS), her most recent book is *Theologizing en Espanglish: Context, Community and Ministry* (Orbis, 2010).

Liliana Naydan earned a Ph.D. in English from Stony Brook University in 2011 and holds a lectureship at the University of Michigan. She is presently researching religious faith in American fiction written in the 1990s and in the aftermath of the 9/11 attacks.

Joanne Robertson-Eletto is Associate Professor of Education and teaches in the Graduate Literacy Program of the School of Education. Her current research explores the power of well chosen books to counter incidents of school bullying. In 2008, she received the Teaching Excellence and Scholarship Award from St. John's University.

Nerina Rustomji is Associate Professor of History at St. John's University. She received her Ph.D. from Columbia University and is a specialist of medieval Islam. Her book *The Garden and the Fire: Heaven and Hell in Islamic Culture* (Columbia University Press, 2009) narrates a history of heaven and hell in Islamic texts, material cultures, and book arts from the seventh century C.E. She is currently completing *Images of Houris and Visions of Islam*, which will examine how contemporary Muslims, American media, and European intellectuals represent one of the most sensational tropes about Islam: pure female companions or *houris* in Islamic Paradise.

Philip Speranza is Assistant Professor in the School of Architecture and Allied Arts at the University of Oregon in Eugene and directs a summer program in landscape urbanism in Barcelona. His design projects in the U.S. and Spain have included private homes, infrastructure, mixed-use development, urban design, and civic art installations in collaboration with the artist Janet Echelman. His design entry, *Foot Hills*, was selected as finalist and third-place honors for the Market Value International Design Competition for downtown Charlottesville.

Jason Steinhauer is a curator, historian and archivist. Among his many exhibition credits is *Ours to Fight For: American Jews in the Second World War*, recipient of the Grand Prize for Excellence in Exhibitions from the American Association of Museums. He currently serves as Liaison Specialist for the Library of Congress Veterans History Project. He is also a touring musician with the band The Grey Area.

Rachel Sykes is a doctoral student in English at the University of Nottingham, having previously studied at the University of York, Mount Holyoke College, and Oxford. Her Ph.D. thesis examines twenty-first-century American fiction, considering the ways in which non-topical novels engage with a history of the present. Her research interests include the American novel after September 11, 2001, cultural memory, and "trauma" studies.

AmyRuth Tobol is currently Associate Dean at SUNY Empire State College, Long Island Center and an Associate Professor in Social Theory, Social Structure and Change. Dr. Tobol holds a B.A. in French, a J.D. and a Ph.D. in American Studies from SUNY Buffalo, and teaches in the areas of sociology, criminal justice, American Studies, and oral history. For the past eleven years, Dr. Tobol has been conducting research on fiber arts and healing and has attended fiber arts study workshops at Penland School of Crafts in North Carolina.

Jennifer Travis is Associate Professor of English and teaches American literature at St. John's University. She is the author of *Wounded Hearts: Masculinity, Law, and Literature in American Culture* (University of North Carolina Press, 2005) and the co-editor of *Boys Don't Cry? Rethinking Masculinity and Emotion in the U.S.* (Columbia University Press, 2002). Her current work focuses on women, accidents, and injury in nineteenth- and early twentieth-century America.

Christopher Vanderwees is an English Ph.D. student at Carleton University in Ottawa, Ontario, whose dissertation studies post-9/11 fiction and representations of falling. He is also the Co-Editor-In-Chief of the *NeoAmericanist*, an online graduate student journal. His current research interests include 9/11 fiction, men and masculinity studies, psychoanalytic theory, and Iraq War memoirs written by female soldiers.

Michael Wolfe is Associate Dean and Professor of History at St. John's University. He is the author or editor of seven books, including most recently (with Natalie Zemon Davis) *A Passion for History* (Truman State, 2010) and *Walled Towns and the Shaping of France* (Palgrave, 2009).

Kenneth Womack is Professor of English at Penn State University's Altoona College and currently serves as Associate Dean for Academic Affairs. He is the author of numerous books on literary and popular culture. His first novel, *John Doe No. 2 and the Dreamland Motel*, was published in 2010.

INDEX